CONTROL OF MACROMOLECULAR SYNTHESIS

MICROBIAL AND MOLECULAR BIOLOGY SERIES

J. R. S. Fincham (*John Innes Institute*):
Genetic Complementation

J. Lascelles (*University of Oxford*):
Tetrapyrrole Biosynthesis and Its Regulation

A. L. Lehninger (*The Johns Hopkins University*):
The Mitochondrion

O. Maaløe and N. O. Kjeldgaard (*University of Copenhagen*): **Control of Macromolecular Synthesis**

CONTROL OF MACROMOLECULAR SYNTHESIS

A Study of DNA, RNA, and Protein Synthesis in Bacteria

Ole Maaløe
Niels Ole Kjeldgaard
University of Copenhagen

W. A. BENJAMIN, INC.
New York Amsterdam
1966

CONTROL OF MACROMOLECULAR SYNTHESIS: A Study of DNA, RNA, and Protein Synthesis in Bacteria

Library of Congress Catalog Card Number 66-13601
Manufactured in the United States of America

*The manuscript was put into production on May 12, 1965;
this volume was published on January 10, 1966*

W. A. BENJAMIN, INC.
New York, New York 10016

EDITOR'S FOREWORD

This book is the fourth to appear in a series of monographs on Microbial and Molecular Biology. The purpose of this series is to encourage and sponsor the publication of carefully selected and edited short monographs on topics in the forefront of research in these fields.

Each book in the series will present a more comprehensive review of its topic, and a broader perspective, than is ordinarily possible in a review article. The presentations are intended to be sufficiently detailed, and thoroughly enough documented and illustrated, so that the advanced student will be able to obtain a comprehensive and up-to-date grasp of an actively developing area without having to refer extensively to original papers. To facilitate access to especially important experimental detail or theoretical development, reprints of key papers will at times be included.

These volumes are not primarily reference works, and they will differ from the traditional monograph in not necessarily covering every relevant reference. The rapid proliferation of the scientific literature makes it increasingly difficult for the experienced investigator, let alone the graduate student, to rely on his coverage of original articles to keep him informed of important advances across the general field of microbial and molecular biology. Hence the editor and publisher believe that appropriate reviews are of increasing value; and for this purpose it seems to us more important that the reviews be critical and lucid than that they be exhaustive. Accordingly, we encourage the authors to be selective, to speculate on immediate problems and on directions of future advance, and to editorialize in much the same way as they would in lecturing to their own students.

I hope that this series of volumes will be of value to the scientific community. Criticisms and suggestions will be welcomed.

BERNARD D. DAVIS

Boston, Massachusetts
October 1965

PREFACE

Most scientists will agree that it is a lot of work to write a book, and those who just finished one sometimes wonder why they ever engaged in such an enterprise. However, it is a great temptation to be asked to write about the particular line of research pursued in one's own laboratory for many years. It provides an occasion for reevaluating what has been done and for presenting such facts and ideas as have remained "viable" in a coherent manner. Since so much of the work has been a joint effort, we decided also to share the responsibility for this book.

The contents and purpose of our monograph are described in the introduction. Here we want to emphasize the role played by the many foreign and Danish scientists who have spent long active periods in our laboratory. Their interest in our research has been a great stimulus and they have contributed many ideas and invested much hard work. We hope they will receive this book as a token of sincere appreciation and of gratitude.

OLE MAALØE
NIELS O. KJELDGAARD

Copenhagen
October 1965

CONTENTS

Editor's Foreword v

Preface vii

INTRODUCTION 1

1 A SURVEY OF RECENT LITERATURE 5

1–1 The General Concepts 5
1–2 The Bacterial DNA 6
1–3 The Bacterial Ribosomes 12
1–4 The Transfer RNA 19
1–5 The Messenger RNA 21
1–6 RNA Synthesis 29
1–7 The Bacterial Proteins 32
1–8 Regulatory Mechanisms 40
1–9 The Operator Model and Some of Its Applications 48

2 STEADY STATES OF GROWTH 56

Cell size, number of nuclei per cell, and DNA content per nucleus

2–1 General Viewpoints 56
2–2 Practical Considerations 57
2–3 Measurements 61
2–4 Concluding Remarks 68

3 STEADY STATES OF GROWTH **70**

Quantities of protein and RNA, and number of ribosomes per cell and per genome

3–1 The Proteins 70
3–2 The Stable RNA 72
3–3 The Relative Quantities of Ribosomal and Transfer RNA 76
3–4 General Remarks about the Theorem 83
3–5 The Numbers and Concentrations of Various Molecules in the Bacterial Cell 86

4 TRANSITIONS BETWEEN STEADY STATES OF GROWTH **97**

4–1 General Principles 97
4–2 The Synthesis of RNA Following a Shift-up 99
4–3 Protein Synthesis Following a Shift-up 109
4–4 DNA Synthesis and Cell Division Following a Shift-up 115
4–5 The Shift-down 117

5 THE REGULATION OF RNA SYNTHESIS **125**

5–1 The Problem in Outline 125
5–2 The Role of Amino Acids in RNA Synthesis 127
5–3 The Possible Mode of Action of Transfer RNA 135
5–4 The Susceptibility of the Different RNA Fractions to Regulation 139
5–5 The Regulation of Ribosomal RNA Synthesis 152

6 THE REGULATION OF DNA SYNTHESIS **154**

6–1 Introductory Remarks 154
6–2 The Duration of the Replication Cycle 157
6–3 A General Principle of Regulation 162
6–4 Thymineless Death and the Initiation of Replication 164
6–5 Thymineless Death 172
6–6 Studies of Replication by Double Labeling Techniques 178
6–7 DNA Replication and the Normal Division Cycle 182

7 THE BACTERIAL NUCLEUS **188**

7–1 The Distribution of Macromolecules in the Cell 188
7–2 Dynamic Aspects of the Transcription Process 192

References **198**

Appendixes **221**

I Dependency on Medium and Temperature of Cell Size and Chemical Composition during Balanced Growth of *Salmonella typhimurium*. M. Schaechter, O. Maaløe, and N. O. Kjeldgaard, *J. Gen. Microbiol.* **19**, 592–606 (1958) 223

II The Kinetics of Ribonucleic Acid and Protein Formation in *Salmonella typhimurium* during the Transition between Different States of Balanced Growth. N. O. Kjeldgaard, *Biochim. Biophys. Acta* **49**, 64–76 (1961) 238

III Regulation of Ribosomal and Transfer RNA Synthesis. C. G. Kurland and O. Maaløe, *J. Mol. Biol.* **4**, 193–210 (1962) 251

IV The Normal DNA Replication Cycle II. P. C. Hanawalt, O. Maaløe, D. J. Cummings, and M. Schaechter, *J. Mol. Biol.* **3**, 156–165 (1961) 269

Index **281**

INTRODUCTION

Content. This book will be concerned with protein and nucleic acid synthesis in bacteria, and more specifically with the rules that govern these syntheses in intact, growing cells. To advance toward an understanding of such complex systems, a proper coordination of *in vivo* and *in vitro* experimentation is essential. In recent years the study of individual synthetic and regulatory processes *in vitro* has been remarkably successful and this area of research undoubtedly will develop further; however, it should continue to be guided as well as checked by *in vivo* studies that reflect the mechanisms of synthesis and control as they operate in the living cell.

The content of this volume has been arranged with this dualism in mind. The first part (Chapter 1) is a selective review of current knowledge of the synthesis of DNA, RNA, and protein. The idea has been to emphasize results, in particular of *in vitro* experiments, that are directly relevant to our main subject, i.e., the integration of cellular activities. In this somewhat arbitrary process the genetic background has been treated very lightly, and readers who want a more comprehensive survey are referred to Watson's recent book.[1] The second part of this volume (Chapters 2–7) deals with *in vivo* experiments. First we describe elementary studies of a series of different steady states of bacterial growth (Chapters 2 and 3), and of the transition between two states (Chapter 4). Then follows a set of more complicated experiments that reveal certain properties of the mechanisms that control RNA and DNA synthesis (Chapters 5 and 6, respectively). Finally we present a somewhat speculative model of the actively working bacterial nucleus (Chapter 7). The main

[1] Watson, J. D. "Molecular Biology of the Gene," W. A. Benjamin, Inc., New York, 1965.

body of the text is followed by a third part, which consists of four original papers. The purpose of this arrangement is to provide easy access to detailed descriptions of the experimental procedures. In a way, the four appendixes constitute a joint "Materials and Methods" section which some readers may find convenient.

Analysis. It will be useful now to consider the relation between problem and experiment in cell biology. Some years ago, in a general discussion of synchronization, it was pointed out that the means by which synchronous division may be achieved can easily distort the normal sequence of events that make up the growth cycle (Maaløe, 1962). Thus the experimenter may, perhaps without realizing it, destroy the object he wants to study. The same kind of mistake can be made when analyzing growth in nonsynchronous cultures, and we have come to the conclusion that only certain very simple *in vivo* experiments permit direct inference concerning the chemical activities during "normal," i.e., undisturbed, balanced growth.

In its simplest form this type of experiment is best described as a "measurement" since it involves nothing more than the determination of a quantity, say that of DNA or RNA, per cell. If such measurements are repeated under different, well-characterized growth conditions, correlations can be established that almost certainly reflect the "normal" behavior of the cell, i.e., the concerted action of all the control mechanisms evolved that permit the bacterial cell to adjust to a large variety of growth conditions. More fancy experiments of the same general type can be visualized; for instance, DNA may be isolated and tested for its transforming activity, or purified RNA may be assayed for its ability to stimulate protein synthesis in an *in vitro* system.

It should be realized that even the simplest of these experiments presents technical problems. Thus, at the critical time, the chemical activities in the cells must be effectively stopped, and the material to be characterized must be preserved in a stable form and must be accounted for quantitatively. These stipulations may seem trivial but they are not always easy to meet. However, it is relatively easy to see what controls are required, and by repetition the reliability of the results can be ascertained. This again means that the correlations eventually established can be trusted, and, most importantly, that their relevance to our problem does not depend on *a priori* assumptions.

The class of *in vivo* experiments we have considered is characterized by a minimum of interference with the growing cells up to the point when everything is "frozen." The other class comprises all experiments in which cells are subjected to treatment, e.g., with an antibiotic or with ultraviolet light, and their response is registered. No comment is called for if the response per se is the subject of study (just as no objection can be raised against the use of an artificial synchronization system if the aim is to find out *why* a particular treatment produces synchrony). On the other hand, if the effects of, say, chloramphenicol are to be used to draw conclusions about the activities and interactions in a normally growing cell, one must be cautious. In such a situation the interpretation of the experiment rests on the *a priori* assumptions made about the direct *as well as* the indirect effects of the antibiotic in the living cell. This uncertainty cannot be reduced by repeating the experiments; however, as our aggregate knowledge increases, we expect to be able to interpret these potentially very powerful experiments with increasing assurance.

The *in vivo* experiments presented in the second part are of both kinds. Nevertheless, our general ideas are to a large extent based on simple experiments of the first class. These ideas were first put forward in a crude form 7 years ago, and later appeared in a more precise and up-to-date version; with some embellishments, they are now presented a third time, and,

as the Bellman explained to his crew,
What I tell you three times is true.

1

A SURVEY OF RECENT LITERATURE

1-1 THE GENERAL CONCEPTS

In 1958 Crick formulated what he called the "central dogma" of biology, postulating that genetic information flows only in the direction from the nucleic acids to the proteins, never in reverse. Our book, which essentially contains a discussion of bacterial growth and of the regulatory mechanisms governing the synthetic activities of the cell, is dogmatic.

From linear, genetic determinants on a DNA strand, the flow of information is assumed to descend to specify the structure of the proteins via the *transcription* into messenger RNA molecules and the *translation* into amino acid sequences by transfer RNA molecules.

The specific structure of the protein molecules determines their affinities toward small molecules, and their properties as enzymes in the synthesis or breakdown of metabolic intermediates. From the level of these low molecular weight products, specific, concentration-dependent signals are thought to reach back to the level of the nucleic acids and to impose a highly specific regulation on the flow of information. This second dogma, formulated by Jacob and Monod (1961a), is also part of our belief.

During the last few years these general ideas have gained enormously in clarity and precision through the ingenious and often laborious efforts of many biologists. Some of the fundamental and to us most convincing experimental contributions will be presented in this chapter as a prerequisite for the discussion of bacterial growth and growth control that follows.

1-2 THE BACTERIAL DNA

DNA as the carrier of genetic information. The best evidence for this property of DNA is still the classical work of Avery, MacLeod, and McCarty (1944) on the transformation of pneumococcal strains from one capsular genotype to another by means of highly purified DNA. Later, the infection of bacteria by bacteriophages was shown by Hershey and Chase (1952) to involve the entry into the cell of new genetic determinants, the viral DNA. In both cases it has been shown that enzymes not previously synthesized in the recipient cells are produced under the influence of the transferred DNA (Smith *et al.*, 1958; Flaks and Cohen, 1959; Kornberg *et al.*, 1959).

The information necessary to specify the protein structure is thought to reside in the sequence of the four different bases in the DNA (adenine, guanine, cytosine, and thymine). The evidence in favor of this notion is now very strong: in the first place, certain chemicals—notably nitrous acid, bromouracil, and aminopurine—produce the so-called "point mutations" that seem to be due to *a single* base pair substitution in the DNA (Freese, 1959a, b); conversely, several mutations in bacteria or bacteriophages, which by recombination could be shown to involve changes in very small regions of a genetic locus, were observed to result in the substitution of *a single* amino acid in the corresponding polypeptide chain (Helinski and Yanofsky, 1962; Henning and Yanofsky, 1962). The logical consequence of these findings, and indeed of the whole concept of a DNA code, is that, for any protein produced by a cell, a DNA sector exists within which the base sequence corresponds, point for point, to the amino acid sequence of the protein. Despite very serious efforts this concept of "colinearity" long remained a postulate. In fact, evidence in favor of a mechanism of protein synthesis that almost demanded colinearity accumulated to the point where many biologists were ready to accept the postulate on this indirect evidence. However, the general notion of a linear DNA code, determining protein structure by specifying amino acid sequences, has recently been confirmed experimentally (see Section 1–4).

The short sequence of base pairs in the DNA molecule assumed to specify a given amino acid has been named the "codon," and the number of base pairs per codon is known as the coding ratio. With 20 different amino acids to be recognized individually, a coding ratio of 3 seemed reasonable although, clearly, this ratio need not be an integer, since all codons need not contain the same number of base pairs. In this book we are not concerned with the coding problem as such, but it should be mentioned that good evidence exists for assuming that the coding ratio is in fact an integer and that the number is 3 (Crick *et al.*, 1961).

With an average molecular weight of the deoxynucleotides of 327, as in *Escherichia coli*, and with an average molecular weight of the amino acids of 131 (from the amino acid composition of *E. coli* proteins) (Waller, 1963), a triplet code means that each protein molecule is specified on a DNA strand by a sequence of nucleotides of a molecular weight 8.3 times that of the protein.

The overall base composition of DNA is known to vary from species to species (Belozersky and Spirin, 1958); however, the molar ratios between adenine and thymine, on the one hand, and between guanine and cytosine, on the other, are always very close to unity (Chargaff, 1955). This fact together with existing x-ray crystallographic data were the chief elements from which the Watson-Crick DNA model was constructed (1953). The double helical structure of complementary DNA strands, with specific base pairing between adenine and thymine and between guanine and cytosine residues, directly suggests a mode of replication that would account for the fact that sister cells receive identical genetic complements (Watson and Crick, 1953).

The two intertwined complementary and antiparallel deoxynucleotide chains are supposed to be held together by hydrogen bonds, although energetically these might be less important than the electrostatic bonds in stabilizing the double helix (De Voe and Tinoco, 1962). Two hydrogen bonds have been suggested to exist between adenine and thymine, and three between guanine and cytosine (Pauling and Corey, 1956). The planes of the purine and pyrimidine rings of a base pair are perpendicular to the axis of the helix and the distance between neighboring planes is 3.4 Å. Each turn of the helix contains ten base pairs and is thus 34 Å long. The diameter of the helix is found to be about 20 Å (Langridge *et al.*, 1960).

At the temperatures and ionic strengths of living cells the

double helix structure of DNA is quite stable, but heating of a solution of DNA results in separation of the two strands (Marmur and Doty, 1959). This collapse of the structure is accompanied by a small change in density, a large decrease in viscosity of the solution, and an increase of about 40% in the optical density at 260 mμ (Marmur and Doty, 1959; 1961). This change in ultraviolet absorption is quite sharp, and the temperature, T_m, at which 50% of the change in optical density has taken place is a function of the base composition of the DNA.

It seems that heating to temperatures above the "melting" point can result in complete separation of the two DNA strands, and that, during subsequent slow cooling, any pair of complementary strands can unite to form a double helix (Schildkraut, Marmur, and Doty, 1961). This was shown by melting and reannealing DNA, labeled with ^{15}N in one strand only. Analysis by cesium chloride density centrifugation of such a DNA solution after slow cooling revealed that, in addition to the original "half-heavy" DNA, two new components had appeared, a heavy-heavy and a light-light DNA.

DNA replication. Conditions that permit DNA synthesis to proceed *in vitro* have been worked out, mainly by Kornberg and his associates. From *E. coli* an enzyme has been isolated and purified that is able to form highly polymerized DNA. The reaction requires a DNA primer plus the deoxyriboside *tri*phosphates of all four bases and, in the presence of Mg^{++}, polymerization occurs with the simultaneous liberation of inorganic pyrophosphate. Under such conditions, DNA can be produced in amounts exceeding by a factor of 10 the quantity of primer added (Lehman *et al.*, 1958a; Bessman *et al.*, 1958).

By using DNA from various sources as primers, it was found that the base composition of the newly formed DNA corresponds exactly to that of the primer (Lehman *et al.*, 1958b). A more detailed investigation revealed that the nearest-neighbor relationships among the nucleotides of the primer were preserved in the product (Josse, Kaiser, and Kornberg, 1961).

The single-stranded DNA isolated from the bacteriophage φX-174 (Sinsheimer, 1959) is an excellent primer for the *E. coli* polymerase system. At early times the product formed was found to have a base composition exactly complementary to the single-stranded primer (Lehman, 1959), and also the nearest-neighbor relationship to be expected in such a complementary strand (Swartz, Trautner, and Kornberg, 1962). At later times the early reaction product seemed to serve as primer for the formation of more double-stranded DNA.

From all the *in vitro* studies it is clear that the DNA polymerase is capable of mediating correct, sequential replication of highly polymerized DNA. Naturally we must ask whether the DNA formed is biologically active. The few observations that bear on this question are barely positive. The synthetic double-stranded φX DNA does not show the same infectivity toward *E. coli* protoplasts as the natural double-stranded replication form of the phage (Sinsheimer, 1961; Sinsheimer *et al.*, 1962). *In vitro* replication of transforming DNA at best takes place to a very limited extent, and the results obtained could represent repair of damage done to the DNA primer (Litman and Szybalski, 1963; Richardson *et al.*, 1963). These somewhat depressing results probably reflect a lack of continuity, at the structural level, of the *in vitro* replication of very long, linear DNA priming molecules. This assumption is not *ad hoc;* it is known that the priming activity of thymus DNA is increased after a short exposure to DNase at low concentrations (e.g., Aposhian and Kornberg, 1962), and it has recently been found that most polymerase preparations are contaminated with nucleases. In the case of the *E. coli* polymerase even highly purified preparations contain a 3′-phosphatase, which seems to promote the *in vitro* synthesis of DNA by creating free 3′-hydroxyl end groups that function as new and "artificial" starting points for replication. This interpretation agrees with the fact that electron micrographs of synthetic DNA show branching chains, a phenomenon never observed with natural DNA (Inman, Schildkraut, and Kornberg, 1965).

It now seems clear that one of the main differences between *in vitro* synthesis and *in vivo* replication of DNA is the mechanism through which the copying process is initiated. *In vitro* synthesis can probably begin wherever the proper free end group presents itself, but *in vivo* initiation seems to be a very special process which probably can occur only at a single, specific site on a DNA molecule.

This question has been successfully approached in bacteria by direct autoradiographic observations of replicating DNA by Cairns (1963), and by short-time density labeling by Bonhoeffer and Gierer (1963). In Cairns' experiments, *E. coli* cells were labeled with ^{3}H-thymidine and lysed with sodium dodecyl sulfate (SDS), and the DNA was released under conditions that minimize shear degradation. The SDS was applied and then removed by dialysis through a membrane filter on which the DNA was eventually collected as it leaked out of the cells. The filter with the extruded DNA molecules attached was mounted directly for autoradiography. In the photographic emulsion the labeled DNA produced about one grain per μ and, with cultures labeled for two or more generations, continuous tracks of 1000–1200μ were observed. This enormously long DNA "molecule" is usually Y-shaped, and the labeling indicates that the fork of the Y actually represents the "growing point" at which replication occurs. If cells are labeled for short periods it is possible to estimate the distance that the growing point has traveled during the incorporation of ^{3}H-thymidine. Experiments of this type again led Cairns to the idea that the bacterial DNA complement (the genome) replicates as one unit with a single growing point (cf. Chapter 6).

In the experiments of Bonhoeffer and Gierer (1963), a thymine auxotroph was allowed to incorporate ^{14}C-labeled bromouracil for about 1% of the time during which the entire DNA complement of the cell replicates. From the work of Levinthal and Davison (1961a) it is known that hydrodynamic shear can break high molecular weight DNA into smaller pieces, the size of which depends on the force applied. In this manner the bromouracil-labeled DNA was broken down to pieces with an average molecular weight close to 1% of that of the genome. Assuming that replication occurs at a single growing point, the ^{14}C-bromouracil incorporated into one genome would be found in one or two fragments. By centrifugation in a cesium chloride gradient, these fragments could be traced by density as well as by radioactivity. The experiment gave evidence for the existence of at most two but more likely a single growing point per genome.

Another important feature of the *in vivo* replication of DNA is that it is semiconservative, i.e., the two sister duplexes produced when a DNA molecule replicates each contains one old and one new polynucleotide strand. This mode of replication, anticipated on structural grounds, was first demonstrated by Meselson and Stahl (1958). *E. coli* cells were grown for several generations in "heavy" medium containing $^{15}NH_4^+$ as the sole source of nitrogen. After transfer to "light" (^{14}N) medium, aliquots of the cells were removed at intervals and the DNA was analyzed for specific density by centrifugation in a cesium chloride gradient. It was observed that, during the first generation of growth after the transfer, heavy (^{15}N-^{15}N) DNA was gradually replaced by half-heavy (^{15}N-^{14}N) DNA. The quantity of half-heavy DNA present at the end of the first generation persisted in subsequent generations during which light (^{14}N-^{14}N) DNA accumulated. By density gradient centrifugation of heated, single-stranded DNA, it was shown that the half-heavy, or hybrid, DNA molecules always contained one heavy and one light strand.

Two features of these experiments should be emphasized: the observed clean separation of heavy, hybrid, and light DNA depends on the fragmentation of the DNA by shear degradation referred to above; and the labeling pattern implies that replication is an orderly unidirectional process, always beginning at a fixed point on the genome. This follows from the observation that no light DNA appears until almost all of the original heavy DNA has been transformed into hybrid material; this would not be so if a DNA segment that had undergone replication late in one cycle were sometimes replicated early in the next cycle. Semiconservative replication of DNA has also been observed during growth of *Chlamydomonas* (Sueoka, 1960) and of mammalian cells (Djordjevic and Szybalski, 1960; Chun and Littlefield, 1961; Simon, 1961).

The formally simple scheme, in which the whole bacterial genome of about 1 mm in length replicates as a unit, is supported by several other lines of evidence.

Genetic experiments of Nagata with *E. coli* (1963) and of Yoshikawa and Sueoka with *Bacillus subtilis* (1963) provide further support for the sequential replication of the bacterial genome, and show that in several of the strains examined replication seems to be initiated in one and the same genetic location in all the cells of a culture. A few exceptions to this rule have been encountered; this probably means that the unique structure responsible for initiating replication may be located in two or more different places on the genome, and that some strains are mixed in this respect. Later in this book, DNA replication will be discussed in more detail both from the point of view of control (Chapter 6) and from a physical and topological point of view (Chapter 7).

The semiconservative replication mechanism strongly suggests that the DNA is metabolically stable under physiological growth conditions. This stability has been demonstrated over long periods of growth by Siminovitch and Graham (1956). Exponentially growing cultures of *E. coli* were labeled with ^{32}P through several generations and subsequently allowed to grow in a nonradioactive medium. Samples withdrawn at intervals were mixed with a large excess of nonradioactive carrier cells. The specific activity of the four deoxyribonucleotides remained constant for about 6 generations, indicating that the nucleotide phosphate groups of the DNA did not exchange with unlabeled material during growth.

1-3 THE BACTERIAL RIBOSOMES

In exponentially growing bacteria the major part of the RNA is metabolically stable, as was demonstrated by Siminovitch and Graham in the study referred to (1956). No turnover of the phosphate group of the four ribonucleotides was observed during about 6 generations of exponential growth of an *E. coli* culture. A turnover of the intact nucleotides among stable RNA molecules might still be imagined. This possibility was excluded by the elegant experiments of Davern and Meselson (1960). Cultures of *E. coli* were grown for many generations in a medium containing the heavy isotopes ^{13}C and ^{15}N. The cells were transferred to a medium containing the corresponding normal, light isotopes, and samples of the culture were harvested after various periods of exponential growth. The RNA was analyzed for changes in specific density by centrifugation through a gradient of cesium formate. Over a period of 3.3 generations only fully heavy and fully light RNA were observed, showing that no mixing occurs between the newly synthesized, light RNA and the old, heavy RNA.

The stable RNA can be divided into well-defined classes according to their sedimentation constants, i.e., according to their molecular weights. In bacterial RNA these fractions are usually referred to as the 23 S and the 16 S ribosomal RNA and the 4 S transfer RNA (tRNA); all three classes of stable RNA have important functions in protein synthesis. In addition, a metabolically unstable RNA fraction, the messenger RNA, is involved as a vector that carries to the sites of protein synthesis a transcription of the information harbored in the DNA.

The particles. Electron micrographs of ultrathin sections of bacteria as well as of higher cells show the presence in the cytoplasm of ellipsoid or spherical particles with a diameter of 150–200 Å. In higher cells these particles, the ribosomes, are largely associated with the membranes forming the endoplasmic reticulum. Breakage of such cells yields fragments of these membranes from which the ribosomes can be isolated by appropriate treatment, e.g., with sodium deoxycholate (Petermann and Hamilton, 1957). In most bacteria the ribosomes can be isolated directly by opening up the cells. Ribosomes are found to be made up of approximately equal parts of RNA and protein, and usually account for the major part of the cellular RNA.

Like the free RNA, isolated ribosomes can be characterized by their sedimentation constants. Particles from different organisms do not vary greatly in size, and their structure and sedimentation constants depend in a characteristic manner on the magnesium concentration of the suspending medium. In the following we shall be concerned mainly with the ribosomes of *E. coli.* When these cells are disrupted at a magnesium concentration below 10^{-3} *M*, ultracentrifugal analysis reveals two classes of particles with sedimentation constants of 30 S and 50 S, respectively. At magnesium concentrations between 10^{-3} *M* and 5×10^{-3} *M*, pairs consisting of one 50 S and one 30 S particle are found in increasing numbers; such pairs have a sedimentation constant of 70 S. At even higher magnesium concentration the 70 S particles aggregate pairwise to form a class of 100 S particles (Tissières *et al.*, 1959; Bolton *et al.*, 1959). All these interactions are reversible. The polyamine, spermine, also has a stabilizing effect on the particles and can partially replace magnesium (Cohen and Lichtenstein, 1960). Polyamines have likewise been found to stabilize yeast ribosomes (Ohtaka and Uchida, 1963).

By very gently opening the cells, aggregates of a higher order, containing up to 20 and perhaps even more 70 S particles, have recently been isolated. These polysomes, or ergosomes, appear to be aligned along a molecule of mRNA (see also Section 1–8). Treatment with low concentrations of ribonuclease (RNase) breaks up the complex, yielding free 70 S ribosomes (Wettstein, Staehlin, and Noll, 1963). These free particles are not attacked by the pancreatic RNase (Tissières *et al.*, 1959; Elson, 1959a).

In the presence of magnesium, ribosomes are very stable; at neutral pH their properties remain unchanged for several days in the cold and for several months in the frozen state. If magnesium is removed, e.g., by ethylenediaminetetraacetate (EDTA), *E. coli* ribosomes break down, and their RNA is degraded to low molecular weight materials due to the liberation from the particles of a latent RNase (Elson, 1958; 1959b; Bolton *et al.*, 1959). In other bacterial species, e.g., *Pseudomonas fluorescens*, no RNase has been found attached to the ribosomes (Wade and Robinson, 1963).

The different particle fractions can be isolated in relatively pure states by centrifugation. In *E. coli* all fractions were found to contain about 60% RNA and 40% protein, and the molecular weights of the 30, 50, and 70 S particles were found to be 7×10^5, 1.8×10^6, and 2.6×10^6 respectively (Tissières *et al.*, 1959). The RNA of the various particles was isolated by Kurland (1960) and characterized by ultracentrifugal analysis. The 30 S particles yielded a single RNA species with a sedimentation constant of 16 S, corresponding to a molecular weight of 5.6×10^5. From the 50 S particles two classes of RNA were isolated, one indistinguishable from the 16 S RNA of the 30 S particles, and a new class with a sedimentation constant of 23 S. The molecular weight of the latter was found to be 1.1×10^6. Considering the size and composition of the different ribosomal particles, a 30 S particle seems to contain a single 16 S RNA unit, while a 50 S particle might contain either two 16 S or one 23 S RNA unit. There is some indication that the 16 S RNA isolated from 50 S particles is, in fact, a breakdown product of 23 S RNA (J. D. Watson, personal communication). If so, both classes of particles may be regarded as homogeneous with respect to their RNA moiety. Ribosomes from *Bacillus cereus* (Takai and Kondo, 1962), and ribosomes from higher organisms, also yield two RNA fractions with sedimentation constants close to 23 S and 16 S (cf. Spirin, 1963). These two RNA units have approximately the same base composition with a high purine (especially guanine) content, irrespective of the base composition of the DNA of the organism (Miura, 1962; Midgley, 1962). This constancy in size and composition indicates that, as a structure, the ribosome has changed little during evolution.

The x-ray diffraction pattern of ribosomal RNA from *E. coli* points to the existence of helical regions (Zubay and Wilkins, 1960), and the presence of hydrogen bonds in free as well as in particle-bound ribosomal RNA is indicated by the hypochromic shift observed at 260 mμ upon heating, or after treatment with 8 *M* urea (Schlessinger, 1960; Zubay and Wilkins, 1960). Similar results have been obtained with rat liver ribosomes by Hall and Doty (1959).

The ribosomal protein. As mentioned above, protein accounts for about 40% of the mass of both the 30 S and the 50 S particles from *E. coli*. The overall amino acid composition of this protein has been analyzed by Spahr (1962) and found to be somewhat different from the average composition of the rest of the proteins from *E. coli;* in particular the basic amino acids, lysine and arginine, are more abundant, and cysteine less abundant, than in the soluble proteins. The NH_2-terminal amino acids have been determined by Waller and Harris (1961), and quite unexpectedly it was found that in most protein molecules methionine, alanine, or serine occupies this position. The pattern is the same for the ribosomal as for the soluble proteins. From these data the average molecular weight of the ribosomal proteins has been estimated to be about 25,000.

The ribosomal protein is not a single molecular species but a complex mixture. Starch gel electrophoresis in 6 *M* urea and at pH 5.6 shows more than a dozen bands (Waller, 1963). It is by no means obvious that all these components are essential constituents of a functional ribosome; nor is it certain that all ribosomes are identical. When the integrity of a ribosome breaks down, the RNA is hydrolyzed by the latent ribonuclease, and at neutral pH and low ionic strength about 50% of the proteins precipitate (Elson, 1959a; Spahr and Hollingworth, 1961). In the intact particle these proteins are probably closely associated with the ribosomal RNA, and form insoluble complexes when the RNA structure is destroyed. These precipitable proteins are soluble at very low or high pH, and at high ionic strength, e.g., in 1 *M* Tris (Spitnik-Elson, 1962).

The ribosomal proteins that are soluble at low ionic strength include several identified enzymes: (a) newly synthesized or even unfinished enzymes not yet released into the cytoplasm (it seems that normally only a fraction of 1% of a "soluble" enzyme is detectable in the nascent state attached to ribosomes), (b) "associated" enzymes whose precise functions are unknown.

Several metabolic enzymes have been found transiently associated with the ribosomes. Thus bound β-glucosidase was found on yeast ribosomes (Kihare, Hu, and Halvorson, 1961), and on *B. cereus* ribosomes a penicillinase was identified (Duerksen and O'Connor, 1963). Among the nascent enzymes, β-galactosidase has been most extensively studied (Cowie *et al.*, 1961; Zipser, 1963). In *E. coli* about 0.5% of the β-galactosidase remained associated with particles after repeated washing. The amount of bound enzyme varies with the state of induction of the cells, but not all of it is "chased" into the cytoplasm when the inducer is removed. Zipser (1963) observed that the amount of bound and chasable enzyme was proportional to the differential rate of synthesis of β-galactosidase. Both interesting and surprising is his further observation that, in the steady state of synthesis, only about 20% of the bound enzyme is ever released from the ribosomes. The relatively large amount of permanently fixed, or nonchasable, enzyme is thought to represent polypeptide chains that, because of "errors," cannot be released (see also Chapter 4). It seems likely that, given sufficiently sensitive assays, most enzymes might be recognized in the nascent state.

The bacterial RNase has been isolated and, like pancreatic RNase, it yields 2′,3′ cyclic nucleotides (Spahr and Hollingworth, 1961). In extracts of bacteria this enzyme sediments quantitatively with the ribosomes (Tal and Elson, 1963a), but this association seems to be an artifact since the enzyme is released into the medium when *E. coli* cells are converted into spheroplasts (Neu and Heppel, 1964). Ribosomes from *Pseudomonas fluorescens* seem not to associate with the homologous RNase (Wade and Robinson, 1963).

About 10% of the deoxyribonuclease (DNase) activity found in *E. coli* cells seems to be associated with the 70 S ribosomes (Tal and Elson, 1963b). When these particles were dissociated into 50 S and 30 S ribosomes the DNase was released, but it reassociated with the ribosomes if 70 S particles were allowed to reconstitute. In view of the existence in *E. coli* of several different deoxyribonucleases (Weissbach and Korn, 1963), the activity associated with the 70 S ribosomes might well represent one enzyme species only.

Other enzymes related to nucleic acid metabolism have also been found in large quantities on the ribosomes. Thus in *Pseudomonas aeruginosa* most of the polynucleotide phosphorylase is associated with the ribosomes (Strasdine, Hogg, and Campbell, 1962), and in *E. coli* about 50% of this enzyme is particle-bound (Sekiguchi and Cohen, 1963).

An RNA-primed RNA polymerase associated with *E. coli* ribosomes (August, Ortiz, and Hurwitz, 1962) catalyzes the incorporation of ATP and of small quantities of other triphosphates into acid-insoluble polynucleotides. This enzyme was found to disappear rapidly upon infection of the cells with T2 bacteriophages (Ortiz *et al.*, 1965). Since no new ribosomes are produced after infection (see below), this is another indication that enzymes that stick to ribosomes *in vitro* need not be directly involved in protein synthesis.

If protein synthesis is inhibited with chloramphenicol (CM), RNA synthesis continues, and new classes of protein-poor ribosomal particles are formed. These "CM particles" have been isolated from *E. coli* cultures (Pardee, Paigen, and Prestidge, 1957; Nomura and Watson, 1959). Similar particles are found when protein synthesis is inhibited by puromycin or by amino acid starvation of a particular mutant, *W6*, of *E. coli* K12 (Dagley *et al.*, 1962). Streptomycin shows much the same initial effect as CM and puromycin (Dubin, 1964). Two types of CM particle can be recognized with sedimentation constants 18 and 25 S, respectively (Kurland, Nomura, and Watson, 1962). These particles contain less than 25% protein but, like the normal particles, contain 16 S and 23 S RNA units. Probably the 18 S particle contains one 16 S unit, and the 25 S particle one 23 S RNA unit. Both particles are stable only at low salt concentrations, and above 10^{-2} *M* NaCl the latent RNase is activated and the RNA degraded. The CM particles are very sensitive to the action of pancreatic ribonuclease, and their physical properties suggest a loosely coiled structure very different from the normal ribosomes, which behave like compact, solvent-impermeable particles.

Since at a suitably high CM concentration no protein is synthesized, the CM-particle protein must be assumed to be present in the cell at the time of drug addition. This prediction was verified by analyzing CM particles formed in the presence of labeled amino acids; the particles contained no radioactivity (see Appendix III). There is now good evidence that CM particles, which accumulate while protein synthesis is inhibited, can develop into normal ribosomal particles during subsequent growth (Aronson and Spiegelman, 1961b; Dagley, Turnock, and Wild, 1963; Nakada, Anderson, and Magasanik, 1964).

The function of the ribosomes. The role of ribosomes as the centers for protein synthesis has been established in a number of different cell types. With bacteria, exponentially growing cultures were labeled for very short periods with ^{35}S sulfate (McQuillen, Roberts, and Britten, 1959). The cultures were poured onto crushed ice to stop further reaction, and the cells were rapidly harvested and disrupted. Analysis of these extracts by sucrose gradient centrifugation showed that most of the cellular radioactivity appeared as amino acid sulfur in association with the 70 S ribosomes. In other experiments a 15-second labeling period was followed by a 2-minute chase at 37°, with a large excess of ^{32}S sulfate and cysteine. In extracts from these cells most of the labeled, newly formed protein had reached the soluble fraction. From the time course of the reaction, it was calculated that the amount of label passing through the ribosomes was sufficient to account for the entire protein synthesis of the cells. This study for the first time demonstrated that ribosomes are involved as the major, if not the only, site of protein synthesis (see also Chapters 3 and 4).

It is important to note that the ribosomes are entirely unspecific with respect to the *kind* of protein being synthesized. Actually, early findings of Cohen (1948) and of Hershey (1953) point in this direction; they showed that net synthesis of RNA, including ribosomal RNA, stops immediately after phage infection, and yet several new protein species, not produced in uninfected bacteria, are formed in large quantities. The nonspecificity of the ribosomes was more rigorously proven in a series of elegant *in vivo* experiments (Brenner, Jacob, and Meselson, 1961) by separating ribosomal particles according to density in a cesium chloride gradient. *E. coli* cells were grown for many generations in a medium containing the heavy isotopes ^{15}N and ^{13}C, harvested, and starved to get rid of traces of unincorporated heavy isotopes. The starved cells were infected with T4 bacteriophages and growth was reinitiated by the addition of normal, light medium. Immediately after infection, ^{35}S sulfate was introduced for 2 minutes to label the newly formed, phage-specific proteins. The harvested cells were mixed with a large excess of phage-infected, "light" cells, and the purified ribosomes were analyzed. In this experiment the radioactivity moved with the "heavy" 70 S ribosomes, formed prior to phage infection, and no activity was associated with the "light" carrier ribosomes. The radioactivity could be removed completely from the "heavy" ribosomes, if the pulse of ^{35}S was followed by a chase with ^{32}S. It is therefore obvious that the phage proteins are formed on "old" ribosomes; furthermore, it is almost certain that the structural RNA of these particles does not contain phage-specific information.

Direct evidence for the nonspecificity of the ribosomes is also obtained from *in vitro* studies. Thus addition of RNA isolated from tobacco mosaic virus to a system containing *E. coli* ribosomes leads to the formation of a protein that, after trypsin digestion, shows a peptide pattern resembling that of the virus protein (Tsugita *et al.*, 1962). Similarly, RNA from the phage f2 (Loeb and Zinder, 1961) induces the formation of rather large quantities of protein when added to an *in vitro* system isolated from *E. coli;* the tryptic digest of this protein is very similar to that of purified phage coat protein (Nathans *et al.*, 1962).

1-4 THE TRANSFER RNA

Physical and chemical characteristics. Transfer RNA (tRNA) is a rather small polynucleotide molecule with a sedimentation constant of about 4 S, corresponding to a molecular weight of about 25,000 and to a chain length of 70–80 nucleotides. This class of RNA was first isolated from ascites tumor cells (Hoagland *et al.*, 1958), but its properties are essentially the same whatever the source. Transfer RNA has the ability to combine with amino acids. This process involves two steps, both mediated by the amino acid-specific, activating enzymes: first an adenosyl-amino acid complex is formed in a reaction with ATP, and in a second step the enzyme couples the activated amino acid to a transfer RNA molecule. Both steps are reversible. The net result is that the amino acid is coupled in an ester linkage to the 3′-hydroxyl group of the ribose moiety of the terminal adenine nucleoside of a tRNA molecule *specific for that amino acid* (Feldman and Zachau, 1964). A rigorous proof of this specificity has been obtained by analyzing RNA fractions obtained by countercurrent distribution (Weisblum, Benzer, and Holley, 1962) or by chromatography on methylated albumin columns (Sueoka and Yamane, 1962). With both methods, bulk tRNA can be resolved into fractions of which the purest show receptor activity for a single amino acid only. The picture is complicated, however, by the fact that in some cases two or even three fractions show the same amino acid specificity (Sueoka and Yamane, 1962; Goldstein, Bennett, and Craig, 1964). Leucine is an amino acid to which correspond more than one tRNA species; if radioactive leucine is first attached to one of the purified tRNA fractions and then added to an *in vitro* protein-synthesizing system, one observes that, depending on the tRNA fraction used, *different* polynucleotides must be used as "messenger" to promote leucine incorporation (Weisblum, Benzer, and Holley, 1962). This clearly shows that the tRNA fractions represent separate codons, both of which are read as "leucine"; a code with this property is called "degenerate."

The same base sequence, · · ·-cytosine-cytosine-adenine, occurs at the amino acid-accepting end of all tRNA molecules (Hecht, Stephenson, and Zamecnik, 1959; Preiss, Dieckmann, and Berg, 1961), and guanosine phosphate is the common end group distal to the amino acid acceptor site (Singer and Cantoni, 1960). Analysis of the overall base composition of *E. coli* tRNA by Dunn, Smith, and Spahr (1960) and Miura (1962), among others, has revealed two important features: (1) the presence of a number of unusual nucleotides, and (2) approximately equimolar quantities of guanine and cytosine, on the one hand, and of adenine and uracil plus the unusual bases, on the other. A fairly high degree of hydrogen bonding might therefore be possible, and is indeed indicated by the reversible hypochromic shift observed when purified tRNA preparations are heated (Tissières, 1959). As in ribosomal RNA the guanine content is high, and no great variation in base composition is observed when comparing tRNA isolated from different organisms (Midgley, 1962; Miura, 1962).

The greatest achievement, however, is the complete base-sequence analysis of one alanine tRNA (Holley *et al.*, 1965). The purified material was isolated from yeast cells by the countercurrent method, each molecule is a linear sequence of 77 nucleotides, and in addition to the four common RNA bases one finds pseudouridine, thymine, dihydrouracil, hypoxanthine, and several methylated bases. The extra methyl groups are derived from methionine and coupled to certain residues of the finished polynucleotide chain (Svensson *et al.*, 1963). The methylations are mediated by enzymes specific for the individual reactions (Fleissner and Borek, 1962; Gold and Hurwitz, 1963).

The nucleotide sequences of at least two other species may soon be known; a serine tRNA (Cantoni *et al.*, 1963; H. G. Zachau and co-workers, personal communication), and a valine tRNA (Ingram and Sjöquist, 1963). It is already evident that, in addition to the end groups, all tRNA species have at least one short nucleotide sequence in common, and it should soon be possible to construct plausible three-dimensional models of these molecules. Progress in this field is significant not only because it will increase our understanding of protein synthesis, but also because the tRNA may play an important role in certain regulatory mechanisms (cf. Chapter 5).

The function of the transfer RNA. In 1958, when nothing was known about the tRNA except that activated amino acids would attach to it and subsequently be incorporated into protein, Crick advanced his adaptor hypothesis. He imagined individual tRNA molecules to have *two* attachment specificities, one for a given amino acid and one for the corresponding codon.

An ingenious proof of the *independent* existence of these two combining sites has been supplied (Chapeville *et al.*, 1962).

The experiment is based on the observation that a copolymer consisting of uridylic and guanylic acid (4:1), when added to an *in vitro* system, promotes the incorporation into peptides of cysteine (and certain other amino acids) but not of alanine. Transfer RNA charged with ^{14}C-labeled cysteine was treated with Raney nickel, thus reducing the cysteine to alanine without affecting the nucleic acid moiety. When this converted tRNA-amino acid complex was tested in the presence of the UG-polymer, alanine was incorporated into peptide linkage. Similarly, von Ehrenstein, Weisblum, and Benzer (1963) showed that, when the same converted tRNA complex was added to a hemoglobin-forming system from rabbit reticulocytes, alanine was incorporated into a peptide that normally contains cysteine but not alanine. Clearly, incorporation is directed by a structural site on the tRNA molecule quite distinct from that responsible for the specific attachment of the amino acid.

The two-step process by which amino acids are coupled to tRNA molecules in the presence of ATP is catalyzed by specific enzymes, some of which have been isolated and purified (Bergmann, Berg, and Dieckmann, 1961). The overall reaction is highly specific; thus Loftfield, Hecht, and Eigner (1963) estimate that mistakes between closely related natural amino acids, e.g., valine, isoleucine, and leucine, occur with a frequency of about 10^{-4}.

The strict specificity of the coupling reaction nevertheless breaks down in the case of some amino acid analogues, and several amino acid auxotrophs will continue protein synthesis, at least for some time, if supplied with an analogue of the required acid. A phenylalanine auxotroph thus incorporates the analogue *p*-fluorophenylalanine and distributes it in a random manner over all the phenylalanine positions of a particular protein, the penicillinase (Richmond, 1963).

1-5 THE MESSENGER RNA

Definition and special properties. The information relating to the structure of a given protein must be transmitted from DNA to a ribosome, since the latter appears to be unspecific with respect to the kind of protein to be synthesized. The connecting link is a class of metabolically unstable RNA molecules, the messenger RNA (mRNA). This concept was derived formally by Jacob and Monod (1961a). Some of the proteins they studied belong to the class of enzymes whose synthesis in the cell requires the presence of a specific inducer. After addition of the inducer, synthesis begins within a few minutes and, more significantly, when the inducer is removed, synthesis stops equally fast. These facts together with genetic evidence suggested to Jacob and Monod that information issued from the genome had to be contained in unstable structures whose synthesis could be rapidly and specifically evoked through the action of small molecules. Thus came into existence the second dogma, mentioned in Section 1–1.

The first indications of a short-lived messenger fraction had already been observed but not clearly recognized in experiments with phage-infected *E. coli.* During infection with T2 bacteriophage no net increase in RNA is observed (Cohen, 1948). However, a small RNA fraction was observed by Hershey (1953) to undergo rapid turnover. This fraction was characterized (Astrachan and Volkin, 1958) through pulse labeling of the RNA by $^{32}PO_4$. The base composition observed was 17% CMP, 31% AMP, 31% UMP, and 20% GMP. These values corresponded to a base ratio of 1.7, as compared to 1.8 for T2 DNA, and 0.9 for both bacterial DNA and total RNA.

These results were further elaborated (Nomura, Hall, and Spiegelman, 1960), by measuring the radioactivity associated with various subcellular fractions of T2-infected *E. coli* labeled for 2 minutes with ^{32}P-orthophosphate. At magnesium concentrations above 5×10^{-3} *M* most of the label was associated with the ribosomes, but at lower magnesium concentration most of the radioactive material had a sedimentation constant around 8 S. The same sedimentation constant was found for the labeled RNA prepared from the ribosomes by phenol treatment. As had previously been observed, the base composition of the pulse-labeled material was essentially that of the phage DNA. It is clear that the unstable RNA fractions observed in these experiments might represent the "information issues" postulated by Jacob and Monod.

Physical and chemical characterization. When synthetic poly*ribo*adenylic and poly*deoxyribo*thymidylic acids are mixed, double-stranded hybrid molecules form spontaneously (Rich, 1960). Hybrids between the rapidly labeled RNA and single-stranded DNA might therefore be expected to form if the RNA molecules were true replicas with base sequences complementary to all or parts of the T2 DNA. Accordingly Hall and Spiegelman (1961) mixed ^{32}P-labeled T2 DNA with ^{3}H-labeled RNA from infected cells; they raised the temperature to obtain strand separation, and found that after cooling a new component had appeared which contained both DNA and RNA label. The hybrid molecules could be separated from both DNA and RNA in a cesium chloride gradient, and the specificity of the hybridization was demonstrated by the absence of interaction of the labeled RNA with DNA from other sources.

The experiments of Brenner, Jacob, and Meselson (1961) discussed in Section 1–3 show that the unstable RNA of a phage-infected cell probably is the messenger that carries information for the synthesis of the phage proteins to the ribosomes. A 2-minute pulse of ^{14}C-uracil was given to *E. coli* cells infected with phage T4, and a cell extract was fractionated in a cesium chloride gradient. The radioactivity was predominantly associated with the 70 S ribosomes, and could be removed if an excess of ^{12}C-uracil was added some time before harvesting the infected cells. The same experiment was done with bacteria that had been labeled with heavy isotopes for several generations before being infected in a medium containing the normal light isotopes. The radioactive RNA was found to be associated exclusively with the heavy ribosomes originating from the infected cells, and not at all with the excess of light ribosomes added as carrier. This experiment is important in indicating that the association is a functional one and not the result of a general affinity between the radioactive RNA and the ribosomes.

By labeling the RNA of exponentially growing, uninfected cells for short periods, a small, labile RNA fraction has been identified in yeast cells (Yčas and Vincent, 1960) and in bacteria (Gros *et al.*, 1961b). Extracts of cells labeled for short periods with ^{14}C-uracil were analyzed by sedimentation through a stabilizing sucrose gradient (Britten and Roberts, 1960). In *E. coli* extracts with 10^{-4} *M* magnesium nearly all the radioactivity was in material with sedimentation constants of 14–16 S; little if any label was associated with the 50 S and 30 S ribosomes. At higher magnesium concentration a considerable fraction of the pulse-labeled RNA was associated with the 70 S ribosomes. RNA purified by phenol extraction appeared as a broad peak with a sedimentation constant of about 8 S. In a number of bacterial strains the base composition of this fraction has been found to be similar to that of the DNA.

In *E. coli* this is not so striking because the base ratios of total RNA and of DNA do not differ greatly. However, in *Pseudomonas aeruginosa* and *Proteus vulgaris* (Astrachan and Fischer, 1961), as well as in *Staphylococcus aureus* (Gros *et al.*, 1961b), the base ratios of total RNA and DNA differ widely, and the 8 S RNA fraction is distinctly "DNA-like." This result was taken to indicate that the short-lived RNA might somehow be derived from DNA. This is almost certainly true, but, as we shall see later, mRNA probably is synthesized by copying one DNA strand only, and the fact that the base compositions of the total DNA and the copy often are very similar is therefore *not* a consequence of the mechanism of synthesis.

The introduction of DNA-agar columns has facilitated the separation and quantitation of RNA species that anneal with denatured DNA (Bolton and McCarthy, 1962). With this technique the rapidly labeled RNA fraction from *E. coli* has been separated into a DNA-like and a ribosomal RNA-like fraction (Midgley and McCarthy, 1962).

At any given time, the messenger fraction should be made up of RNA copies of a large number of genetic loci. However, copies representing completely "closed," or repressed, loci are not expected to be present, and a sufficiently sensitive method might therefore permit recognition of the specific mRNA expected to be formed in response to enzyme induction. Successful experiments of this kind have been done with the galactose enzymes (Attardi *et al.*, 1963b) and with β-galactosidase (Hayashi *et al.*, 1963). In both cases the assay can be made extremely sensitive by using bacteriophage DNA with extensive homology toward the messenger in question. As expected, much more hybridizing RNA could be extracted from induced than from uninduced cells.

Messenger RNA and protein synthesis *in vitro*. The *in vitro* system described by Matthaei and Nirenberg (1961) contains ribosomes, soluble enzymes, and tRNA, together with ATP and an energy-yielding system. By preincubation with a complete amino acid mixture the protein-forming capacity of such a system can be exhausted, probably because the messenger present on the ribosomes eventually breaks down completely. Further incorporation of radioactive amino acids into peptide linkage depends on the addition of new RNA. It is thus possible *in vitro* to assay different RNA species, natural as well as synthetic, for their "messenger" activity.

Of the RNA species naturally occurring in bacteria, the 8–14 S fraction stimulates amino acid incorporation more than either ribosomal or tRNA (Willson and Gros, 1964). Furthermore, Bautz (1963a) showed that RNA selected by hybridization to DNA stimulated amino acid incorporation much more than the RNA fraction that did not hybridize. At this point one may ask whether ribosomal or tRNA shows any stimulating effect at all *in vitro*. We shall see later that, at best, their effect is extremely weak, and the efficiency with which an RNA preparation stimulates amino acid incorporation *in vitro* may thus be used to estimate its messenger content (cf. Section 5–4).

The size of a messenger molecule is determined by the coding ratio and the number of amino acids coded for. If the ratio is 3, the molecular weight of a messenger should be about 8 times that of the corresponding polypeptide chain (or chains). Apparently several chains are often coded for on the same messenger and the existence of very large messenger molecules would therefore be expected. With new isolation techniques, designed to avoid accidental enzymatic degradations, it has in fact been possible to demonstrate that about 50% of the pulse-labeled RNA from *E. coli* consists of very large units with sedimentation constants ranging from 16 to 25 S (Sagik *et al.*, 1962; Bautz, 1963b).

Polyribosomes (polysomes or ergosomes) consisting of groups of 70 S ribosomes have recently been identified in bacteria as well as in mammalian cells (Risebrough, Tissières, and Watson, 1962; Warner, Knopf, and Rich, 1963; Gierer, 1963; Wettstein, Staehlin, and Noll, 1963; Schaechter, 1963; Schlessinger, 1963). Short-time labeling with radioactive amino acids shows that the polysomes probably are the active centers of protein synthesis, and it is believed that the ribosomes are attached in series to long messenger molecules. In rabbit reticulocytes which synthesize globin only, most of the polysomes seem to contain five 70 S particles (Warner, Knopf, and Rich, 1963). Cells producing a larger variety of proteins show a correspondingly wide distribution in the size of the polysomes, and units with 15–20 70 S ribosomes are not uncommon (Wettstein, Staehlin, and Noll, 1963; Noll, Staehlin, and Wettstein, 1963). Even higher numbers are reported: thus 40–60-unit polysomes seem to be formed in HeLa cells infected with polio virus (Penman *et al.*, 1963), and polysomes with 30–50 units have been implicated in the synthesis of β-galactosidase in *E. coli* (molecular weight about $4 \times 120{,}000$) by Kiho and Rich (1964).

It is natural to assume that the size of a polysome is related to the size of the message. This assumption has been tested by extracting the RNA from polysomes of specific size isolated from cells that had been labeled with ^{32}P for a short time. The molecular weight of the radioactive messenger RNA was measured by sedimentation, and a definite, positive correlation was established between the size of the mRNA and the number of ribosomes per polysome. It was estimated that the distance between ribosomes attached to the same messenger molecule corresponds to a piece of RNA of molecular weight around 28,000, i.e., a chain of about 90 nucleotides (Staehlin *et al.*, 1964). This value is in fair agreement with the 300 Å distance measured on electron micrographs (Warner, Knopf, and Rich, 1963).

These figures, together with the fact that reticulocytes contain mainly pentameric polysomes, permit a crude estimate of the coding ratio. Thus the mRNA corresponding to a pentamer should contain somewhere around 450 nucleotides, and the hemoglobin synthesized by the reticulocytes contains chains with about 150 amino acids. This gives a coding ratio of 3 (Staehlin *et al.*, 1964). The most gratifying thing about this result is not that it corroborates the already strong evidence for a triplet code, but rather that it supports the idea that the pentamer is in fact the unit that synthesizes globin molecules.

Instability of messenger RNA. Originally mRNA was identified by its rapid turnover, and it is therefore necessary to consider the rate of synthesis as well as that of breakdown. Together these parameters define the steady-state concentration of messenger. The breakdown of either specific or total messenger has been measured in different ways, all of which suggest exponential decay.

In *B. subtilis*, breakdown has been studied by means of actinomycin D, which rapidly and specifically inhibits all DNA-dependent RNA synthesis. After pulse labeling of the RNA, actinomycin may be added to prevent the reutilization of the nucleotides that might be produced during messenger decay, and the loss of acid-precipitable radioactivity with time should therefore measure the breakdown of the rapidly labeled RNA. With this technique two very significant observations were made (Levinthal, Keynan, and Higa, 1962): (1) decay to the level of acid-soluble material occurs exponentially; (2) after addition of actinomycin the rate of protein synthesis decreases in step with the decay of the labeled RNA. Thus protein can be synthesized in the presence of actinomycin. When measured at different temperatures the rate of decay was found to vary approximately as the growth rate, or the rate of protein formation. Thus, the "messenger" half-life was determined to be about 0.7 minute at 37°, about 2.5 minutes at 25°, and about 1 hour at 10° (Fan, Higa, and Levinthal, 1964).

In *E. coli*, which is not susceptible to the action of actinomycin, high concentrations of dinitrophenol or proflavine have been used to inhibit RNA synthesis (Woese *et al.*, 1963; Soffer and Gros, 1964). Both these inhibitors probably act less specifically on RNA synthesis than does actinomycin D, which may explain why the half-life (at 37°) of pulse-labeled RNA was found to be 6–8 minutes with dinitrophenol and 3–4 minutes with proflavine. As mentioned before, the *in vitro* protein-forming system of Matthaei and Nirenberg (1961) responds to the addition of an mRNA fraction. RNA from *E. coli* cultures treated with dinitrophenol or with proflavine has been tested in this way, and decay of messenger activity could actually be observed (Woese *et al.*, 1963; Gros *et al.*, 1963b).

The breakdown of specific messenger has been studied by means of "pulse induction" of β-galactosidase (Képès, 1963; Nakada and Magasanik, 1964) and of histidase (Hartwell and Magasanik, 1963). This type of experiment measures the enzyme-producing capacity that remains after removal of the inducer, and the loss of capacity with time is assumed to reflect the decay of mRNA. With this technique the *in vivo* half-life of the β-galactosidase messenger in *E. coli* has been estimated to be about 1 minute at 37° (Képès, 1963), and about 2.5 minutes at 30° (Nakada and Magasanik, 1964). The histidase messenger of *B. subtilis* seemed to decay with a half-life of 2.4 minutes at 37° (Hartwell and Magasanik, 1963).

Starvation of a uracil auxotroph of *E. coli* of the required pyrimidine causes rapid decrease and eventually an almost complete loss of the stimulating activity of the RNA as measured *in vitro* (see Chapter 5).

At present it is very difficult to test whether different species of mRNA within a cell, or within an organism, decay at the same or perhaps at quite different rates. We have discussed two cases in which the decay of a specific messenger seems to occur at about the same rate as total messenger. This one would expect on the simple assumption that all messengers are chemically alike and that, in bacteria, protein synthesis takes place in a single compartment in which a common mechanism of messenger breakdown might operate. It is therefore puzzling to learn that the penicillinase messenger of *B. subtilis* may have a much longer half-life than other messenger molecules in the same cell (Pollock, 1963). In higher organisms more diversity might be expected (Revel and Hiatt, 1964), and one extreme case is actually known: the highly specialized reticulocytes, in which the globin messenger seems to be stable for days.

There is now very good evidence that the synthesis of all protein molecules starts from the NH_2-terminal end (Dintzis, 1961; Goldstein and Brown, 1961; Bishop, Leahy, and Schweet, 1960). The information harbored in a given mRNA molecule must therefore be read from the codon that corresponds to the N-terminal amino acid. If breakdown always began at the same end, no incomplete protein molecules would be formed, and it is therefore a reasonable first choice to visualize messenger breakdown as somehow coupled to protein synthesis. Actually, the rate of decay of total messenger decreases by a factor of about 5 when protein synthesis is inhibited by chloramphenicol (Fan, Higa, and Levinthal, 1964; Gros *et al.*, 1963b). On the other hand, decay of the specific messengers for β-galactosidase or histidase seems to be unaffected either by chloramphenicol or by removal of a required amino acid (Képès, 1963; Hartwell and Magasanik, 1963; Nakada and Magasanik, 1964). This apparent contradiction cannot be resolved at the moment; but it should be kept in mind that a system which registers the function of only intact messenger molecules will be sensitive to one or a few chain breaks. Such slight damage to a messenger molecule would not be registered either in actinomycin experiments or in *in vitro* assays for messenger activity.

If energy metabolism is blocked, the stability of total messenger (Fan, Higa, and Levinthal, 1964), as well as that of specific β-galactosidase messenger, is greatly increased (Nakada and Fan, 1964). The antibiotic puromycin, which stops protein synthesis by releasing unfinished protein chains from the ribosomes (Allen and Zamecnik, 1962; Gilbert, 1963b), affords no protection to messenger, and even seems to reverse the protection offered by chloramphenicol or anaerobiosis (Fan, Higa, and Levinthal, 1964; Nakada and Fan, 1964). The problem of messenger decay will be discussed again (Chapter 5).

Quantitative estimates of messenger RNA. Several attempts have been made to estimate the amount of messenger present in growing bacteria. Levinthal, Keynan, and Higa (1962) found that approximately 8% of the RNA of *B. subtilis* decayed in the presence of actinomycin D. If all the labile RNA is assumed to be messenger the cells would contain, per ribosome, a piece of messenger about 1500 Å long. If the polysomes that have been isolated from various sources are typical of the living cells, this figure implies that, in *B. subtilis*, only a fraction of the messenger could be tied up in polysomal structures, i.e., one would have to assume the existence of a large pool of free messenger.

The size of the messenger fraction in *E. coli* has been estimated by pulse labeling of the RNA (Gros *et al.*, 1961a). In this semiquantitative study, mRNA was estimated to account for only about 3% of the total RNA.

The quantity of mRNA has also been estimated by hybridization. About two parts of uniformly labeled RNA were mixed and incubated at 60° with one part of single-stranded, homologous DNA embedded in an agar gel. Most of the radioactivity could be washed out of the gel at 60°, but the RNA that had annealed with DNA was not released except at higher temperatures. With *E. coli* RNA, this second fraction amounted to 1.2% of the RNA applied to the gel. Renewed hybridization of the first RNA fraction with fresh DNA led to retention of about 0.2% of the radioactivity. This gives an estimated messenger fraction of 1.4% of the total RNA (Bolton and McCarthy, 1962). A messenger fraction of this size means a piece of messenger of about 300 Å per ribosome, which is the same as the estimated distance between adjacent ribosomes on a polysome (Staehlin *et al.*, 1964).

Finally, the T4 specific messenger present 8 minutes after phage infection of *E. coli* has been measured by hybridization with T4 DNA adsorbed onto a cellulose column (Bautz, 1963c). Of the RNA applied to the column at 51°, 4% was retained in hybrid structures and could be eluted at low salt concentration.

In our opinion, a critical comparison of the several estimates of the messenger fraction must wait. The problem is elusive because differences between strains, growth conditions, and techniques may all contribute to the observed variability.

1-6 RNA SYNTHESIS

Enzymology. The double-stranded hybrid molecules formed between single-stranded DNA and complementary RNA molecules are very resistant to degradation by ribonuclease. This property has greatly facilitated the recognition of true hybrid structures in cases where only very small fractions of the RNA in a mixture actually anneal. It has thus been possible to show that not only mRNA but also the stable RNA species can hybridize with specific regions on homologous DNA molecules. The 23 S and the 16 S ribosomal RNA seem to be represented by distinct DNA regions, each of which accounts for about 0.2% of the *E. coli* genome (Yankofsky and Spiegelman, 1963), whereas only about 0.04% of the genome hybridizes with tRNA

(Giacomoni and Spiegelman, 1962; Goodman and Rich, 1963). The numerical relationship between the different RNA species, and between them and the sites on the genome, will be discussed in Chapter 3.

Since all RNA species seem to be copied from specific DNA regions, *all* RNA synthesis might be catalyzed by the same enzyme. A polymerase that performs the characteristic DNA-dependent RNA synthesis *in vitro* has actually been isolated from bacteria and from plant and animal cells (Weiss and Gladstone, 1959; Stevens, 1960; Hurwitz *et al.*, 1961; Ochoa *et al.*, 1961; Chamberlin and Berg, 1962). In the presence of DNA and the four natural riboside triphosphates (ATP, GTP, UTP, CTP), this enzyme catalyzes the production of high molecular weight RNA in great excess over the amount of DNA in the system; during the reaction inorganic pyrophosphate is liberated. The polymerase precipitates with the nucleic acids (Furth, Hurwitz, and Goldman, 1961), and in rat liver cells it is found exclusively in the nuclei (Weiss, 1960). The enzyme from *E. coli* has been purified and crystallized (J. Hurwitz, personal communication). In the form in which it is active in the cell it has a high molecular weight, between 5×10^5 and 10^6, and seems to be a nearly spherical polymer containing several subunits (Doerfler *et al.*, 1962; Fuchs *et al.*, 1964).

The most important properties of the enzyme are: (1) it is primed by different sorts of DNA, and (2) the RNA produced has the same base sequence as one, or the other, strand of the DNA template. Both these properties, of course, are necessary for accepting this polymerase as the general catalyst of RNA synthesis *in vivo*.

Natural double-stranded DNA from many sources has been used as primer, but the synthetic copolymers, deoxyadenylic-thymidylic acid and deoxyguanylic-cytidylic acid, as well as the single-stranded DNA isolated from the bacteriophage φX-174, are also active (Hurwitz *et al.*, 1961; Chamberlin and Berg, 1962).

When double-stranded DNA is used as primer, the RNA synthesized has the same base composition as the DNA (Hurwitz *et al.*, 1962; Weiss and Nakamoto, 1961a; Chamberlin and Berg, 1962) but, with single-stranded DNA as primer, a product is obtained whose base composition is approximately complementary to that of the DNA. Thus, *in vitro*, both strands of a double-stranded primer may give rise to complementary RNA strands (Hurwitz *et al.*, 1962; Chamberlin and Berg, 1962) with the same nearest-neighbor frequencies as the DNA primer (Weiss and Nakamoto, 1961b; Hurwitz *et al.*, 1962).

The DNA-dependent RNA synthesis is inhibited by the antibiotic, actinomycin D, both in living cells and *in vitro* (Reich *et al.*, 1961; Goldberg and Rabinowitz, 1962; Hurwitz *et al.*, 1962). The inhibition does not involve the enzyme itself, but results from the antibiotic combining with deoxyguanylic acid residues in the DNA. The amount of actinomycin bound is directly related to the content of guanine-cytosine base pairs, and neither binding nor inhibition is observed if the synthetic deoxyadenylate-thymidylate copolymer is used as primer (Goldberg, Rabinowitz, and Reich, 1962; Kahan, Kahan, and Hurwitz, 1963).

***In vivo* versus *in vitro* synthesis.** The close resemblance in base composition between the bacterial DNA and the messenger fraction originally led to the view that both strands of the DNA were copied *in vivo*. At this point we shall concentrate on recent evidence *against* this notion.

Indirect evidence has been obtained from studies of point mutations in the *rII* locus of bacteriophage T4 (cf. Benzer, 1961). In contrast to wild-type T4, the *rII* mutants fail to reproduce in the K strain of *E. coli*. A number of the *rII* mutations are known to have been caused by a substitution in the phage DNA of an adenine-thymine pair for a guanine-hydroxymethylcytosine pair, and, if the K strain is infected with one of these *rII* mutants, in the presence of fluorouracil, about half of the infected cells produce a few progeny particles. This phenomenon is purely phenotypic, since the *rII* genotype is preserved in this progeny (Champe and Benzer, 1962). The effect is explained by assuming that the analogue substitutes for uracil in messenger molecules replicated from the *rII* locus, and that the substituted messenger will have a certain probability of producing a normal, wild-type protein molecule. Presumably a few of the normal protein molecules, synthesized early enough, will ensure that one or a few mature phage particles are present in the cell at the time of lysis. The fact that only half the *AT* mutants respond to fluorouracil was taken to indicate that the messenger molecule is replicated from one DNA strand only.

Direct evidence, that *in vivo* only one DNA strand is copied, comes from studies with the DNA bacteriophages α of *Bacillus megaterium* (Tocchini-Valentini *et al.*, 1963) and SP8 of *B. subtilis* (Marmur and Greenspan, 1963). In these phages, the sister strands in the DNA differ enough in base composition so that they can be separated on the basis of their different buoyant densities. In both cases, labeled mRNA from phage-infected bacteria combined to form ribonuclease-resistant complexes with one of the DNA strands *only*. A completely analogous situation was studied by Hayashi, Hayashi, and Spiegelman (1963). They found that the mRNA produced in bacteria infected with bacteriophage φX-174 hybridizes with the double-stranded, replicating form of φX-174 DNA, but *not* with the single-stranded DNA isolated from the free phage. The same authors (1964) also showed that one strand only is copied when circularized, double-stranded φX DNA is used as primer *in vitro*. The product obtained behaved as the natural mRNA in hybridization experiments.

1-7 THE BACTERIAL PROTEINS

Structure and stability. The one-way flow of genetic information in the cell brings us from a sequence of nucleotides to a colinear array of amino acids. In the terminology of Linderstrøm-Lang (1952), such an amino acid chain constitutes the primary structure of a protein molecule. The chain, however, is known to be folded into secondary and tertiary structures, both of which are prerequisite for the biological function of the molecule. The secondary structure is produced mainly by hydrogen bonding between amino acids *close* together in the chain, as exemplified by the α-helix of Pauling, Corey, and Branson (1951). The final and more compact tertiary structure is maintained by *distant* intrachain hydrogen bonds, hydrophobic bonds, and covalent disulfide bonds (Schachman, 1963).

Sarabhai *et al.* (1964) recently succeeded in demonstrating colinearity between the genetic map and the peptide sequence of the head protein of the bacteriophage T4; strong indication of colinearity has also been obtained in the case of tryptophan synthetase of *E. coli* (Yanofsky, 1963; Yanofsky *et al.*, 1964).

It was suggested early that the natural folding might be a direct result of the order of the amino acids, i.e., that the secondary and tertiary structures are "contained" in the information specifying the primary structure (Crick, 1958). This hypothesis is supported by recent experiments. Most proteins are enzymes and do not function as such unless their secondary and tertiary structure is intact. Treatment with denaturing agents almost invariably leads to loss of the biological activity, and at the same time the molecule changes into a "fibrillar protein" (Linderstrøm-Lang, 1950). Bovine pancreatic ribonuclease (RNase) is a small protein molecule, containing only 124 amino acids, whose sequence has been completely resolved (Hirs, Moore, and Stein, 1960). Among the amino acids, 8 cysteine residues pair to form 4 disulfide bonds in the intact molecule. If these bonds are reduced, the molecule unfolds, and in this process the enzymatic activity is lost. After removal of the denaturing agent, the enzyme can be renatured by bubbling oxygen through the solution. Anfinsen *et al.* (1961) showed that such reoxidation can restore the enzymatic activity almost completely, and that disulfide groups reappear during the renaturation process. It appears that randomly formed S-S bridges are slowly rearranged until the thermodynamically most stable and enzymatically active configuration is reestablished (Epstein, Goldberger, and Anfinsen, 1963). Similar results have been obtained with alkaline phosphatase (Levinthal, Signer, and Fetherolf, 1962) and with egg-white lysozyme (Imai, Takagi, and Isemura, 1963), both of which contain disulfide bonds. Reversible denaturation has also been demonstrated with bacterial α-amylase (Isemura and Imanishi, 1962) and bacteriophage lysozyme (Merigan and Dreyer, 1963), neither of which contains S-S bonds.

These experiments show that the secondary and tertiary structure of a protein molecule can in fact be determined solely by the amino acid sequence, and there is no strong reason to think that this is not the rule. However, even under optimal conditions, *in vitro* renaturation of proteins is a very slow process compared to enzyme synthesis *in vivo*. Nothing definite is known about the "naturation" process, i.e., the transition from a polypeptide chain to a finished molecule *in vivo*. With two enzymes containing disulfide bonds, an RNase and a lysozyme, renaturation *in vitro* has been shown to be greatly accelerated by special proteins isolated from rat liver microsomes (Goldberger, Epstein, and Anfinsen, 1963; 1964). Hence the intracellular naturation process may be facilitated by catalysts, whose mode of action, however, is unknown.

In growing bacteria the proteins are very stable. Using an extremely sensitive radiochemical assay, Koch and Levy (1955) found their average half-life to be about 30 days in an exponentially growing culture of *E. coli* with a generation time of about 1 hour. The average half-life of the proteins of yeast has been similarly determined and found to be about 18 days in exponentially growing cells (Halvorson, 1958). In *nongrowing* cells the protein undergoes degradation and resynthesis at a rate of about 5% per hour at 35° (Mandelstam, 1958). Although not impressive, this turnover rate is much greater than that observed in growing cells.

Protein synthesis mediated by natural messenger RNA. As mentioned earlier, this process takes place on the 70 S ribosomes. The individual polypeptide chains are built up sequentially, beginning with the N-terminal amino acid, as shown by experiments with rabbit reticulocytes (Naughton and Dintzis, 1962; Dintzis and Knopf, 1963) and with bacteria (Goldstein and Brown, 1961; Goldstein, Goldstein, and Lowney, 1964).

In the reticulocyte experiments, cells were labeled with ^{3}H-leucine for short times and the soluble hemoglobin was isolated. When the radioactivity of the peptides from a tryptic digest was measured, a gradient could be established indicating that synthesis starts at the N-terminal valine and proceeds unidirectionally toward the C-terminal end of the chain. Similar results have been obtained *in vitro* by analyzing the very small quantities of labeled hemoglobin synthesized by isolated ribosomes (Hardesty *et al.*, 1963).

In bacterial experiments a technique had to be developed that would permit analysis of a mixture of many proteins. A leucine auxotroph of *E. coli* was first starved of the required amino acid and then brought to 0°; at this temperature ^{14}C-leucine was incorporated for short times. The isolated mixed proteins and peptides were degraded by means of a carboxypeptidase known to cause partial hydrolysis from the C-terminal end of a chain. This type of experiment showed that the shorter the pulse of ^{14}C-leucine, the greater the *fraction* of the label that is released by the enzyme. Clearly, this is the result to be expected if the most recently added amino acids are those that are split off first by the enzyme, i.e., if the chains grow from the N-terminal end (Goldstein, Goldstein, and Lowney, 1964). Experiments of this type can also be used to estimate the average time it takes to add an amino acid to a growing chain (this aspect of the work of Goldstein *et al.* will be discussed in Section 3–5).

If polypeptide chains always grow from the same end, the individual codons of a messenger molecule must present themselves in the right order at the proper site on a ribosome. Thus a messenger molecule must have directional orientation and, at one end, a point at which ribosomes first make contact and from which the message is to be read. Both these properties could be simple functions of the polynucleotide structure. Synthetic mRNA molecules with partly or completely defined sequences can now be synthesized (see, e.g., Khorana, 1964), and it should soon be possible to decide unequivocally whether the translation of a message proceeds in the same direction as the transcription. This is often taken for granted, but the problem should be settled experimentally, since it is of great importance when considering models for the regulation of enzyme synthesis by induction and repression (see Sections 1–8 and 1–9, as well as Chapter 5).

From existing crude estimates of the quantity of mRNA in bacteria, it can be calculated that the cell contains at least five ribosomes per messenger molecule, if the latter is assumed to code for a protein of average molecule weight. More than one ribosome might thus be associated with one messenger molecule, and aggregates of this kind were actually observed (Risebrough, Tissières, and Watson, 1962). *E. coli* cells infected with T2 bacteriophage were labeled with ^{14}C-uracil in the messenger fraction. The cells were broken in the presence of $10^{-2}\,M$ magnesium and the ribosomes were isolated, care being taken to keep the temperature below 4°. When these ribosomes were centrifuged through a sucrose gradient, most of the associated radioactivity sedimented with units larger than the 100 S particles. Furthermore, ribosome aggregates were incubated with labeled amino acids in a protein-synthesizing system, and again the radioactivity was found to sediment with the very large units. Finally, treatment of the amino acid-labeled aggregates with RNase brought the sedimentation constant of the radioactive material down to 70 S.

The role of polyribosomes (polysomes) as active protein-forming centers has now been demonstrated in reticulocytes (Gierer, 1963; Marks, Burka, and Schlessinger, 1962; Warner, Knopf, and Rich, 1963), in rat liver cells (Wettstein, Staehlin, and Noll, 1963), and in bacteria (Schaechter, 1963; Schlessinger, 1963; Staehlin *et al.*, 1963). In sedimentation diagrams of extracts a number of discrete peaks can be observed, corresponding to polysomes containing anywhere from 2 up to more than 20 70 S ribosomes. In agreement, electron micrographs show the polysomes as clusters in which the number of particles is related to the sedimentation constant of the polysome fraction (Warner, Rich, and Hall, 1962; Rich, Warner, and Goodman, 1963).

It is not an accident that ribosomes were studied for a relatively long time before the existence of polysomes was recognized. These large structures are fragile, and disintegrate unless the cells are opened carefully and the extracts treated so as to minimize nuclease activity. Now that it is known how to avoid extensive destruction, it may be time to ask what the evidence is that polysomes are not preparation artifacts. We know that aggregates form when ribosomes are mixed with synthetic polynucleotides (Barondes and Nirenberg, 1962; Spyrides and Lipmann, 1962; Gilbert, 1963a). It is possible, of course, that the ribosomes found in these aggregates attached themselves individually at one end of the polynucleotide chain and moved along to make room for the next. However, if this is *not* the way polysomes form *in vitro*, it means that free ribosomes can attach more or less anywhere along a polynucleotide chain, and artificial aggregates *could* thus be produced, or existing aggregates enlarged, during the preparation of cell extracts. The best indication that polysomes exist in living cells probably is to be found in electron micrographs of sectioned reticulocytes; in these cells nearly all the ribosomes occur in clusters of 4–6 particles, which is a "reasonable" size for a polysome synthesizing globin chains (cf. Section 1–5).

Protein synthesis can be studied *in vitro* by using polysomes of known size isolated from living cells (Wettstein, Staehlin, and Noll, 1963; Noll, Staehlin, and Wettstein, 1963; Goodman and Rich, 1963). In this way, it has been found that the quantity of protein formed per 70 S particle increases as the average number of these particles per polysome goes up, and that single ribosomes do not take part in protein formation. Furthermore, the aggregates break down during protein synthesis in such a manner that the increase in the number of *free* 70 S particles equals the increase in the *total* number of units of all sizes. This indicates that the polysomes break down by releasing one 70 S particle at a time. In striking contrast to this systematic breakdown, treatment with low concentrations of RNase was found to produce random cleavage of the polysomes, yielding progressively smaller and smaller aggregates.

All these observations support the notion that, during protein synthesis, ribosomes move along the mRNA molecule, and that when the entire message has been translated a particle leaves the aggregate and the nascent protein molecule is released. The complications arising when this simple model is applied to messenger molecules coding for several proteins will be discussed below (Section 1–9).

Protein synthesis mediated by artificial messenger RNA. Let us now consider the formation of polypeptides in *in vitro* systems primed by synthetic polynucleotides. We have dis-

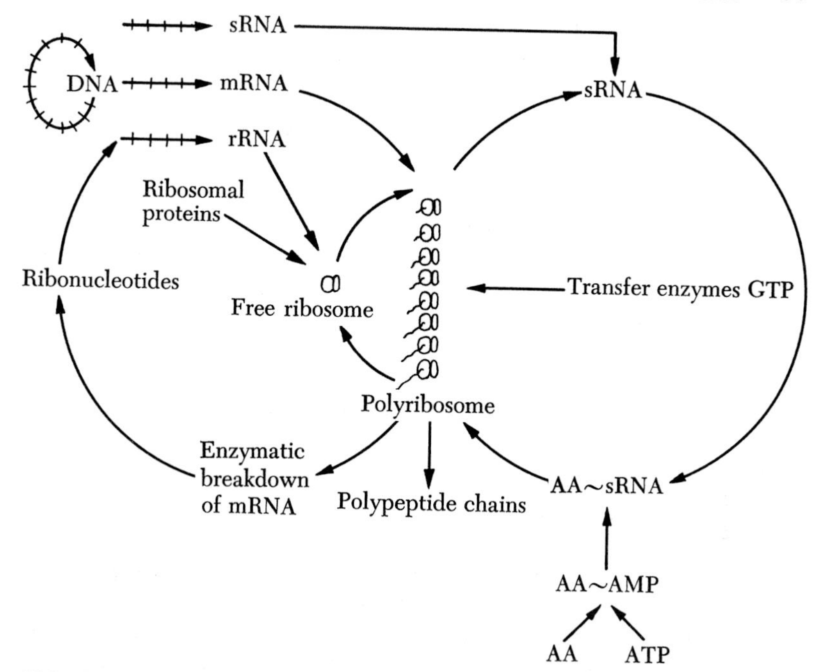

FIGURE 1-1 Schematic view of protein synthesis. (From Watson, J. D., 50th anniversary meeting of the French Biochemical Society, Paris, April 6, 1964.)

cussed the enzymatic activation and coupling of an amino acid to a specific molecule of tRNA (Section 1-4). In this process ATP is cleaved and the energy is conserved in the aminoacyl-RNA. Nevertheless, when purified ribosomes and polyuridylic acid are incubated with ^{14}C-phenylalanyl tRNA, the formation of polyphenylalanine depends on the further addition of GTP and two soluble enzymes (Fessenden and Moldave, 1961; Nathans and Lipmann, 1961; Nakamoto *et al.*, 1963). One of these enzymes may be specific for the binding of an aminoacyl-tRNA to the ribosome, while the other may be involved in peptide bond formation (Shaeffer, Arlinghaus, and Schweet, 1965).

The polyphenylalanine chains formed in this system are not spontaneously released from the 70 S ribosomes. When these particles dissociate at low magnesium concentrations the polypeptide chains are found to remain associated with the 50 S subunits. When this complex is dissociated further by sodium dodecyl sulfate, the polyphenylalanine chain remains attached to a tRNA molecule. This double unit can be identified by sedimenting, in a sucrose gradient, material labeled with ^{32}P in the RNA and with ^{14}C in the incorporated amino acid. Final dissociation can be achieved by breaking the aminoacyl-RNA bond at pH 10 and separating the ^{32}P-labeled tRNA from the ^{14}C-labeled polyphenylalanine (Gilbert, 1963b). The strong initial binding of the polypeptide chain to the 70 S ribosome seems to involve a special site on the surface of the 50 S subunit onto which tRNA molecules can be firmly attached (Canon, Krug, and Gilbert, 1963; Takanami, 1962). Several more tRNA molecules are often found on the ribosomes, but are not held as firmly (cf. Section 3–4).

From what we have just seen, the growth of a polypeptide chain must represent a series of steps in which the finished part of the chain is transferred from one tRNA molecule to another. The actual mechanism by which a codon on the messenger directs the attachment of the proper tRNA molecule is not known. The hydrogen bonds between the codon and the corresponding triplet on the tRNA molecule are definitely too weak to keep this molecule and the growing polypeptide chain attached to the ribosome (Lipsett, Heppel, and Bradley, 1961); presumably a larger region on the tRNA molecule is involved in the attachment. The mRNA, on the other hand, seems to combine with the 30 S subunit of the ribosome (Okamoto and Takanami, 1963; Takanami and Zubay, 1964).

The newly synthesized protein molecule probably has assumed its definitive secondary and tertiary structure by the time its connection with the ribosome is broken. The most direct indication is the observation that the enzymatic activity of a protein molecule can be expressed while the molecule is still attached to a ribosome. The picture is complicated, however, by the fact that many enzymes are active only when a polymer has been formed consisting of two or more individually folded polypeptide chains. β-Galactosidase is such an enzyme, and it has been possible to study the formation of active polymers *in vitro* by mixing monomers obtained from different, lactose-negative mutants (Perrin, 1963). This act of complementation also takes place if one of the monomers has remained attached to a ribosome, and in this case the process is much faster (Zipser and Perrin, 1963). The significance of these observations is not clear. It could mean that a free monomer associates most readily with an attached one, because the latter has not yet assumed its definitive configuration.

The effects of antibiotics on protein synthesis. Three antibiotics, viz., puromycin, chloramphenicol, and streptomycin, specifically inhibit protein synthesis both *in vivo* and *in vitro*. They are valuable tools in the study of protein synthesis.

The close similarity in chemical structure between puromycin and the terminal end of an aminoacyl-tRNA was first recognized by Yarmolinsky and de la Haba (1959), who showed that the antibiotic inhibits the transfer of amino acids from tRNA to the growing polypeptide chains. Puromycin labeled in the amino acid moiety of the molecule when added to a hemoglobin-forming *in vitro* system was found in the liberated peptide to the extent of one molecule of puromycin per N-terminal valine residue (Allen and Zamecnik, 1962). Similarly, radioactive puromycin is incorporated into acid-precipitable material when added to a culture of *E. coli* at concentrations which inhibit growth and amino acid incorporation.

The incorporation of intact puromycin was rigorously demonstrated by reisolation and crystallization (Nathans, 1964). These experiments indicate that puromycin, occasionally, takes the place of an aminoacyl-tRNA complex, that the drug is incorporated in the C-terminal position of the growing polypeptide chain, and that the chain is released because no tRNA is present to keep it attached to the 50 S particle. In polysomal systems the addition of puromycin produces an accelerated, but still GTP-dependent, breakdown of the polysomes (Noll, Staehlin, and Wettstein, 1963; Villa-Trevino *et al.*, 1964). To explain this, Noll (1965) suggests that puromycin causes the ribosomes to move faster along the mRNA molecule, thereby producing polysomes with increased spacing between neighboring ribosomes.

Like puromycin, chloramphenicol arrests growth and protein synthesis. The concomitant effect of this drug on RNA synthesis will be discussed in detail (Chapter 5). *In vitro* chloramphenicol blocks the transfer of amino acids from the tRNA molecules to the polypeptide chains on the ribosomes (Nathans and Lipmann, 1961; Nirenberg and Matthaei, 1961; Wood and Berg, 1962). Similarly, the incorporation by *E. coli* cells of radioactive puromycin into insoluble material is inhibited (Nathans, 1964). It has been suggested that chloramphenicol interferes with the attachment of mRNA to the ribosomes (Jardetsky and Julian, 1964; Kućan and Lipmann, 1964; Weisberger, Wolfe, and Armentrout, 1964).

Streptomycin, the third antibiotic to be discussed, inhibits protein synthesis by an entirely different mechanism. Genetically, bacteria can be sensitive to, resistant to, or dependent on, streptomycin. All three phenotypes can be shown to represent alleles at the same genetic locus. Streptomycin-dependent strains grow only in the presence of the drug, and it has been shown that removal of streptomycin seriously reduces protein synthesis without affecting RNA synthesis (Spotts, 1962). On this evidence it was suggested that streptomycin might act on the ribosomes, and that the streptomycin locus might be involved in determining the structure of the ribosome (Spotts and Stanier, 1961). This notion is strongly supported by the fact that protein synthesis *in vitro* is inhibited only if the ribosomes are prepared from streptomycin-sensitive bacteria (Speyer, Lengyel, and Basilio, 1962). Pushing the analysis further, 70 S ribosomes were prepared *in vitro* by recombining 50 S and 30 S particles, one of which was derived from streptomycin-sensitive and the other from streptomycin-resistant cells. With such artificial ribosomes, the *in vitro* synthesis of polyphenylalanine was inhibited by streptomycin only when the 30 S particles came from sensitive cells. However, streptomycin does not seem to interfere with the actual binding of polyuridylic acid to the 30 S particles.

The interaction between streptomycin and mRNA has been found in some cases to modify the translation of the genetic code. Thus certain bacterial mutants, defective for ornithine transcarbamylase or for galactose transferase, will produce small amounts of these enzymes if streptomycin is added to the growth medium (Gorini and Kataja, 1964; Lederberg, Cavalli-Sforza, and Lederberg, 1964). This effect can be explained by assuming that streptomycin causes occasional misreading of the messenger, and that *mis*reading may make sense out of a mis-sense or non-sense codon. In other words, streptomycin is supposed in these cases to act as a phenotypic suppressor. This interpretation is strongly supported by *in vitro* experiments. When streptomycin-sensitive ribosomes are used with polyuridylic acid as messenger the normal event, i.e., incorporation of phenylalanine into hot TCA-insoluble material, is strongly inhibited by the drug; at the same time, however, incorporation of isoleucine, serine, and leucine is stimulated (Davies, Gilbert, and Gorini, 1964). The mechanism by which streptomycin acts in the living cell is not known in detail.

1-8 REGULATORY MECHANISMS

We shall now discuss evidence showing that small molecules assimilated from outside or produced inside a cell can modify both the *activity* and the *production* of individual enzymes. Both these regulatory mechanisms have been studied intensively in recent years and we are beginning to understand the principles involved in molecular terms. The rapid advances in these areas of research have led to the development of a set of concepts of almost universal applicability, but at the same time it has become a little too easy to describe many biological phenomena in a vague and general way by invoking new regulatory functions. Since the number of possible functions and interactions is very large, descriptions of this kind are not of much interest; in fact they do little more than affirm the truth that, with a sufficient number of variables, any observation can be "explained." In this and in later chapters we shall therefore try to concentrate on cases in which it is possible to be quite specific about the mechanisms as well as the cell components that are invoked to "explain."

Regulation of enzyme activity, or feed-back inhibition. The chief characteristic of this mechanism is that the *end* product of a linear biosynthetic sequence specifically inhibits the enzyme that catalyzes the *first* reaction of that sequence. This mechanism was first suggested by Novick and Szilard (1954) and its existence has been demonstrated in several systems, both in intact, growing cells and *in vitro* with isolated enzymes. The first clear case of feed-back inhibition was that of isoleucine, which is formed from threonine by a sequence of reactions, and was shown to inhibit the enzyme that deaminates threonine to α-ketobutyrate (Umbarger, 1956; Changeux, 1963). The lysine and threonine pathways are other examples. Thus lysine inhibits one of the two aspartokinases and dihydropicolinic acid synthetase, while threonine inhibits a different aspartokinase and homoserine kinase (Stadtman *et al.*, 1961; Cohen and Patte, 1963). In both instances the amino acid inhibits at a branch-point where two separate synthetic chains begin, or two different enzymes perform the same catalytic step. In the pyrimidine pathway the first enzyme, aspartate transcarbamylase, is inhibited by cytidine triphosphate (CTP), which is the end product of the reaction sequence and one of the substrates for RNA synthesis (Yates and Pardee, 1956) (see also Section 4–2).

In the examples just mentioned it is evident that the end product is structurally quite different from the substrate, as well as the product of the reaction it inhibits. To explain this fact, Monod, Changeux, and Jacob (1963) assumed that, in addition to the *active site* which combines with the substrate, an enzyme may possess an *allosteric site* whose structure is complementary to the metabolite, the allosteric effector, which inhibits the activity of that enzyme. In the most general form the theory postulates that the effector stabilizes the enzyme in a configuration in which the active site, and with that the biological activity of the molecule, is altered (Monod, Wyman, and Changeux, 1965). Aspartate transcarbamylase seems to exhibit such an allosteric effect. This enzyme has a molecular weight of 300,000, and can be separated into units of molecular weights of about 100,000 and 30,000, respectively. The large unit carries the catalytic sites, whereas the small unit is specific for the binding of the feed-back inhibitor, CTP. One may therefore assume that the interaction between the subunits, and perhaps their position relative to each other, can be changed by CTP in such a way that enzyme activity is lost (Gerhart and Pardee, 1963; J. C. Gerhart, 1965, personal communication). It is believed that allosteric effects are most readily, if not exclusively, produced when the protein involved contains two or more subunits.

Regulation of enzyme synthesis. The genome of a bacterial cell contains the information necessary for the synthesis of one or a few thousand different proteins. In a steady state of growth the concentration of a given enzyme in a cell must reflect the rate at which information flows from the corresponding genetic locus. *A priori,* this flow rate might be thought to be regulated at the level of *transcription,* at the level of *translation,* or at both.

In 1961, Jacob and Monod presented strong genetic and enzymological evidence for the regulation of protein synthesis at the transcription level. Their model holds a central position in modern biology, and we shall therefore discuss in some detail the studies of inducible and repressible enzymes on which the new ideas are based. The model itself will be described in the next section.

Enzyme induction. The inducible enzymes are found chiefly among those that catalyze the entry into the cell and the breakdown of metabolites supplied in the growth medium. These catabolic enzymes are produced in quantity only if the relevant metabolite, or a close analogue thereof, is present in the medium. Of the inducible enzymes, β-galactosidase is by far the most thoroughly studied, largely as a result of the remarkable work of Monod and his colleagues during the last two decades.

Most wild-type strains of *E. coli* can use lactose (*lac*) as their main carbon source, and when they do the cells contain β-galactosidase. This enzyme acts as a transgalactosidase which splits lactose and a number of other β-galactosides (cf. Cohn, 1957).

The formation of β-galactosidase can be induced by lactose which, however, undergoes transgalactosidation in the cell before acting as inducer (Burstein *et al.*, 1965). The two analogues, methylthio-β-D-galactoside and isopropylthio-β-D-galactoside are the most potent inducers known, and none of them is hydrolyzed by the enzyme. This is of great importance for kinetic studies, since the enzyme formed does not affect the concentration of inducers of this kind, nor does it produce new catabolites from them. This very favorable experimental condition is called *induction gratuit* (Monod and Cohn, 1952).

Induced enzymes are always formed directly from amino acids (Rotman and Spiegelman, 1954; Hogness, Cohn, and Monod, 1955), and under conditions of maximum induction, β-galactosidase constitutes about 4–6%, and in special cases as much as 25%, of the protein produced in the cells (Jacob and Monod, 1961a,b; Horiuchi, Tomizawa, and Novick, 1962). In uninduced cells the β-galactosidase concentration is low, and in wild-type strains it is about 1000 times less than the maximum concentration.

At saturating inducer concentrations the full rate of enzyme synthesis is reached in about 3 minutes at 37° and, when the inducer is removed from the medium, synthesis stops within 5 minutes (Pardee and Prestidge, 1961; Boezi and Cowie, 1961). We have seen earlier that information is released by the inducer in the form of specific mRNA molecules, and the pulse induction experiments discussed in Section 1–5 show that messenger production is initiated very rapidly, and that it takes only about $1^1/_2$ minutes at 37° to produce sufficient messenger to establish the steady-state level in which there is balance between synthesis and decay (Képès, 1963).

In typical *E. coli* strains, induction of β-galactosidase also releases the synthesis of the galactoside permease, which is responsible for the specific transport of galactosides into the cells, and of a transacetylase of unknown physiological significance (Rickenberg *et al.*, 1956; Zabin, Képès, and Monod, 1959). The transacetylase is always produced in amounts strictly proportional to those of β-galactosidase, and the two enzymes are said to be under *coordinate control* (Monod, Jacob, and Gros, 1962).

The molecular weight of β-galactosidase is approximately 540,000 (Sund and Weber, 1963; Craven, Steers, and Anfinsen, 1965). It seems to contain four identical subunits (Zipser, 1963; Karlsson *et al.*, 1964; Steers *et al.*, 1965), each of which may consist of three monomers of about 45,000 molecular weight (Zabin, 1963a). The transacetylase has a molecular weight of 65,000 and is probably a dimer with two identical halves (Zabin, 1963a,b). When these figures are used to calculate the number of monomers of β-galactosidase and of transacetylase, respectively, that are synthesized during induction, the ratio proves to be about 30:1 (Zabin, 1963a). We shall discuss later how this striking inequality may be reconciled with the fact that the two enzymes are under coordinate control (see next section).

Mutants have been isolated which are defective either in β-galactosidase or in permease and transacetylase production. The genetic loci involved (*z* and *y*, respectively) map close together within a region that accounts for only about $^1/_{500}$ of the *E. coli* linkage map (Jacob and Monod, 1961a,b). Other mutants are known which produce β-galactosidase and permease constitutively, i.e., the enzymes are synthesized whether or not inducer is present. Two genetic determinants for constitutivity are located near each other and within the lactose region (Jacob and Monod, 1965); they are referred to as the regulator (*R*) and the operator (*O*) locus, respectively. The R^- and O^c mutants, both constitutive, can be distinguished by their behavior in diploid cells. Finally, mutants have been isolated which under no circumstance synthesize any of the three enzymes, although genetic analysis shows that they possess the intact structural genes. Some of these mutants, designated R^s, map in the *R* locus (Willson *et al.*, 1964), whereas others, the O^o mutations, map at the extreme end of the *z* locus and very close to the O^c locus (Beckwith, 1964). The behavior of the different classes of mutants in the presence and absence of inducer is illustrated in Figure 1–2.

When tested for the production of specific mRNA (by the hybridization method discussed earlier), the O^c mutants produce enzymes as well as specific messenger in the absence of inducer, whereas the O^o mutants never produce either enzyme or messenger (Attardi *et al.*, 1963b; Beckwith, 1963). The so-called "polarity mutants" will be discussed in the next section.

In *E. coli*, the utilization of another sugar, galactose (*gal*), depends on three enzymes, galactokinase, galactose transferase, and galactose epimerase; they are all induced by galactose or by the gratuitous inducer, fucose (the 6-deoxy derivative of *gal*) (Kalckar, Kurahashi, and Jordan, 1959; Buttin, 1961). The three enzymes are closely linked genetically (Lederberg, 1960), and are under coordinate control (Yarmolinsky, Jordan, and Wies-

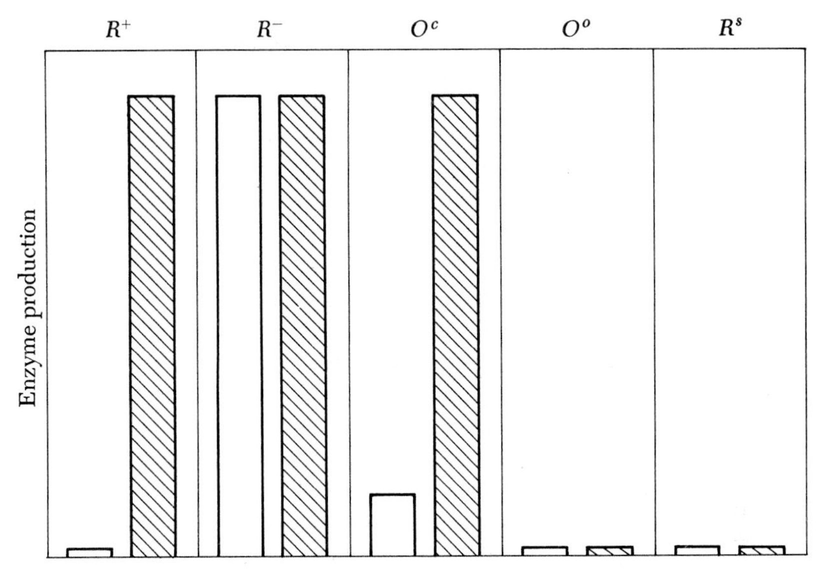

FIGURE 1–2 The production of β-galactosidase in various genotypes of *E. coli* in the absence of inducer (white columns) and in the presence of inducer (hatched columns).

mayer, 1961; Buttin, 1963). The phage λdg, which transduces the galactose region with a high frequency, has been used as source of *gal*-specific DNA in hybridization experiments to test for the production of *gal* messenger in induced and uninduced cells. As with β-galactosidase, induction was accompanied by an increase in the production of specific mRNA (Attardi *et al.*, 1963a).

Among the constitutive *gal* mutants, one class which may be of the *R* type is not linked to the *gal* region. Other mutants are of the O^c type and map at one end of the *gal* segment close to the structural gene for galactose epimerase (Buttin, 1963). Like the O^c mutants in the *lac* region, the O^c *gal* mutants seem to produce the specific mRNA in the absence as well as in the presence of inducer (Attardi *et al.*, 1963b). Mutants of the O^o type have also been isolated. These mutants map between the transferase and the epimerase genes and *not* (as in the case of the analogous *lac* mutants) at one extreme end of the gene cluster (Adler and Kaiser, 1963). The O^o *gal* mutants produce no specific messenger even in the presence of inducer (Hill and Echols, 1965).

When *E. coli* grows with arabinose as energy and carbon source, four enzymes are induced, L-arabinose isomerase, Lribulokinase, L-ribulose-5-phosphate-4-epimerase, and arabinose permease. The structural genes for the three first enzymes are very closely linked, and the distance between this cluster and the permease locus is too great to be estimated by transduction experiments (Englesberg, 1961; Lee and Englesberg, 1963). In several isomerase or kinase mutants the loss of one enzyme is accompanied by very significant changes in the quantities in which the other enzymes of the group are synthesized (Lee and Englesberg, 1962; 1963). Certain mutants that map at one end of the arabinose segment show no activity for any of the three closely linked enzymes, but, since they also lack the unlinked permease, are not quite analogous to the O^o mutants described above (Helling and Weinberg, 1963).

Enzyme repression. Most of the enzymes we shall now be concerned with have biosynthetic functions. When the end product of a given synthetic sequence, e.g., an amino acid, is added to growing bacteria, the synthesis of *all* the enzymes of that sequence is greatly reduced; the system as a whole is said to be repressed. If the amino acid is removed the system returns to the original, more or less completely derepressed state. In both directions the transition is as fast as with induction. The first examples of enzyme repression, described by Monod and Cohen-Bazire (1953) and Cohn, Cohen, and Monod (1953), concerned the tryptophan and the methionine synthetases of *E. coli*, respectively. The effects of repression and derepression upon the concentrations of enzymes in the cells will be discussed later (Chapters 2 and 4).

We shall now present some data concerning the four best known repressible systems: the enzymes involved in the synthesis of histidine, arginine, and the pyrimidines, respectively, and the alkaline phosphatase.

Histidine is formed from ATP and phosphoribosyl-pyrophosphate in ten steps, all of which have been characterized enzymatically (cf. Ames and Hartman, 1962). The synthesis of all ten enzymes can be repressed by adding histidine to the growth medium. Four of them have been studied sufficiently to show that they are repressed coordinately (Ames and Garry, 1959).

Transduction analysis of more than 1000 independently isolated histidine-requiring mutants of *Salmonella typhimurium* shows that the structural genes for the ten histidine enzymes are clustered in a small region of the bacterial chromosome (Hartman, Loper, and Šerman, 1960; Ames, Garry, and Herzenberg, 1960; Ames, Martin, and Garry, 1961). Mutants that can grow in the presence of the histidine analogue triazole-alanine are permanently derepressed for the histidine enzymes; in some the genetic change was found to have occurred near the end of the histidine region (O^c-type mutants), whereas other mutants mapped outside this region (R^--type mutants) (Ames and Hartman, 1963). The O^c-type mutations could be localized close to or inside of the structural gene of the first enzyme in the biosynthetic sequence. Finally, certain mutants with a deletion in this gene do not synthesize any of the histidine enzymes, and might therefore be classified as O^o mutants (Ames, Hartman, and Jacob, 1963).

In *E. coli*, the synthesis of the six enzymes in the pyrimidine pathway are repressed by uracil (Yates and Pardee, 1956). The structural genes for three of the enzymes in the sequence map together in a small chromosomal segment, while the other three genes map separately and away from the cluster. When cultures of pyrimidine-requiring strains are supplemented with different pyrimidine precursors or derivatives, the enzyme levels change. Four of the enzymes in the sequence, including the three that map together, were found to vary in a coordinate fashion; the remaining two enzymes follow the same pattern qualitatively but not quantitatively (Beckwith *et al.*, 1962; Taylor *et al.*, 1964). Nonrepressible mutants have not been found in this system.

Carbamate kinase supplies carbamyl phosphate not only for pyrimidine biosynthesis but also for the synthesis of arginine. Interactions between the control mechanisms of these two pathways could therefore be expected, and it has in fact been observed that the partial repression of the synthesis of carbamate kinase, caused by uracil, is followed by increased synthesis of the enzymes of the arginine pathway. Thus the addition of uracil brings the arginine system from a partially repressed to a more derepressed state (Gorini and Kalman, 1963).

In *E. coli*, the seven enzymes involved in the biosynthesis of arginine are repressed when arginine is added to a growing culture (cf. Vogel, 1961; Maas, 1961). Studies of arginine mutants have provided one of the key observations concerning repression: in mutants in which one of the seven enzymes is missing, arginine will repress the synthesis of *all* the other six, i.e., those that function before as well as those that function after the block in the reaction sequence. Thus repression of a given enzyme in the series does *not* depend on accumulation in the cell of either the substrate or the immediate product of the defective, or missing, enzyme (Gorini and Maas, 1957). It has further been shown that the arginine analogue canavanine will repress, whereas the intermediates ornithine and citrulline, which are structurally quite different from arginine, have no effect (Schwartz and Maas, 1960).

The structural genes of the arginine enzymes have been mapped by means of recombination and transduction. Three, possibly four, of these genes form a cluster, while the remaining ones map singly and at great distances from each other and from the cluster (Gorini, Gundersen, and Burger, 1961; Maas, 1961; Vogel, Bacon, and Baich, 1963). Nonrepressible mutants have been isolated by selecting for the ability to grow in the presence of canavanine. These mutations map close to the locus for streptomycin resistance; they are not linked to any of the arginine enzymes and, since they affect the latter collectively, are classified as *R* mutations (Maas, 1961). This interpretation is strengthened by the observation that the R^+ allele is dominant in zygotes and in diploid cells (Maas *et al.*, 1964; Maas and Clark, 1964). Repression of the arginine enzymes seems *not* to be coordinate (Vogel, 1961; Gorini, Gundersen, and Burger, 1961; Maas, 1961). Finally, it has been shown that, as one would expect, the activating enzyme that couples arginine to its tRNA is not repressed by arginine (Boman, Boman, and Maas, 1961).

The alkaline phosphatase of *E. coli* is formed only when the concentration of inorganic phosphate is very low; at high concentrations, enzyme synthesis is almost completely repressed. Nonrepressible mutants fall into two groups, both genetically and with respect to the amount of enzyme they produce. Mutants with alterations in the *R1* locus, which is very close to the structural gene of the phosphatase, are "low-level" constitutives and produce about 20% of the maximum amount of enzyme in the presence of inorganic phosphate. Mutations in the *R2* locus, which map far away from the structural gene, result in complete loss of repressibility (Echols *et al.*, 1961). Certain other properties of the *R1* and *R2* mutants will be discussed below.

1-9 THE OPERATOR MODEL AND SOME OF ITS APPLICATIONS

It is now generally accepted that, at least in bacteria, information is released from DNA in the form of unstable mRNA molecules. Nevertheless, this idea was probably the most provoking element of the unifying theory for the regulation of enzyme synthesis proposed by Jacob and Monod (1961a,b). In their model, the bacterial chromosome is divided into units of genetic expression, or *operons,* whose activity is governed by a special genetic element, the *operator.* The unit function of an operon is reflected in the coordinate repression of clusters of structural genes, and the role of the operator is revealed by the O^c mutants in which phenotypic expression of the operon is more or less unrestricted.

The small molecules to which the regulatory mechanism responds are thought primarily to interact with an "operator-specific" repressor substance. The structure of this key substance is defined by an *R* locus, and its function is to regulate the flow of information from the corresponding operon. In induction, the primary interaction between the repressor substance and the small inducer (effector) molecule is imagined to "inactivate" the repressor molecule, i.e., to alter it so that it no longer is able to interfere with messenger production (or release). In a repressible system, the theory postulates that it is the *complex* between the repressor substance and the effector that is active in interfering with messenger production. Thus, induction and repression are looked upon as complementary expressions of the same basic mechanism.

An interesting situation, which seems directly to reflect this dual property of the model, has been observed with the arginine enzymes. As a result of mutation, the production of one of these enzymes is stimulated instead of being repressed when arginine is added to the culture. In this mutant the other arginine enzymes are repressed in the normal way (Vogel, Bacon, and Baich, 1963).

The model of Jacob and Monod leads to definite predictions, several of which have been verified experimentally. Thus, mutations in the *R or* in the *O* locus might be expected to produce the same phenotype. With β-galactosidase, both types of mutant might be expected to produce the enzyme constitutively because either the repressor substance or the site of repression would have been altered. This ambiguity can be resolved by separating the *R* and the *O* loci. In *E. coli,* partial diploids can be constructed that carry one set of *O* and *R* alleles in the bacterial genome, and another set in an episome that has been transferred to the cell from another strain (Jacob and Adelberg, 1959). According to theory, an *O* mutation would be expected to affect only the expression of genes on the *same* "chromosome" (i.e., genes in the cis position), and its effect would be independent of the presence, in cis or in trans position, of an R^+ allele. In other words, an *O* mutation would be dominant over an *R* mutation, but only with respect to genes in the cis position. In agreement with this, $[O^c z^+/i^+ z^-]$ heterozygotes[1] are found to synthesize β-galactosidase constitutively; furthermore, if the z^- allele is one that allows the production of cross-reacting material,[1] *this* protein will be synthesized only in the presence of inducer. Together, these observations show that repressor substance is present in the cell, but cannot interfere with the mutated operator, the O^c locus (Jacob and Monod, 1961a). Analogous effects have been observed in the galactose system (Buttin, 1961).

The O^c mutations in the *lac* and *gal* regions are localized at the extreme end of the operon. In the histidine region, nonrepressible mutants have been isolated in which the mutations also map at one end of the gene cluster. It is logical to assume that they are operator mutants, but it has not yet been possible to construct diploid strains in which the crucial test for dominance could be made.

If an *R* locus is assumed to be the structural gene for a repressor substance which is freely diffusible in the cell, it is clear that an R^+ gene should be dominant over an R^- gene in a heterozygote. This relationship has been demonstrated, both in the β-galactosidase and in the alkaline phosphatase system, by introducing the appropriate episomes (Jacob and Monod, 1961b; Echols *et al.*, 1961).

A so-called "superrepressed" *R* mutant in the *lac* system (i^s) has the peculiar property that any *z* locus in the cell, whether in cis or trans position relative to i^s, is *in*sensitive to induction. Thus a diploid of the constitution $[i^s/i^+z^+]$ does not produce β-galactosidase. This has been interpreted to mean that the mutated *R* gene gives rise to a repressor substance so modified that it fails to interact with the inducer, and therefore remains an active repressor under all conditions. In aggreement with theory, an $[i^s/O^c z^+]$ diploid was found to be constitutive, i.e., the mutated operator (O^c) is insensitive also to the i^s product, the "superrepressor" (Willson *et al.*, 1964).

The nature of the repressor substance. Recombination experiments in which an R^+ gene is introduced into a constitutive

[1] The symbols *z* and *i* represent the structural gene for β-galactosidase and the corresponding *R* gene, respectively. "Cross-reacting material" refers to a *z* product without enzymatic activity which, however, reacts with an antiserum against β-galactosidase.

(R^-) mutant show that repression, i.e., expression of the R^+ allele, can be established in the presence of inhibitors of protein synthesis (Pardee and Prestidge, 1959). This indicates that the repressor substance might *not* be a protein, and, consequently, a polynucleotide structure was suggested. However, it is extremely difficult to see how a great variety of structurally different effector molecules could act, unless each kind were "recognized" in the cell by a specific protein. As with feed-back inhibition, an allosteric effect can be invoked as follows: the effector may interact specifically with a protein whose configuration is thereby changed in such a way that it is no longer active (in the case of induction) or becomes active (in the case of repression) in blocking the synthesis, or release, of the relevant mRNA. A model like this, of course, does not exclude the possibility of an RNA component as intermediate between the allosteric protein and the operator.

Strains with mutations in the *R* locus (the *i* gene) have recently been isolated that produce β-galactosidase constitutively at 42°, but require induction when growing at 32°; in some strains the *i* product itself is unstable at the higher temperature, and in others the finished product is stable but its synthesis (or "naturation") is abnormally temperature-sensitive. The existence of such mutants shows that the *i* product probably is a protein, and experiments by Sadler and Novick (1965) indicate that the active form of this protein is *more* stable in the presence than in the absence of inducer. This could be due to an allosteric effect. It has furthermore been shown that normal amounts of the *i* product are formed in the absence as well as in the presence of an inducer of β-galactosidase (Novick, McCoy, and Sadler, 1965).

No assay has yet been devised that would permit identification of the product of an *R* locus by testing it *in vitro* for repressor activity. However, genetic evidence strongly indicates that some *R* products in fact are proteins. Several suppressor mutations are known that have the effect of correcting a mutational alteration in a structural gene. This has been demonstrated with certain mutants with alterations in the alkaline phosphatase gene (Garen and Siddiqi, 1962), or in one of the *rII* cistrons of phage T4 (Benzer and Champe, 1961). In both cases, cells carrying the suppressor gene (su^+) produce a functional protein, although the corresponding structural gene carries an altered, or non-sense codon that could not be translated in the wild-type strain (su^-). Certain constitutive mutants ($R1^-$ or $R2^-$) of the phosphatase system respond similarly, and recombinants (R^-, su^+) behave phenotypically like the wild type (R^+). It was therefore concluded that the *R1* and the *R2* gene products are proteins (Garen and Garen, 1963). This was verified in part when Garen and Otsuji (1964) isolated a protein which is not produced by strains carrying a deletion in the *R2* locus. The *R2* protein and the phosphatase seem to be under coordinate control, but no specific regulatory function has been ascribed to the former.

The size of the messenger molecule. In their original paper, Jacob and Monod (1961a) describe two possible ways of transcribing a complex message: on the one hand, individual messenger molecules might be produced, one corresponding to each of the proteins defined in the operon; on the other hand, the entire information might be transcribed as a single, continuous messenger molecule. It is clear, however, that the authors feel that the most direct way to account for the very striking phenomenon of coordinate control would be to accept the second alternative.

Under this view it is necessary to postulate that the beginning, possible interruptions between parts, and the end of the total message, respectively, are indicated by special codons, or punctuation marks. At the transcription level we have to visualize specific base sequences (perhaps containing unusual, or substituted bases) that mark the sites at which the polymerase synthesizing the mRNA can engage with and, later, disengage from the DNA template. The structure of these special sites is not known. However, a different type of punctuation mark has recently been identified by analyzing two special classes of suppressible mutants (called "amber" and "ochre"). A mutation of one of these types is expressed at the *translation* level by the release of an unfinished polypeptide chain (Sarabhai *et al.*, 1964). If the proper suppressor gene is introduced, translation can proceed past the critical point and, in the finished protein, serine is found to have replaced the amino acid normally present in the position corresponding to an "amber" mutation. In fact, two triplets have been identified, one for "amber" and one for "ochre," which are *not* read as amino acids but are used to specify "end and release of chain" (Brenner, Stretton, and Kaplan, 1965).

Very long messenger molecules may in fact exist that represent continuous transcripts of large operons. This is indicated by analysis of mixtures of pulse-labeled RNA from repressed cells (labeled with ^{14}C-uracil) and from derepressed cells (labeled with ^{3}H-uracil). When the histidine and lactose operons were studied in this way, the highest $^3H/^{14}C$ ratio was found in RNA fractions larger than the 23 S ribosomal RNA. The mRNA molecules from these operons would therefore seem to contain more than 4000 nucleotides each; i.e., one messenger molecule could code for proteins with a total of 1300 or more amino acids (Martin, 1963; Attardi *et al.*, 1963b).

As mentioned above, the one operon–one messenger hypothesis suggests that enzymes coded for in the same operon are under coordinate control because the entire message is transcribed in one continuous process. On the other hand, we have seen, in the *lac* operon, that two enzymes may be under coordinate control *without* being produced in equimolar amounts (Zabin, 1963a), and similar results have been obtained with the histidine enzymes. These observations have given rise to much speculation, most of which is based on experiments with a certain type of mutant, the so-called polarity or dual-effect mutant. In these strains a mutation in one structural gene affects the *quantities* of other enzymes produced in the same operon (Jacob and Monod, 1961b; Lee and Englesberg, 1962; Ames and Hartman, 1963). An extensive analysis of the histidine system has shown that genes situated between the operator and the gene carrying a polarity mutation are normally expressed, whereas all genes distal to the mutated site are greatly reduced in their activity. Of the histidine mutants tested about half were of this type, and the polarity effect could be observed in the repressed as well as in the derepressed state.

Some of the phenomena just described could be accounted for by assuming that the chance that protein synthesis continues past certain special codons is low and that, in most cases, the ribosome dissociates from the messenger at such a point. Codons with this property might, if placed between neighboring genes, account for the nonequimolar production of different enzymes belonging to the same operon; moreover, since the enzymes whose structural genes are close to the operator would always be produced in greater amounts than the more "distant" enzymes, the polarity effect could be explained. All this is quite speculative, and at least one case is known that does not fit the hypothesis. The arabinose operon contains the four loci, *D, A, B,* and *C,* and it has been found that a dual-effect mutation in *B* changes the production of enzyme *A* quantitatively, and vice versa (Lee and Englesberg, 1962).

Up to this point we have adhered strictly to the "dogma" of Jacob and Monod, which says that repression occurs at the level of the gene. This mechanism seems to be the general one in bacteria, but instances in which regulation occurs at the ribosomal level are not thereby excluded (see, e.g., McAuslan, 1963).

Catabolic repression. In bacteria the production of many metabolic enzymes is controlled by a relatively nonspecific repression mechanism in which different catabolites play the role of effector (Magasanik, 1963). The first observation of this kind was that glucose almost completely prevents the induction of β-galactosidase (Monod, 1942).

In certain situations it can be shown that the glucose effect is counteracted by inducer. When wild-type *E. coli* cells grow with glycerol as carbon source, and if inducer *and* glucose are added, the response depends on the order of addition. If inducer precedes glucose by a few minutes, a steady state can be established in which the cells will continue for many generations to synthesize β-galactosidase despite the presence of glucose. Less enzyme is produced than in the absence of glucose, but very much more than in a parallel culture to which glucose was added before inducer (Cohn and Horibata, 1959a,b). This "memory effect" is restricted to inducible strains that produce the galactoside permease (Novick and Weiner, 1957). When inducer is added first, one or a few permease molecules are presumably synthesized before glucose is introduced, and the cells are therefore able to maintain an internal inducer concentration high enough to reduce considerably the glucose effect or catabolite repression. However, this type of repression is not limited to the inducible system, as shown by the fact that constitutive strains of both the i^- and the O^c types produce less enzyme when glucose is present than they do when glycerol alone is available (Brown, 1961; Loomis and Magasanik, 1964).

It is not only glucose that exerts a catabolite effect on the synthesis of β-galactosidase. Clark and Marr (1964) showed that, under special conditions, strong catabolite repression could be established with carbon sources other than glucose; furthermore, under no circumstance was repression more than partly neutralized by inducer.

Catabolite repression tends to disappear in cultures that are starved of their main carbon source and, conversely, repression is greatly increased when the carbon source is present in excess and the culture is starved of, say, nitrogen or sulfur. It is extremely important to keep this rule in mind when experiments are designed, because seemingly simple operations—such as the temporary removal of a required amino acid—may cause serious fluctuations in the degree of catabolite repression.

The actual compounds that effect catabolite repression are largely unknown. It is almost certain that different compounds are active and that they affect separate groups, or families, of enzymes. We shall not discuss this problem here but refer the reader to the papers of Magasanik (1963) and Kornberg (1963).

2

STEADY STATES OF GROWTH

Cell size, number of nuclei per cell, and DNA content per nucleus

2-1 GENERAL VIEWPOINTS

Living cells will respond in many ways to changes in their immediate environment. The physiological effects of such changes can be studied experimentally, but the subject is by nature a complicated one—first of all because the cells must remain alive and intact, but also because the permissible changes in the environment and the ease and precision with which they can be produced often severely limit the scope of the study. From an experimental viewpoint a primitive, unicellular organism would be preferred that can grow under a wide variety of conditions. Bacteria not only fit this description, but, once the growth conditions have been chosen, the cells can be cultured in a virtually unchanging environment for long periods during which they simply repeat the same cycle of mass increase and division. This completely undifferentiated behavior is at once a limitation and an advantage: on the one hand, the number of observable characters is reduced to a minimum, but, on the other hand, we may assume that such general features as can be observed in these growing cells reflect functions of considerable ecological significance.

Ten years ago, when we began to study the growth physiology of some of the common enteric bacteria, many elementary and seemingly trivial data still had to be collected. In particular, few systematic observations had been made on cells that could be expected to have reached a steady state of growth determined exclusively by temperature and by the *kinds* of nutrient available to the cells.

These stipulations are important. The bacteria we have studied were selected mainly because they can be cultured in a great variety of well-defined media, and it is clear that the extent to which cells will adjust to a particular medium can be fully appreciated only when they are given time to equilibrate under constant conditions. *A priori*, it must be assumed that the equilibrium is approached slowly; hence our insistence on making observations on cells that have exhibited growth at a constant rate for several generations, and at a culture density that has been kept reasonably low and constant by dilution.

As part of these very general considerations, it should be stressed that the equilibrium we are concerned with is characterized by two special properties: first, its very existence is inferred from the fact that, in a given medium, a unique growth rate will establish itself; second, the system is so complex that the equilibrium can be described only by means of a large number of parameters. One way of doing so would be to list the ratios between all the different cell components.

2-2 PRACTICAL CONSIDERATIONS

To pass from generalities to experiments, it is necessary to decide on values for such vague terms as "several generations" and "reasonably low and constant," and to select a small set of cell components for the study. For practical reasons we had to fix the two values and to choose a small set of components, and these decisions had to be made on meager and indirect evidence. The procedure on which we settled will be discussed in some detail to provide background for judging the results.

The principal concern is to make sure that a constant growth rate has established itself in the experimental culture, since this is the only simple evidence of a steady state of growth. In a liquid medium it is convenient either to measure total cell mass turbidimetrically or to count the total cell number by means of an electronic counter. However, the steady state is often approached gradually, and in our experience neither method is adequate unless frequent readings indicate that the growth rate has remained constant over approximately a 10-fold increase in mass or in cell number. In other words, one should observe a culture through whatever lag it may exhibit, and not be satisfied until at least three doublings at a constant rate have been registered. Ideally, both mass and cell number should be followed.

One may ask whether this procedure is acceptable theoretically. To answer this question we must know how the equilibrium is approached if, at some time in the history of the cultures, the degree of repression of one or more enzyme systems has changed. If the change involves a large number of systems in the cell the problem may be very complicated, because different systems may interact and transitional states may be produced (cf. Chapter 4). Here we shall consider only the simple situation in which, at a given time, a single system is changing from one level of repression to another. It can be shown that the approach to the new equilibrium follows the equation

$$E_t/M_t = E_0/M_0\{\alpha + e^{-kt}(1-\alpha)\}$$

where E/M denotes the ratio of the mass of, e.g., an enzyme system (E) to the total cell mass (M), and α is the *factor* by which this ratio will have changed at equilibrium. Thus, repression corresponds to α values < 1, derepression to α values > 1. In either case the new equilibrium ($\alpha E_0/M_0$) is approached in the same way, and the quantity, $e^{-kt}(\alpha - 1)$, is reduced by a factor 2 for each doubling in mass. According to this simple model, during the observation period of three doublings advocated above, the "distance" ($\alpha - 1$) between the initial ratio, E_0/M_0, and the definitive ratio, $\alpha E_0/M_0$, would be reduced 8-fold. In many cases this would be considered a satisfactory approach to equilibrium.

In actual experiments the approach to equilibrium may be faster than predicted by our equation; thus repression (or derepression) may initially be more or less complete and quickly lead to an E/M ratio near the equilibrium value, at which time the maintenance level of repression may establish itself. On the other hand, the kinetics may be complex, as in the case of derepression of the arginine enzymes. Thus, upon removal of arginine, the ornithine transcarbamylase is initially synthesized at an excessively high rate and the quantity of this enzyme overshoots the equilibrium level, which is reached slowly "from above" as a result of secondary, intracellular repression (Gorini and Maas, 1957).

Finally, it should be emphasized that the reasoning just presented is valid *only* if the system, E, is small compared to the mass of the cell, M; if this is not the case, repression or derepression of the synthesis of E cannot be considered independently of the rest of the activities of the cell. A case in which E is *not* small will be discussed (Section 4–5).

The culture density and the steady state of growth. To allow a steady state of growth to be established and maintained, the density of a culture must be kept so low that the overall process of bacterial growth does not significantly change the physical or chemical properties of the medium. In cultures of *E. coli* and related species, the growth rate usually begins to decrease at densities between 2 and 5×10^8 cells/ml. However, a distinction must be made between the rate of division and the rate of mass increase, because the cell size changes in a characteristic manner during the "growth cycle" of a whole culture (see, e.g., Hershey and Bronfenbrenner, 1938). Figure 2–1 shows two growth curves, representing the increase in mass and in cell number, respectively, which together form a pattern much like a hysteresis loop. At early times, mass increases considerably before division begins, i.e., the cells grow bigger; as saturation approaches, the process is reversed and the cells return to their initial small size. In practice, we are most often concerned with the late phase and, consequently, the turbidimetric measurements will reveal that the growth rate has begun to decrease long before this can be detected by means of cell counts.

At this point it should be mentioned that certain cell properties may change long before the culture density is reached at which the rate of mass increase begins to go down. This was observed in the case of lysogenization of cells of *Salmonella typhimurium* by a temperate bacteriophage (Maaløe and Lark, 1954). In broth cultures, lysogenization occured with a constant frequency at densities between 2×10^7 and 10^8 cells/ml, when the multiplicity of infection was controlled by exposing the cells for a short time to a very high phage concentration. However, at densities above 10^8 cells/ml the frequency dropped sharply, despite the fact that no decrease in the growth rate could be observed turbidimetrically during the next doubling time. This rather special case has not been analyzed further, and it is reported only to explain why in our studies care has been taken not to get too near the culture densities at which the growth rate begins to decrease.

A broth culture of *S. typhimurium* with 10^8 cells/ml contains about 83 μg dry weight of cells per ml. Under our conditions of

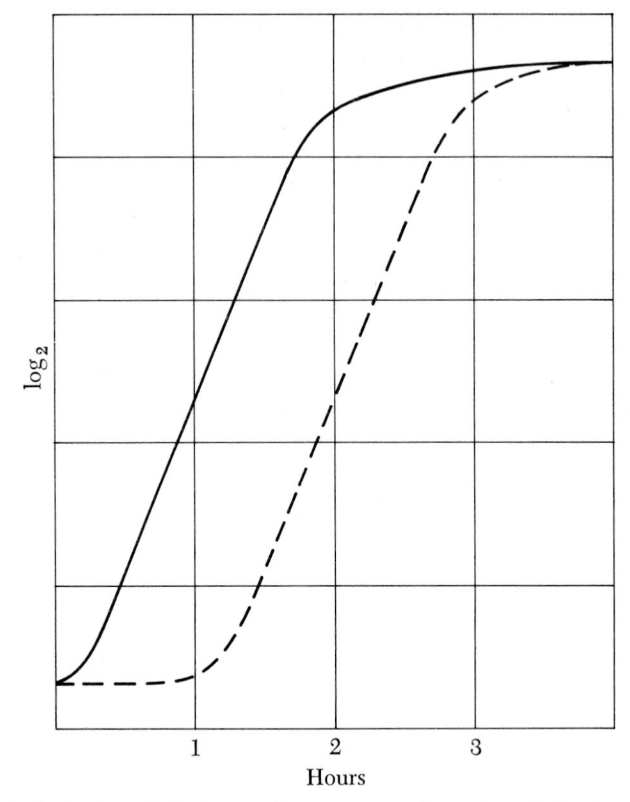

FIGURE 2–1 Growth in terms of mass and cell number. Ordinate: mass in arbitrary units (*curve on left*) and cell number (*curve on right*). The log unit represents one doubling. The curves correspond to growth in broth at 37° with a doubling time of 25 minutes, or 2.4 doublings/hr. Note that the mass/cell ratio first increases and then decreases about 4-fold.

measurement this gives an optical density (OD) close to 0.450 (see "Materials and Methods" in Appendix I). Most of our experiments have been conducted in such a way that, when the OD approached 0.500, the culture was diluted 2-fold with fresh, prewarmed medium. Growth generally continues at an undiminished rate until an OD of at least 0.800 is reached; but, except in a few cases, it has not been a problem to carry the experiments through at lower densities and we have felt safer doing so.

Finally, it should be mentioned that, when the cells are grown in media with carbon sources that are poorly utilized, special caution is necessary because waste products excreted into the medium may reach significant concentrations at relatively low cell densities.

The cell components chosen for the present study. At the time when we began to look for correlations between growth conditions and chemical composition of the cells the decision was relatively easy. Little was known about the relative importance of single components, e.g., individual enzymes, during growth in different media. It was therefore natural first to look for changes in major quantities such as cell mass and number of "nuclei," on the one hand, and the relative amounts of DNA, RNA, and protein, on the other. In the course of this work it became clear that the three major RNA fractions—ribosomal, transfer, and messenger RNA—had to be measured separately. The study of the ribosomal proteins and of the enzymes involved in DNA replication and in RNA synthesis has recently advanced so rapidly that quantitative analysis of these specific components under different growth conditions may soon be undertaken. These future possibilities will be discussed later; at present we shall confine ourselves to a presentation of the well-established quantitative relationships that have proved useful for the characterization of different steady states of growth.

2-3 MEASUREMENTS

Cell mass. In many previous studies of bacterial growth, the main emphasis has been on the changes in cell size and composition that occur during the "growth cycle" of a whole culture in a particular medium (cf. Figure 2-1). In the present study we also emphasize differences in size and composition, but the comparison is made between the steady states of growth that establish themselves in different media. Most of the observations have been made on cultures of *S. typhimurium*, and the original data are presented as Appendix I; very similar results may be obtained with various strains of *E. coli*.

First, some general comments should be made concerning the interpretation of results obtained when optical density measurements are used to estimate total cell mass. With particles the size of bacteria the dependency of light scattering on particle size and shape is difficult to analyze. Special caution is therefore necessary when comparison is made between cultures with varying cell size. We have found *empirically* that, in *Salmonella* cultures with less than about 150 μg dry cell weight per ml, OD values, measured at a wavelength of 450 mμ in a 1-cm cuvette in the Zeiss PMQ spectrophotometer, are proportional to cell mass. Furthermore, the proportionality factor is independent of the variation in the average cell size encountered in our experiments. This factor is known to depend on the geometry of the optical system and the wavelength used, and measurements made under different conditions may therefore not be independent of cell size to the extent we have observed (cf. "Materials and Methods" in Appendix I).

Consider now the observed values for mass/cell in the different media (see Figure 2–2, and Table 2–1). Qualitatively, our data confirm the classical finding that fast-growing cells are big, and slow-growing and resting cells are small. This striking contrast between the resting state and the state of exponential growth has frequently led to the notion that nothing but these two alternative physiological states exist. The ill-defined transition forms have not attracted much attention. In contrast to this simple view, it has become evident that a large number of well-defined, steady states of growth exist, and can be distinguished merely on the basis of the growth rate and the *corresponding* average cell mass, or size (Figure 2–2).

The variation in cell volume, both within and between cultures, is illustrated in Figure 2–3. The measurements were made by means of an electronic particle analyzer (Ecker and Schaechter, 1963; their Figure 1). Two important features emerge from this diagram. First, within a culture the cell volume varies by a factor of approximately 4, i.e., considerably more than the 2-fold variation that would be expected if the volume of a cell were always the same at the time of division. Second, the two volume distributions are unimodal and reasonably similar. We may therefore assume that the average figures for cell mass of Figure 2–2, which presumably also express average

TABLE 2–1 Representative Weights per Cell and per Nucleus in *Salmonella typhimurium* [a]

Medium	μ at 37°	Cells ($\times 10^{-12}$) per g dry weight	Dry weight (g) per 10^{12} cells	Average number of nuclei per cell	Dry weight (g) per 10^{12} nuclei
Broth	2.4	1.3	0.756	2.45	0.308
Glucose	1.2	3.1	0.322	1.50	0.215
Glycerol	0.6	4.8	0.210	1.25	0.168

[a] The composition of the media is given in Appendix I, Table 1. μ = doublings per hour. Weights calculated from Equation (3–1). Average number of nuclei from Appendix I, Figure 4.

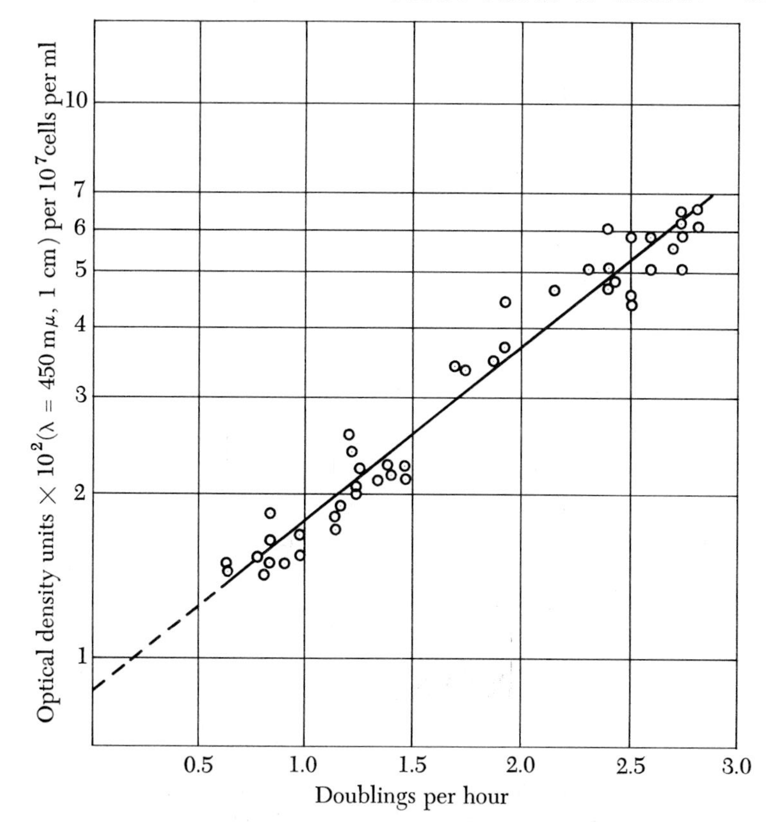

FIGURE 2–2 *Salmonella typhimurium:* dependency of cell mass on growth rate at 37°. From the optical density (mass) measurements and the viable counts in the different media, values for optical density/10^7 cells/ml were calculated. The logarithm of these values is plotted against the growth rate expressed as doublings per hour.

cell volumes, represent the actual cell populations in a fairly straightforward manner. With respect to the shape and dimensions of the cells, it should be noted that the big, fast-growing cells are thicker as well as longer than the small, slow-growing cells (see Appendix I).

The characteristic physiological growth states may conveniently be described as states of *balanced growth*, by which we mean that, over any time interval, every extensive property of the whole system increases by the same factor (Campbell, 1957). In this definition, the system being considered usually is a large population of cells. In the following we shall extend

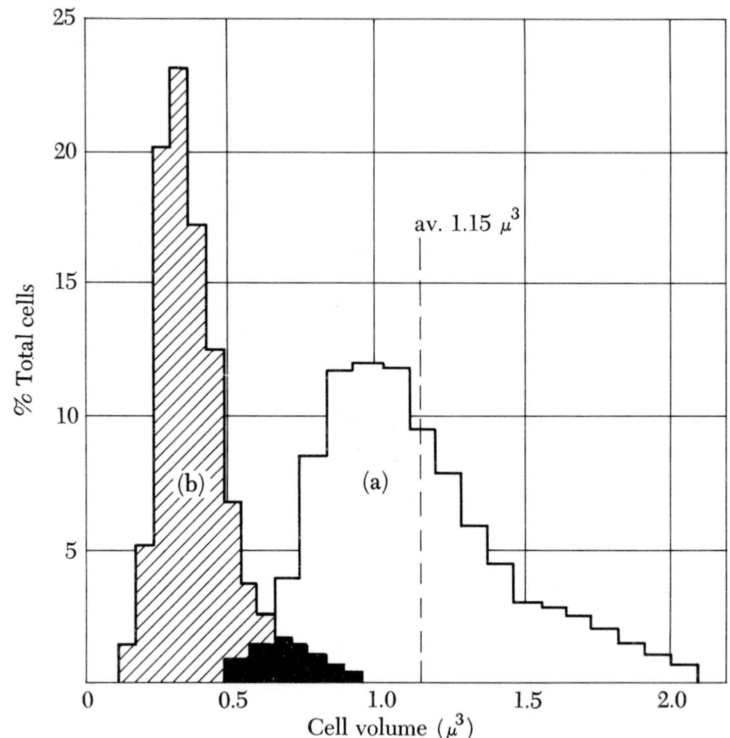

FIGURE 2–3 Distribution of cell sizes in balanced growth of *Salmonella typhimurium:* (a) cells grown in glucose minimal medium enriched with casamino acids, growth rate 2.0 doublings per hour, and (b) cells from a glucose limited chemostat, growth rate, 0.13 doublings per hour. (From Ecker and Schaechter, *Ann. N.Y. Acad. Sci.,* **102,** 549, 1963.)

the definition of balanced growth to imply that, apart from small statistical fluctuations, every component of the *individual* cell doubles in quantity between successive divisions. It should be clear from this definition that the transition states referred to above are not states of balanced growth. We shall see later that they are fundamentally different despite the fact that, during the transition, growth rate and cell mass may assume values characteristic of known states of balanced growth (see Chapter 4).

The number of nuclei per cell and the DNA content per nucleus. In the following the term "nucleus" will be used to designate the often irregular, but nevertheless closed, regions in which the DNA of the bacterial cell is seen in stained prepara-

TABLE 2–2 The Numbers of Nuclei per Cell in Stained Preparations

	Growth medium			
	Broth		Glucose-minimal	
Preparation	**I**	**II**	**I**	**II**
Nuclei/cell				
1	0	2	157	138
(1–2)[a]	0	0	39	18
2	132	104	104	153
(2–4)[a]	72	57	1	0
4	146	139	1	1
(4–8)[a]	7	4	0	0
Nuclei/cell (average)	3.12	3.13	1.45	1.54

[a] Cells in these classes could not be scored unequivocally; the arbitrary values of 1.5, 3, and 6 nuclei/cell, respectively, were used to calculate averages.

tions or in electron micrographs (Lark, Maaløe, and Rostock, 1955; Birch-Andersen, 1955). After the demonstration by means of phase-contrast microscopy that living cells show corresponding regions which divide in step with cell division, the nuclei seen in stained or fixed preparations can no longer be suspected to be artifacts (Mason and Powelson, 1956).

Our cytological observations on *S. typhimurium* show that a given growth rate is characterized not only by a given cell mass but also by a fixed average number of nuclei/cell. Like the mass, this number increases with the growth rate (see Figure 2–2, and Table 2–1). Examples of the distribution of nuclei at two different growth rates are presented in Table 2–2. At the high as well as at the relatively low rate, mixed populations are found; nevertheless, the rapidly growing cultures consist almost exclusively of cells with two *or* four nuclei, whereas cells with one *or* two nuclei are equally predominant in the more slowly growing cultures. Of the individual cells, 10–20% were classified as having 1–2 or 2–4 nuclei, because it is impossible always to decide whether a large stained body of irregular shape should be registered as 1 or 2 nuclei. Cells in these classes were scored as having 1.5 or 3 nuclei, respectively; it should be emphasized, however, that a cell with 3 distinct nuclei is hardly ever seen.

To permit direct comparison between cells in different growth states, we decided to express mass and other quantities on a per nucleus basis. This convention was first adopted because a single nucleus, with its share of cytoplasm, etc., seemed to constitute a natural unit. At very low growth rates most cells are in fact uninucleated. A more important reason for expressing the quantities of different cell constituents in this way is that, eventually, we want to discuss growth in terms of numbers, e.g., of ribosomes, tRNA units, or molecules of a particular protein, that are synthesized per time unit and per genome. Finally, we want to eliminate the changes in the number of nuclei/cell from our discussion as much as possible.

In parallel with the cytological study, DNA determinations were made, and Figure 2–4 shows a set of these values plotted against the corresponding numbers of nuclei per cell. The correlation is reasonably good and permits a crude graphical estima-

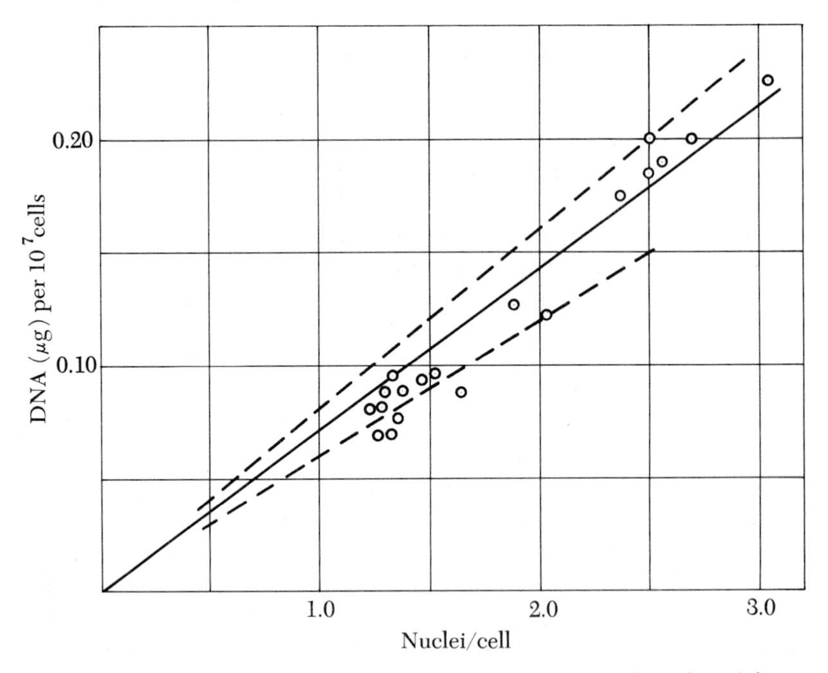

FIGURE 2–4 Correlation between DNA content and number of nuclei per cell in cultures of *Salmonella typhimurium*. This representative set of observations covers growth rates between 0.63 and 2.00 doublings per hour. Most of our observations fall between the lines drawn through the origin. The few aberrant points correspond to cells with "too few" nuclei; we attribute this to imperfections in the stained preparations.

tion of the DNA content per nucleus. The most probable value is about 7×10^{-15} g of DNA, and the upper and lower limits may be put at 8 and 6×10^{-15} g, respectively.

To estimate the amount of DNA per genome, we first consider a relatively fast-growing cell. There is good reason to believe that in such a cell the process of DNA replication occupies nearly the whole period between successive divisions, and that it proceeds at a constant rate (see Chapter 6). If we disregard the possibility that, cytologically, a nucleus could appear to have divided before replication has been completed, it is clear that, on a time average, a nucleus contains 1.5 genomes. However, because of the age distribution in an exponentially growing culture, the "average cell" is not halfway but approximately 0.41 of the way through the cycle; consequently, in the nuclei whose DNA we determine the average content would be 1.41 genomes.

At very low growth rates, when the large majority of cells are uninucleated, this figure may be somewhat different, because replication seems not to occupy more than, say, half the time between divisions. Thus if replication were completed early in the division cycle, and if the nucleus did not divide, cytologically, until later, the average number of genomes per nucleus would be between 1.5 and 2. Experiments (presented in Chapter 6) indicate that this is indeed the case. On the basis of these general arguments we obtain a value of $4\text{–}5 \times 10^{-15}$ g per genome.

An independent and very direct estimate of this quantity has been obtained by Cairns from autoradiograms (1963). Tracks corresponding to a closed ring structure have been observed, and it is natural to assume that, in such cases, the entire genome has been isolated intact. Measurements of tracks that form a ring have given figures of $1\text{–}1.2 \times 10^{7}$ Å for the length of the genome, which is equivalent to $3.2\text{–}3.8 \times 10^{-15}$ g of DNA, or $3\text{–}3.6 \times 10^{6}$ base pairs.[1] These values refer to the genome of *E. coli* strain B, but its genetic homology with *S. typhimurium*

[1] It should be noted that, on a molecular scale, the resolution of the DNA autoradiograms is poor since on an average only one grain is produced per μ. The grain track therefore does not directly show to what extent the DNA thread is extended. Consequently, the length of the bacterial genome as estimated from an autoradiogram could be a serious *under*estimate of the true length. The justification for assuming that this is not the case is to be found in comparative studies of phage DNA by means of autoradiography on the one hand, and direct electron microscopy on the other (Kleinschmidt *et al.*, 1962). The two methods give almost identical estimates of the length of the relatively long DNA molecule of T2 phage (over 50μ), indicating that the measurements made on autoradiograms quite accurately represent the true length of a DNA molecule.

is so extensive that one would expect their genomes to be very similar in length (Falkow, Rownd, and Baron, 1962). The fact that our estimate of the size of the *Salmonella* genome exceeds Cairns' figure for *E. coli* would find a natural explanation, if episomes contribute to the DNA content of the cells in our *Salmonella* strain. When needed in later chapters, we shall use Cairns' figure of 3–3.6 $\times 10^6$ base pairs per genome, but in no case is the difference critical between this value and our estimate.

2–4 CONCLUDING REMARKS

So far we have seen that, in a variety of media, cultures of *S. typhimurium* readily reach the state of balanced growth, i.e., a dynamic equilibrium is established between the cell and the medium it grows in. The most remarkable feature of this system is that a simple relationship exists between the growth rate and the average cell mass. In other words, the state of balanced growth which establishes itself in a given medium can be characterized by *either* the growth rate *or* the average cell mass, one of these parameters defining the other in a unique manner. Experiments to be discussed later show that the same general principle applies to the strains of *E. coli* that have been examined.

A second important point should be mentioned here, although some of the relevant experiments cannot be described until later: With a few media that support very different growth rates, balanced growth produced the same average cell mass independently of temperature, in the range 25–37°. In the media tested so far the growth rate at 25° is almost exactly half that at 37°, and Figure 2–2 could therefore be made to represent the relationship between growth rate and cell mass at 25° simply by dividing the μ values by 2. It is not clear how general this temperature independence of cell mass may be. It would not be surprising if, in some media, the temperature coefficient pertaining to the growth rate were quite different from that usually observed, and what the corresponding cell mass would be in such a case cannot be predicted. The very existence of temperature mutants, which grow normally in minimal media at, say, 25° but not at all at 37°, indicates that wild-type *Salmonella* or coli strains may exist that do not double their growth rate between 25° and 37°.

Finally, we have seen that DNA and the number of nuclei/cell increase with the growth rate. Table 2–1 shows that this increase can be eliminated, and that the average cell mass per nucleus, or per genome, still increases with growth rate. In the next chapter we shall examine this residual increase in terms of the chemical composition of the cells in the different states of balanced growth.

3

STEADY STATES OF GROWTH

Quantities of protein and RNA, and number of ribosomes per cell and per genome

In Chapter 2 we were concerned with quantities and measurements more or less directly related to bacterial cytology. This is true even of the chemical determinations of DNA, which could be correlated with microscopically observed nuclei or with autoradiograms of free DNA. We now turn to a series of chemical and physical measurements relating to smaller structures, which are visible, if at all, only in a fixed and dried state in the electron microscope.

3–1 THE PROTEINS

In any state of growth, whether balanced or not, the bulk of the bacterial cell mass is protein. Between the highest and the lowest growth rates realized in our experiments, 2.8 and about 0.2 doublings per hour, respectively, at 37°, total protein increases from approximately $^2/_3$ to $^5/_6$ of the dry weight of the cell. These values were obtained by analyzing hot TCA-extracted *Salmonella* cultures, using TCA-treated *Salmonella* protein as reference standard (Kjeldgaard, 1963). The lower figure, 67%, agrees well with the data of Roberts *et al.* for *E. coli* (1955). In cultures of *Aerobacter aerogenes,* Neidhardt and Magasanik

(1960) found little if any change in the ratio protein/total mass, suggesting that also in this organism total protein accounts for the major part of the cell mass under different growth conditions.

The small changes in protein content observed in *Salmonella typhimurium* are paralleled by an increase in the DNA/mass ratio such that, per nucleus or per genome, the total protein content of the cell is very nearly constant (see Table 3–2). This is equivalent to saying that, per genome, the number of amino acids that must be put into peptide linkage during a division cycle is more or less independent of the growth rate. We may therefore assume (but cannot rigorously conclude) that a corresponding and equally constant number of nucleotides must be joined to form mRNA. Some of these basic numbers are given in Table 3–3.

The protein fraction must vary greatly in composition from one state of growth to another. Certain components, such as the amino acid-activating enzymes, the DNA- and RNA-synthesizing polymerases, and the ribosomal proteins will always be present, although not necessarily in constant quantities. On the other hand, a large fraction of the protein of the cell may even change qualitatively, enzymes present in great quantities during growth in one medium being almost completely absent under other conditions. It is by no means obvious why the total quantity of protein per genome is the same under different growth conditions, i.e., why the total amount is independent of the *kinds* of protein that are being synthesized. At the moment we can only carry the reasoning one step back and conclude that the total quantity of mRNA produced per generation probably also is constant.

The state of balanced growth can be described formally as the result of a definite partitioning of energy and matter among all the components being synthesized. A very large share of the energy and matter consumed must be devoted to the synthesis of enzymes. We are, of course, far from being able to account in detail for the pattern of partitioning in any given state of growth, but it is reasonable to assume that this pattern is completely defined by the primary repressions, derepressions, and inductions imposed on the cells by the various components of the medium. In principle, it should be possible to distinguish between the direct effects caused by these components themselves, and indirect or spreading effects due to interactions in the cell between different systems. In practice this can be very difficult (see Chapter 5).

Two distinctive states present themselves when cells growing in minimal medium are compared to cells growing in broth. In the former case, all the amino acids are being synthesized in the cell, a process involving something like one hundred enzymes, which together probably constitute a large fraction of the protein of the cell. In the second case, these enzymes are under repression and, since the total amount of protein per nucleus is the same, other enzyme systems must have expanded considerably. We shall return to this particular situation in the next chapter, when discussing the precision with which the control by repression is able to adjust the size and capacity of an enzyme system to the needs of the cell.

3-2 THE STABLE RNA

As we have seen, $^1/_6$–$^1/_3$ of the cell mass is *not* protein. This residue contains DNA in an amount corresponding to 3–4% of the total mass, and RNA in amounts varying from about 10 to 30% (see Table 3–2).

Large variations in the RNA content of individual cells have been observed in several different organisms (Brachet, 1942; Caspersson, 1950), and until quite recently the positive correlation between total RNA content and the protein-synthesizing activity of a cell was the only evidence suggesting that RNA might be involved in protein synthesis. As regards bacteria, this correlation was established for several species by comparing the RNA contents of resting and growing cells (Wade and Morgan, 1957). We have collected further evidence along these lines: First, figures for total RNA were obtained, corresponding to states of balanced growth representing many different but well-defined rates of growth and of protein synthesis. Second, in selected cases the total RNA was analyzed to account separately for ribosomal and transfer RNA. We shall discuss these experiments and the correlations they reveal in the natural order.

Figure 3–1 is similar to Figure 2–2, except that, instead of mass, total RNA per cell is plotted against the growth rate (μ). In both diagrams a logarithmic scale is used on the ordinate, and lines suggesting linear relationships have been drawn. The experimental values distribute themselves harmoniously around the straight lines, but it should be noted that the RNA values, which increase about 10-fold, are the only ones that could not possibly be fitted to a straight line in an arithmetic plot. It is

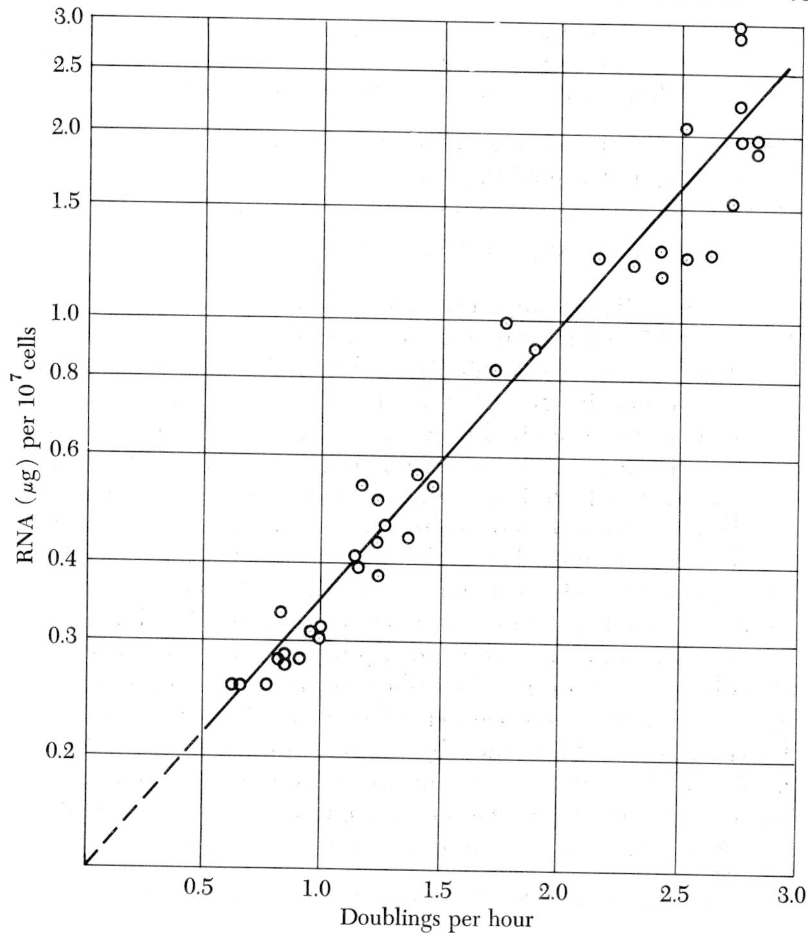

FIGURE 3–1 Dependency of cellular ribonucleic acid on growth rate at 37°. The RNA content of the cultures was calculated from the ribose determination (μg RNA = μg ribose × 4.91). The logarithm of the RNA values, in $\mu g/10^7$ viable cells, is plotted against the growth rate.

therefore for convenience and *not* for theoretical reasons that semilogarithmic plots have been used when mass or other quantities are presented as functions of the growth rate.

From the graphs relating mass and RNA to the growth rate (Figures 2–2 and 3–1, respectively), simple, empirical equations, in which the quantities are expressed in $\mu g/10^9$ cells, can be written as follows:

$$\log_{10}(\text{mass}) = 0.31\mu + 2.14 \quad (3\text{–}1)$$
$$\log_{10}(\text{RNA}) = 0.45\mu + 1.31 \quad (3\text{–}2)$$
$$\log_{10}\{(\text{RNA}/\text{mass}) \times 100\} = 0.14\mu + 0.83 \quad (3\text{–}3)$$

A DNA diagram, corresponding to Figure 3–1, is shown in Appendix I, and Equation (3–4) is derived from that graph and from the DNA values per g dry weight listed in Table 3–2:

$$\log_{10}(\text{DNA}) = 0.23\mu + 0.75 \quad (3\text{–}4)$$

It is immediately apparent that the DNA determinations in Appendix I scatter more than do the mass and RNA values. However, the slope estimate derived from the early analysis has been confirmed by our later determinations, and we therefore assume that it is reliable. For $\mu = 0$, Equation (3–4) gives a value of 5.6 mg DNA per 10^{12} cells. At zero growth rate practically all cells are uninucleated, and this nucleus must be assumed to contain between one and two genome equivalents of DNA. It is tempting to speculate that, in the resting state, the nucleus might be reduced to a single genome; however, the DNA value for $\mu = 0$ is too high to support such an assumption. To obtain estimates of the number of genomes (in terms of DNA equivalents) per cell we have adopted the following somewhat arbitrary procedure: total DNA has been calculated from Equation (3–4) and the values obtained divided by 4.5, which is a reasonable figure for the DNA content in mg per 10^{12} genomes (see Figure 2–4). On the basis of this procedure the number of genome equivalents of DNA, as a function of μ, can be expressed as

$$\log_{10}(\text{genome equivalents}/\text{cell}) = 0.23\mu + 0.10 \quad (3\text{–}4\text{a})$$

Considering the nature of the experiments and the assumptions on which this expression is based, systematic errors might be involved that would make the true numbers of genome equivalents per cell as much as 20% higher or lower than values calculated from Equation (3–4a). A proper statistical analysis would be difficult and has not been attempted.

Combining Equations (3–1) and (3–2), respectively, with Equation (3–4a) we obtain:

$$\log_{10}(\text{mass}/\text{genome equivalents}) = 0.08\mu + 2.04 \quad (3\text{–}5)$$
$$\log_{10}(\text{RNA}/\text{genome equivalents}) = 0.22\mu + 1.21 \quad (3\text{–}6)$$

where the quantities are expressed in μg per 10^9 genome equivalents of DNA.

As emphasized above, our six equations are meant as convenient descriptions of empirical relationships. It is therefore necessary to consider separately the very low μ values, i.e., the interval corresponding to values between 0 and 0.6, within which no measurements have so far been reported. Between μ values of 0.6 and 2.8, respectively, a large number of determinations exist, and from this region extrapolations were made to obtain estimates of mass and of total RNA per cell at zero growth rate. Several observations indicate that such estimates are meaningful: in the first place, measurements have been made on cultures in a glucose-minimal medium from which, after several generations of balanced growth, the nitrogen source was withdrawn. The cells in these cultures remained viable, and the values for mass and RNA per cell gradually fell to the levels indicated by the extrapolations to zero growth rate in Figures 2–2 and 3–1, respectively. Furthermore, comparable values were obtained by analyzing resting cells taken from an outgrown broth culture. Finally, mass and RNA values that fit the extrapolations have been observed at the very low growth rates, of the order of 0.2 doubling per hour, realized in later experiments (see next section).

In Chapter 2 it was shown that cell mass, and mass per genome, can be used to characterize growth in a given medium, and that these parameters do not change with temperature in the range 25–37°. Since the RNA content of the cells varies much more with the growth rate than does cell mass, a particularly sensitive test for temperature independence is obtained by studying the rates of RNA synthesis at several temperatures. Figure 3–2 shows the differential rates of incorporation of ^{14}C-uracil during growth of *S. typhimurium* in glucose-minimal medium at 37, 31, and 25°, respectively. The label is incorporated into both nucleic acids, of which DNA, however, constitutes only about $^{1}/_{6}$. The fact that identical slopes are obtained when counts per minute are plotted against optical density shows that at all three temperatures a constant fraction of the total cell mass is RNA (and DNA).[1]

This result strongly supports the idea that the growth medium defines in a unique manner not only cell mass, but also one important aspect of the chemical composition of the bacterial cell.

[1] A word of caution should be injected here. In some strains, e.g., in *E. coli* strain 15T$^-$ and its derivatives, much larger quantities of capsular material are produced at 25° than at 37°. In such cases, the RNA/*mass* ratio might be significantly lower at 25° than at 37° without implying a change in the quantity of RNA/*genome*.

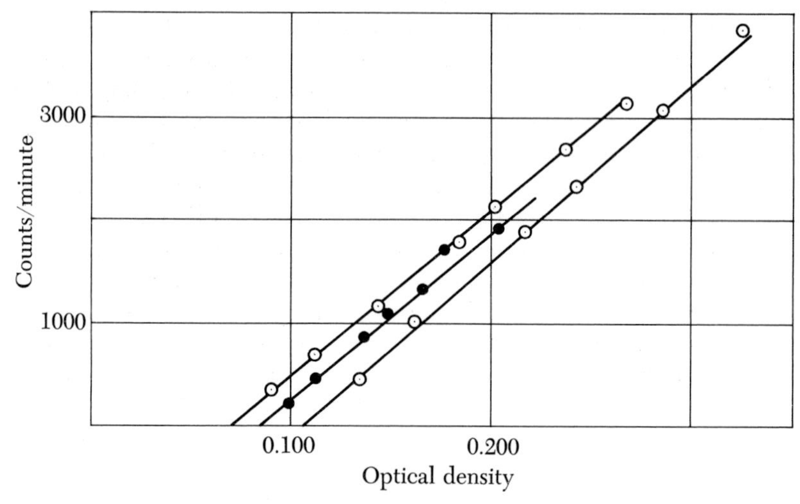

FIGURE 3-2 Incorporation of ^{14}C-uracil in cultures of *Salmonella typhimurium* grown in glucose minimal medium at 37°, 31°, and 25°. Each culture was grown for several generations and diluted into radioactive medium containing 10 μg per milliliter of uracil. Samples were taken at intervals for measurements of optical density and of radioactivity. The results are plotted against the optical density at the time of sampling; from left to right the curves represent growth at 37°, 25°, and 31°.

Thus mass and RNA content are characteristics of the steady state of growth that develops in a given medium, and, in contrast to the growth rate, these parameters are independent of temperature over a considerable range.

3-3 THE RELATIVE QUANTITIES OF RIBOSOMAL AND TRANSFER RNA

The values for total RNA per cell at various growth rates have revealed the expected correlation between the rates of protein synthesis and the RNA content of the cells. In fact, a more than 4-fold increase in growth rate, and *pari passu* in the rate of protein synthesis, was accompanied by a barely significant increase of about 50% in the amount of protein produced per time unit and per unit of RNA. This observation suggests that the RNA content of these cells might be regulated in such a way that, once a steady state of growth is established, ribosomes are not produced in excess (see Appendix I). In other words, at a given temperature, the tendency would seem to be for individual ribosomes to produce proteins with an efficiency characteristic of the cell and not of the rate at which it grows. If this principle proved to be generally valid, it would mean that, once the synthesis of a polypeptide chain has been initiated on a ribosome, the chain would grow to completion at a rate uniquely defined by temperature (it is of course possible, but does not seem likely, that the rate is influenced by the amino acid composition of the chain). The overall rate of protein synthesis would then depend exclusively on the *number* of chains being initiated, or completed, per unit time.

It was realized early in this study that the principle of constant efficiency at the ribosomal level might not be valid at very low growth rates. As already pointed out, resting cells contain a

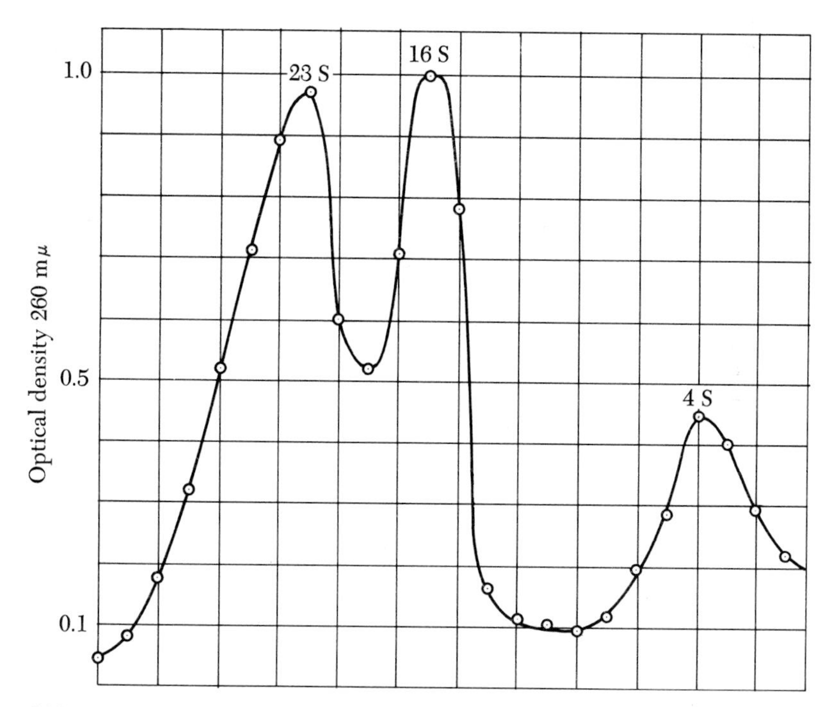

FIGURE 3–3 Sucrose gradient centrifugation of RNA from *Salmonella typhimurium* growth in glucose-minimal medium. The cells were lysed with SDS only, and the RNA was prepared as described by Kjeldgaard (1963). The gradient was centrifuged at 25,000 rpm for 14 hours and analyzed for ultraviolet-absorbing material.

definite and by no means negligible quantity of RNA (cf. Figure 3–1). In such cells protein turnover takes place, but the rate of synthesis is very low and would correspond to a doubling time of approximately 24 hours at 37° (Mandelstam, 1958; own unpublished experiments). In this "resting" state the rate of protein synthesis per unit of *total* RNA is obviously lower than during growth at rates of 0.6 or more doublings/hr. To test the general validity of the principle of constant efficiency, it is therefore necessary to determine the quantity of *ribosomal* RNA, or the actual number of ribosomes, and if possible to include in the analysis cells that grow very slowly (see Table 3–2).

We shall first consider the experiments of Kjeldgaard and Kurland (1963), which deal with isolated and purified RNA. In principle, this analysis is simple because the 4 S transfer RNA and the 16 S and 23 S ribosomal RNA species are readily separated by centrifugation through a sucrose gradient (see Figures 3–3 and 3–4), and the results of a large number of experiments of this kind are shown in Figure 3–5, which illustrates both the

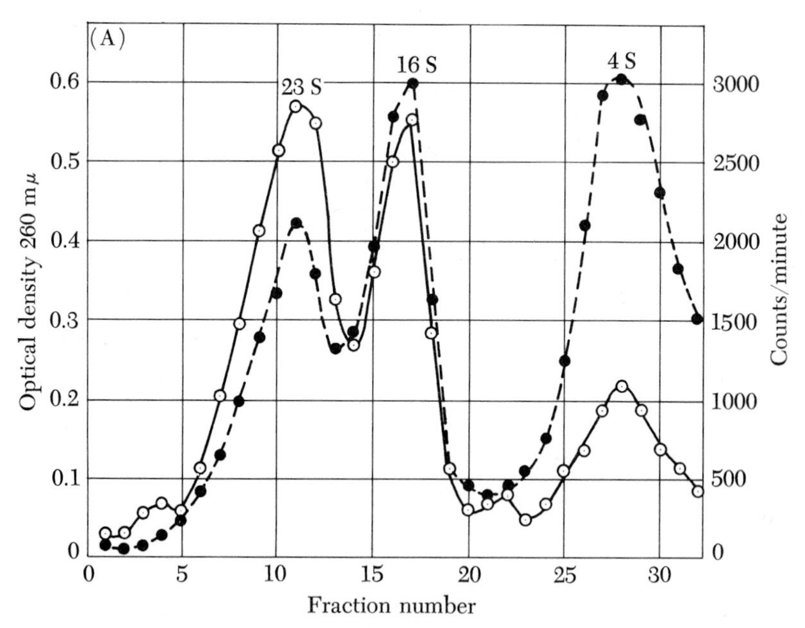

FIGURE 3–4 The relative quantities of ribosomal and transfer RNA at different growth rates. (*A*) Zone centrifugation analysis of RNA prepared from a mixture of carrier cells grown on casamino acid medium (○), and cells labeled with $^{32}PO_4$ in glucose-minimal medium (●).

systematic *de*crease in the tRNA fraction with *in*creasing growth rate, and the variation between experiments. The average figures for the ribosomal and tRNA fractions will be used later, together with figures for total RNA, to obtain estimates of the numbers of ribosomes and of tRNA molecules per genome (Table 3–3).

The data of Figure 3–5 could be seriously biased if either transfer or ribosomal RNA were lost preferentially during preparation and, since the loss of total RNA amounts to 25–50%, this is a real concern. The purification and extraction procedures have therefore been examined as carefully as possible:

(1) The phenol method for separating protein and RNA was tested separately to eliminate the possibility that the relatively small tRNA molecules might be preferentially dissolved in the

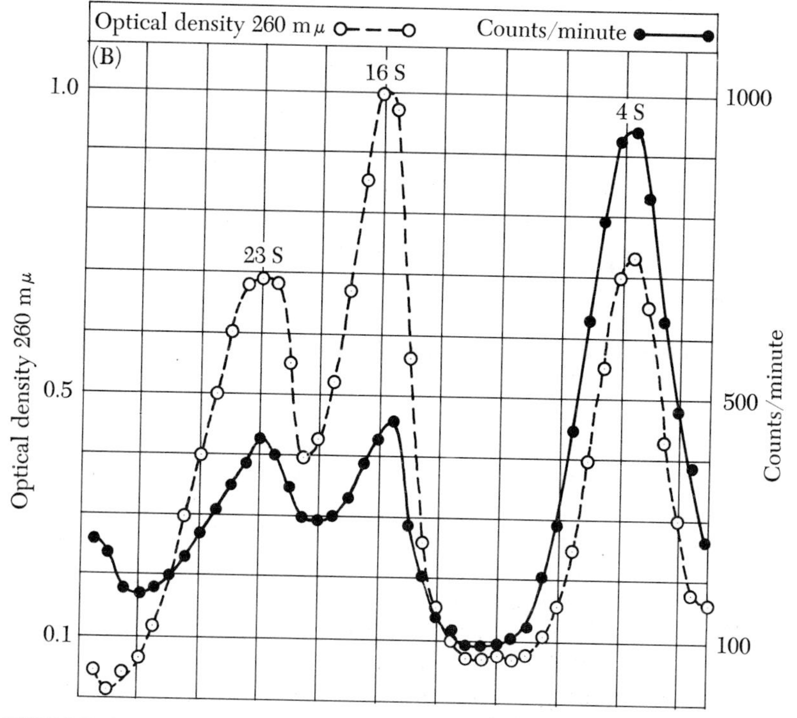

FIGURE 3–4 (*B*) Zone centrifugation analysis of RNA prepared from a mixture of carrier cells grown on glucose-minimal medium (○), and cells labeled with $^{32}PO_4$ in glutamic acid-minimal medium (●).

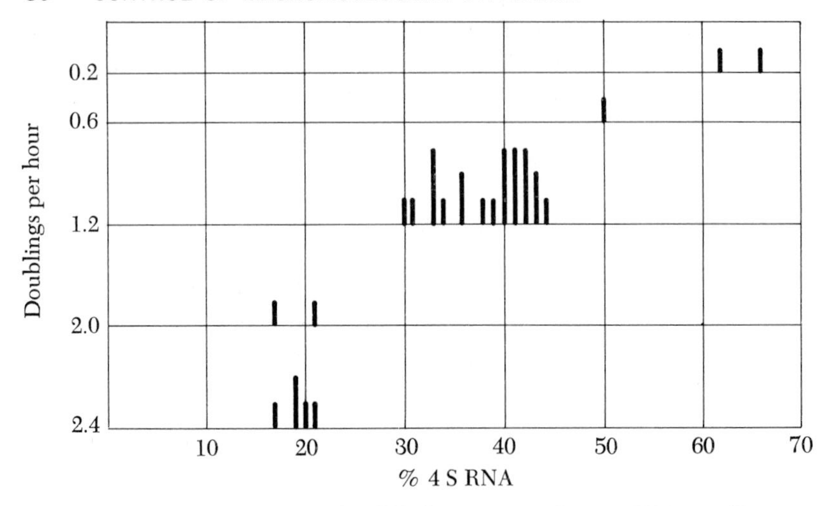

FIGURE 3–5 The amount of sRNA in percent of total RNA at different growth rates.

phenol phase. For this purpose a small quantity of cells, grown in a glucose-minimal medium and labeled uniformly with ^{32}P, and a large quantity of broth-grown cells were prepared. The two cultures were concentrated and one part of the labeled cells was mixed with 40 parts of carrier cells. In this mixture the specific activity of the tRNA will be particularly high, because the labeled cells are richer in this fraction than are the carrier cells. Three samples of the mixture of cells were lysed with SDS and shaken with phenol; the water phase of one of the samples was analyzed directly; the two remaining water phases were shaken with phenol a second time, and one of them a third time, before the RNA was analyzed by sedimentation through sucrose gradients. Table 3–1 shows that the specific activity of the total RNA remained constant. This would not have been the case had the tRNA of relatively high specific activity been lost selectively during the second and third phenol treatments. Similarly it was shown that selective loss did not occur during additional ethanol precipitations.

(2) The problem of controlling the extraction of RNA from the cells is more difficult. The data of Table 3–1 show that the process is reproducible, since replicate samples give identical specific activities. This, however, does not exclude the possibility that the three RNA components might be liberated from the cells with unequal efficiencies. No definite answer to this problem can be had until methods for quantitative RNA extraction

TABLE 3–1 Specific Activity of Radioactive RNA Fractions during Phenol Treatments

RNA fraction	Number of phenol shakings 1	2	3
	(specific activity in counts per min per OD unit at 260 mμ)		
23 S	350	360	340
16 S	550	545	500
4 S	1580	1500	1470
Total RNA	850	825	850

are available. Meanwhile, control experiments have been made using ultrasonic treatment as an alternative method to disrupt the cells. In our hands, this technique has given a somewhat higher yield of RNA than is obtained after lysis with SDS. Comparisons have been made between the partitioning of the RNA among the three major fractions in samples lysed directly with SDS, and in samples to which SDS was added after the cells had been disrupted in an ultrasonic field. With broth-grown cells the two methods gave identical patterns, showing that the improved yield of RNA did not affect the partitioning. With the very slow-growing cells from the glutamate medium, the 4 S fraction tended to decrease from the values of 60–65% reported above (Figure 3–5) to 50–60% when sonic treatment was used to disrupt the cells. Thus, if there is a real tendency for the different RNA components to be extracted unequally, it would seem to be due to a small number of ribosomes being retained with the cell debris.

To sum up: analysis of the stable RNA components from cells in balanced growth, at rates ranging from about 0.2 to 2.4 doublings/hr, shows that the quantity of *ribosomal* RNA increases more sharply with the growth rate than does total RNA. Since, as we shall see later, the tRNA/DNA ratio does not vary significantly with the growth rate, it can be shown that the ribosomal RNA/DNA ratio increases by approximately the same factor as the growth rate (cf. Table 3–3).[2]

[2] In connection with experiments to be described (Section 5–4), the partitioning of transfer and ribosomal RNA has been studied in *E. coli* strain 15T⁻ (Forchhammer, Kjeldgaard, and Moldave, 1965). The trend illustrated in Figure 3–5 was again observed, but the percentages of tRNA were somewhat less, with extreme values of about 15 and 40 as compared to 20 and 60, respectively, for *S. typhimurium*. We do not yet know whether the correlation between the quantity of ribosomal RNA and the rate of protein synthesis is as extensive in strain 15T⁻ as in *S. typhimurium*.

The same close correlation we have observed between the quantity of ribosomal RNA and the growth rate has been demonstrated for the *number* of ribosomal particles by Ecker and Schaechter (1963). Like the RNA analysis just described, their study of whole particles was carried out with cultures of *S. typhimurium;* the range of very low growth rates was covered by means of glucose limitation in a chemostat. Cells were collected by centrifugation, washed once with buffer containing 0.01 *M* $MgCl_2$, and broken in the French press. The lysates were immediately analyzed by sedimentation in the optical ultracentrifuge at 20°. Some of the results are presented graphically in Figure 3–6. The total quantities of ribosomes (70 S particles + polysomes) are expressed as fractions of the total quantity of slowly sedimenting material. This reference material consists almost entirely of soluble protein, a quantity which we believe to be present in a fixed amount relative to DNA, irrespective of

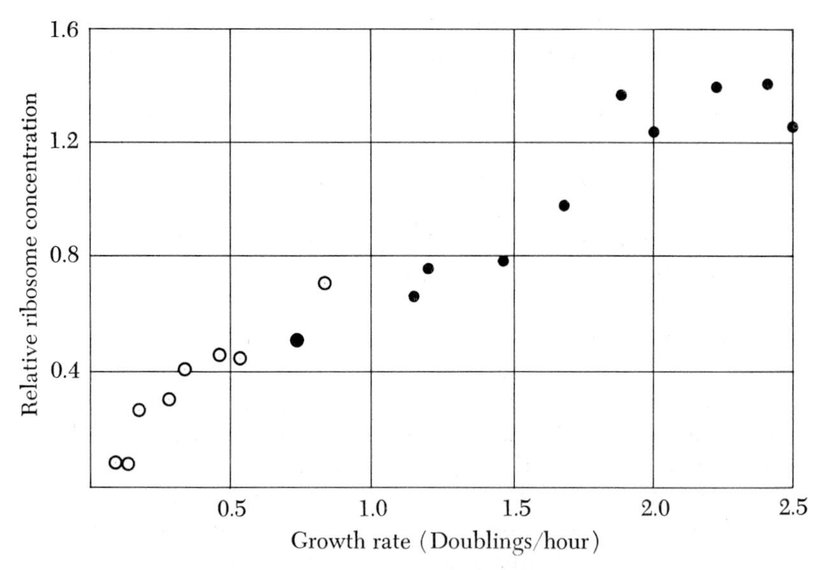

FIGURE 3–6 Relative total ribosome concentration as a function of balanced growth rate in cultures of *Salmonella typhimurium.* For this purpose, ribosome concentration is defined as the total area under the ribosome peaks divided by the area under the peak representing the soluble macromolecules. Open circles represent glucose limited chemostat growth, solid circles refer to batch cultures. (From Ecker and Schaechter, *Ann. N.Y. Acad. Sci.,* **102,** 549, 1963.)

growth rate. To a good approximation the figures on the ordinate of Figure 3–6 thus are proportional to the *number* of ribosomes per genome.

3–4 GENERAL REMARKS ABOUT THE THEOREM

Together, the analysis of the purified RNA and that of whole particles indicate that the number of ribosomes is proportional to the rate of growth and of protein synthesis. This correlation seems to hold for all rates examined. As regards the control of ribosome synthesis, we are thus led to assume the existence of a mechanism that responds effectively at any rate at which the cell can grow.

This general statement is critical for the analysis of much of our work, and a few qualifying remarks are therefore in order.

First, an examination of the composition of the media used shows that essentially they differ in two respects only: if the glucose-minimal medium, i.e., the "fastest" of the very simple media, is taken as a point of reference, it appears that high growth rates are always obtained by *supplementing* the basic glucose medium with elements that are synthesized in bulk by the cells themselves, and that low rates are obtained by *substituting* other carbon and energy sources for glucose. Generally speaking, a comparison between the different media of this series is a study of the efficiency with which the regulatory mechanisms of the cell respond to changes in the availability of carbon and energy; more specifically, we have been concerned with the way in which RNA synthesis is adjusted. The control mechanisms that effect this adjustment presumably have developed gradually in the course of evolution, and an efficient coupling between RNA synthesis and the flow of carbon and energy must therefore have been of considerable selective value (cf. Chapter 5).

It cannot be taken for granted that the same precise adjustment of ribosome number to growth rate would be obtained in a medium with a "poor" nitrogen source as in one with a poor carbon source. The studies of Magasanik, Magasanik, and Neidhardt (1959) and of Fraenkel (1961) with *A. aerogenes* include pairs of media that differ only with respect to the nitrogen source. In some of these cases quite large differences in growth rate were observed, and their data show that the RNA/mass ratios actually changed almost as indicated by our Equation (3–6).

These results suggest that the regulation of RNA synthesis may be as efficient in response to a change of nitrogen source as it is in the case of changes in carbon and energy sources.

Second, reservation must be made for the possible failure to liberate *all* ribosomes from the disrupted cells. Since we are interested only in establishing a proportionality, this source of error would be relevant only if it turned out that a more or less constant number of ribosomes always remained with the debris. If so, the correlation between number of ribosomes and growth rate would be less striking at the very low rates. In terms of control this would mean that the control mechanism failed to "respond adequately" at these low rates. We believe that systematic errors of this kind are small or absent; this view is based mainly on the finding that the *fraction* of total RNA sedimenting with the debris is not greater at low than at high growth rates (R. E. Ecker and M. Schaechter, personal communication).

Third, an unexpected observation made with our usual strain of *S. typhimurium* calls for comments. If a rapidly growing culture of this strain is homogeneously labeled with ^{14}C-uracil, the cells disrupted, and the crude extract analyzed by sedimentation in a sucrose gradient, nearly *all* the label remains associated with the 70 S ribosomes; i.e., in cell extracts rich in ribosomes practically all the tRNA seems to stick to these particles. In this extract the tRNA is firmly associated with the ribosomes, since dialysis against a buffer solution with low magnesium concentration (10^{-4} *M*) fails to dissociate the complexes. The presence of a normal complement of 4 S RNA in these cells was demonstrated by analyzing the RNA extracted from disrupted cells. When the same experiments were done with slow-growing cells containing relatively few ribosomes, the crude extract contained a more or less normal 4 S fraction of free tRNA (Figure 3–7).

The experiments just described show that as many as 20–40 tRNA molecules can stick to one 70 S ribosome. What this means is not clear; first, because some strains, e.g., the $15T^-$ strain of *E. coli*, do not show association to nearly the same extent, and, second, because we do not know whether the phenomenon occurs *in vivo* or not. At the moment our observation is therefore mainly of technical interest, and indicates that the data of Ecker and Schaechter, presented in Figure 3–6, probably should be corrected for association between ribosomes and tRNA. The figures corresponding to the high growth rate would be reduced by about 20% if the adsorbed tRNA is subtracted. At lower growth rates progressively less tRNA would remain associated, and the effect of the correction would be, to a first approximation,

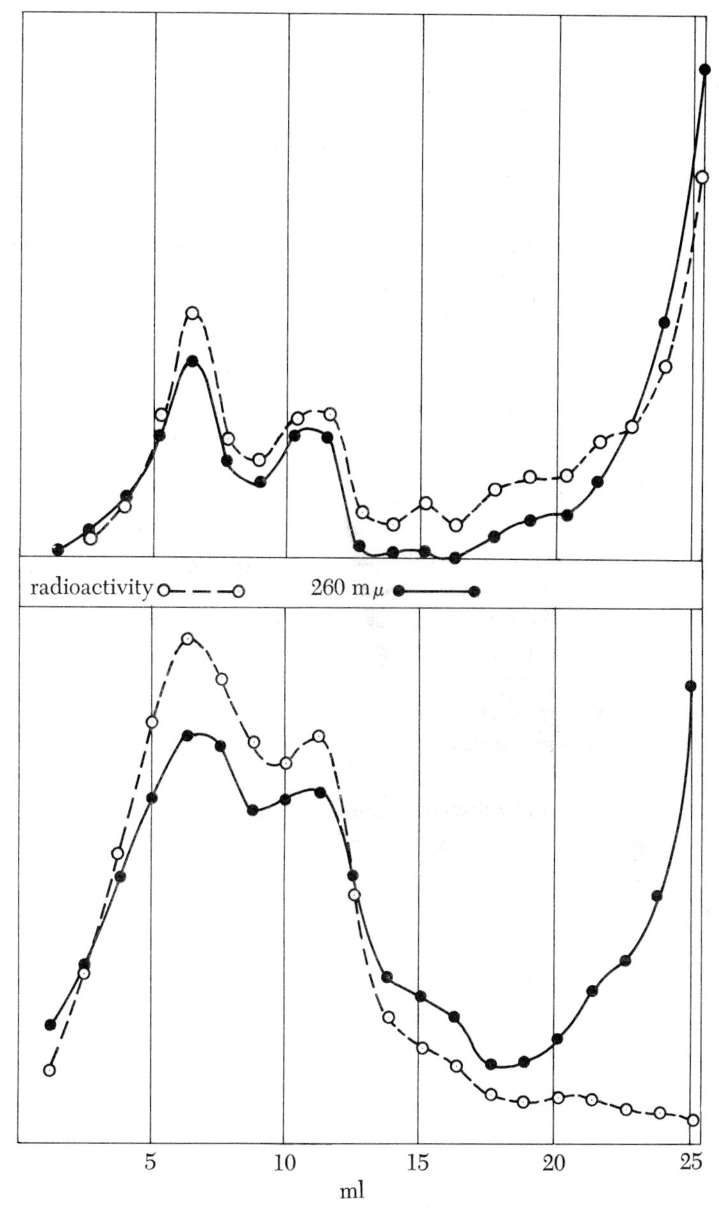

FIGURE 3–7 Association between ribosomes and transfer RNA in *Salmonella typhimurium.* Density gradient analysis of cultures labeled for several generations with ^{14}C-uracil. The cells were disrupted in buffer with 10^{-2} *M* Mg^{++} and spun to display the ribosomes. *Upper frame:* preparation from a slow-growing culture of *S. typhimurium* (μ = ca. 0.2). *Lower frame:* preparation from a culture in glucose-minimal medium ($\mu = 1.2$).

to reduce the slope of the line by about 20%. We shall therefore assume that even the corrected data would agree reasonably well with our general conclusion that the number of ribosomes is proportional to the growth rate.

Electron microscopic evidence. The striking contrast between fast- and slow-growing cells has been illustrated by means of thin-section electron microscopy. It is extremely difficult, if at all practicable, in this way to obtain precise estimates of the number of ribosomes per cell, because (a) actual counting can be attempted only in very thin sections, and (b) it is almost hopeless to collect a sufficient number of uniformly thin serial sections for this purpose. However, a semiquantitative comparison has been obtained by examining mixtures of fast- and slow-growing cells in the electron microscope. In this manner cross-sections of the two kinds of cells can be compared without regard to possible differences in the intensity of "staining" or in the thickness of the preparation. Figure 3–8 shows fields containing both cell types, and as expected they are easy to tell apart. Measurements made on a number of sections indicate that the "fat" cells may well contain 10 times as many ribosomes per nucleus as the "skinny" ones. This approximate figure should be compared to the growth rates of 2.4 and about 0.2 doublings/hr, respectively, in the two cultures.

3–5 THE NUMBERS AND CONCENTRATIONS OF VARIOUS MOLECULES IN THE BACTERIAL CELL

Currently, very exciting results are being obtained by isolating individual components from broken cells and reenacting *in vitro* even such complex biochemical processes as protein synthesis. However, beyond these studies of the physical and chemical properties of particular components, or complexes, lies the problem of understanding how they work and cooperate in the living cell. As a first step in this direction we have analyzed a number of steady states of growth, and obtained a realistic picture of the bacterial cell in terms of absolute numbers and concentrations of the different sorts of macromolecule (see Table 3–3).

In living cells interactions of great biological significance occur, and many properties of the complete system therefore cannot be inferred directly from results obtained by studying fragments of the system *in vitro*. This general and rather obvious problem is one that all biologists face, but it is not the only one, and not even the first to be considered when we try to understand how a biochemical reaction known to occur *in vitro* may proceed in the living cell. Quite apart from the subtle biological properties that manifest themselves only *in vivo*, the physical and chemical environment in the intact cell differs from most test-tube systems in two important respects: On the one hand, the *concentration* of the nucleic acid components, and of many enzymes, is 100 or more times greater in the cell than in most *in vitro* systems. On the other hand, the effective concentrations (or the chemical activities) of the small molecules and ions in the cell are difficult to determine and remain largely unknown.

The precise significance of these differences is not easy to assess, but it is clear that they introduce considerable uncertainty. Thus, the very high concentrations of macromolecules suggest that phenomena like aggregation and gel formation may normally occur in the cytoplasm (see, e.g., Appel, Alpers, and Tomkins, 1965); and our *lack* of knowledge about metabolite and metal ion concentrations implies that it is sometimes difficult to predict in which direction a given enzyme reaction will proceed *in vivo*. Later in this book, specific problems of both kinds are the subject of analysis—and speculation. At this point some relevant numbers, volumes, and overall rates of synthesis will be listed.

Specific numbers and rates. In Chapter 2 the relation between growth rate (μ) and cell mass was derived. For our present purpose we need the numbers of cells per g dry weight for different μ values, and figures for the various macromolecular components expressed in mg per g dry weight. These figures were published by Kjeldgaard (1963) and are reproduced in our Table 3–2. The numbers of genome equivalents of DNA per cell have been calculated from Equation (3–4a), and are used in Table 3–3 to arrive at figures for the numbers of ribosomes, tRNA molecules, etc., per genome.

Let us first consider the dry weight per unit cell volume. Most estimates of the water content in bacteria are based on the weights of the wet and dried cells, respectively; these figures usually indicate that 75–80% of the wet weight is water. This again gives a water *volume* of 80–85%, using the buoyant density of approximately 1.30 measured on living cells in CsCl solutions (S. D. Silver, personal communication), or in solutions of sodium tartrate (R. E. McDonald, personal communication). It is difficult to say to what extent extracellular water contributes to

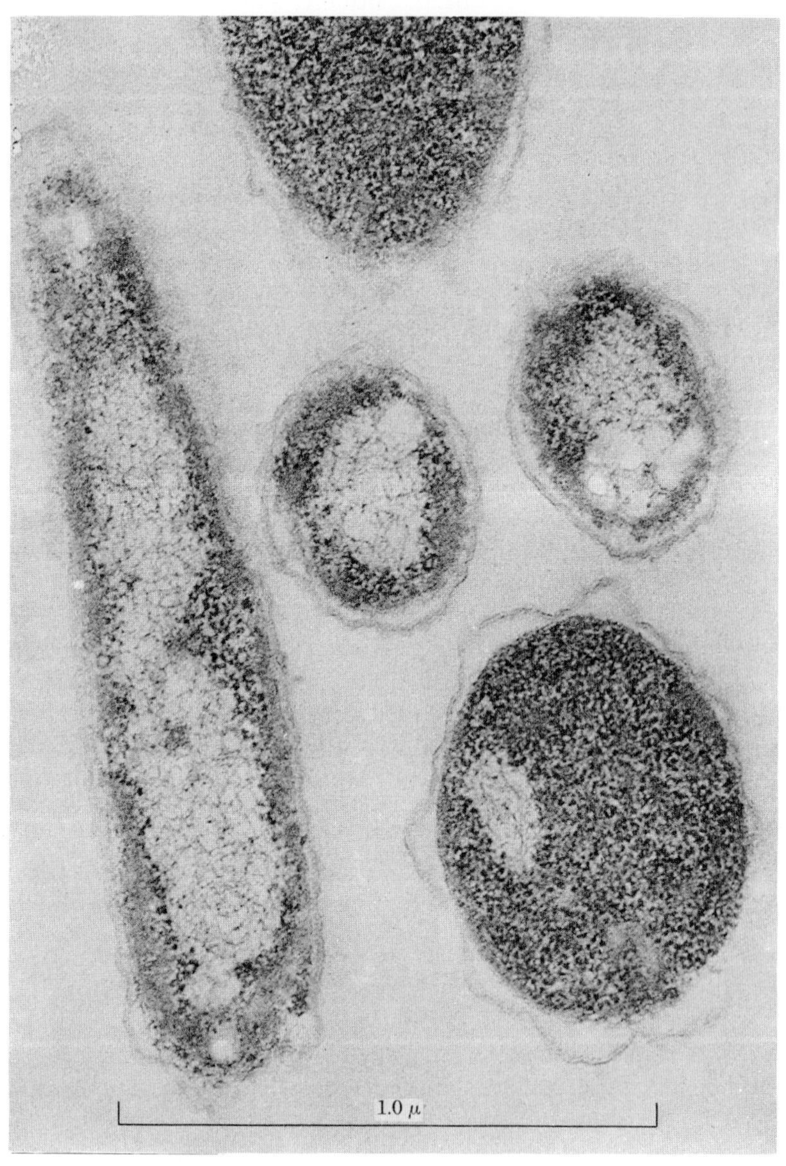

FIGURE 3–8 Thin sections of a mixture of cells from a fast- and a slow-growing culture of *Salmonella typhimurium*. Both cultures had been maintained at their definitive growth rates of $\mu = 2.4$ and approximately 0.2, respectively, for 4–5 generations before being mixed, and processed for microscopy. Fixation and embedding according to Ryter *et al.* (1958). Note that the cyto-

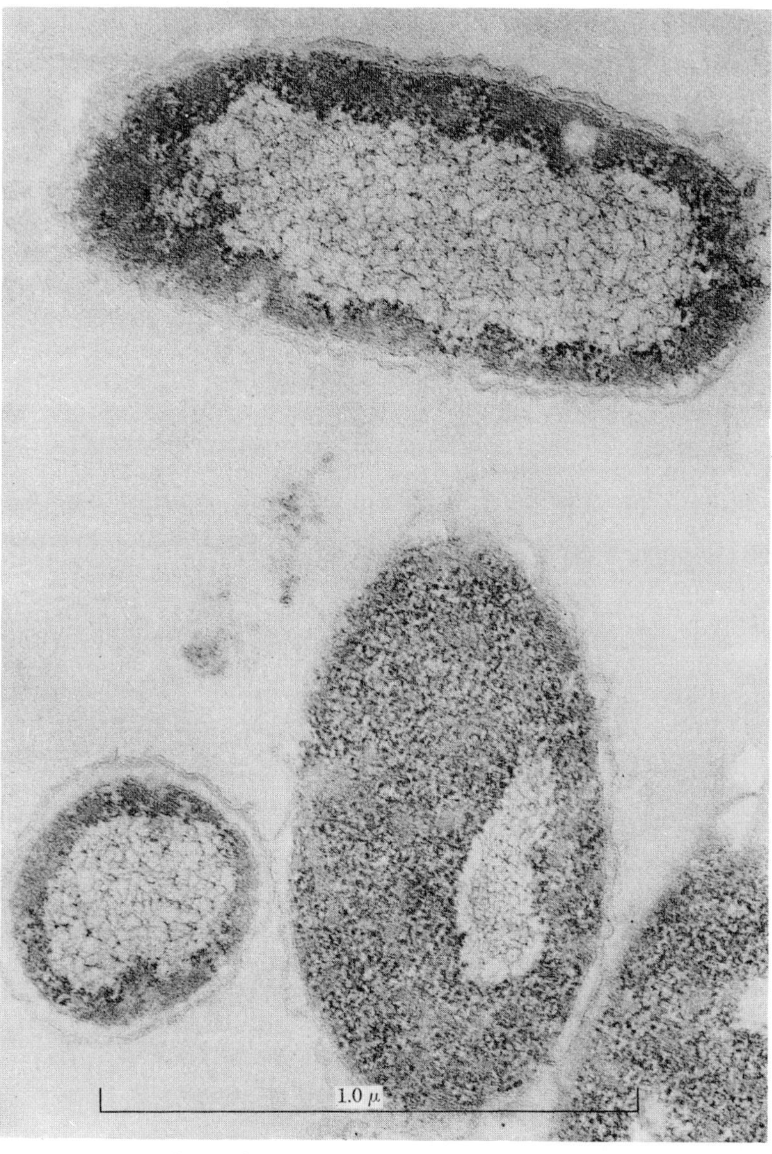

plasm of the "fat" cells (a) from the rapidly growing culture is uniformly packed with ribosomes, whereas in the "skinny" cells (b) from the slow-growing culture the few ribosomes present tend to cluster around the nuclear regions. We are grateful to Professor D. v. Wettstein and Miss Annelise Jensen for having prepared the specimens and taken the electron micrographs.

TABLE 3–2 Number of Cells and Quantities of DNA, RNA, and Proteins [a]

μ	Cells ($\times 10^{-12}$) per g dry weight	DNA (mg/g)	Total RNA (mg/g)	rRNA (mg/g)	tRNA (mg/g)	Protein[b] (mg/g)
2.4	1.3	30	310	250	60	670
1.2	3.1	35	220	135	85	740
0.6	4.8	37	180	90	90	780
0.2	6.3	40	120	35	85	830

[a] Per g dry weight.
[b] To a certain extent, membranes and cell-wall material are included in this figure. We have not attempted to estimate these quantities separately in *S. typhimurium*.

the figures, and an independent estimate of the water content of the *S. typhimurium* strain used in our study is therefore of some interest. Such a value can be derived from Equation (3–1) and from direct volume measurements. The growth rates of the two cultures represented in Figure 2–3 were $\mu = 0.13$ and 2.0, respectively, and the corresponding mean cell volumes were 0.39 and $1.2\mu^3$ (Ecker and Schaechter, 1963). The volume percents of water calculated from these figures are 69 and 70, respectively, i.e., these cells would seem to be more "solid" than is commonly thought. It should be noted that, apart from the reliability of the density measurements, the accuracy of these new figures depends on the precision with which the electronic particle analyzer can be calibrated for measurements of bacterial cell volumes.

Table 3–2 shows the quantities of protein and of the nucleic acid components as functions of μ, and these figures directly show that the ratios of protein and of tRNA to DNA are independent of the growth rate, whereas the ratio of ribosomal RNA (rRNA) to DNA changes dramatically. Table 3–3 shows the actual numbers of amino acids, 70 S ribosomes, and tRNA molecules per gènome, i.e., the numbers that, in a steady state of growth, must be synthesized per generation and per nucleus; or, expressed differently, the numbers of ribosomes, etc., present per genome at the beginning of the cycle during which the genome itself replicates once.

Some basic relationships can be derived from these numbers. Without making any assumptions about how the ribosomes function in protein synthesis, we can calculate the minimum number of amino acids that must be joined together in peptide

TABLE 3–3 Numbers of the Nucleic Acid Molecules and Rates of Protein Synthesis per Ribosome

μ	Genome equivalents[a] (per cell)	70 S ribosomes (per genome)	tRNA molecules (per genome $\times 10^{-5}$)	Amino Acids[b] (per genome $\times 10^{-8}$)	Amino Acids[c] (per 70 S ribosome per second)
2.4	4.5	15,500	2.4	5.4	16
1.2	2.4	6,800	2.8	4.9	17
0.6	1.7	4,200	2.7	4.7	14
0.2	1.4	1,450	2.3	4.5	14

[a] Calculated from Equation (3–4a).
[b] Based on an average molecular weight of 125 for the amino acids.
[c] Calculated on the basis of the average number of ribosomes present in the cell during the cycle, i.e., the figures of column 3 multiplied by 1.5.

linkage per ribosome and per second. As shown in Table 3–3, this number does not change significantly between the μ values of 2.4 and 0.2, and it proves to be about 16 (at 37°). In other words, if *all* ribosomes were engaged *all* the time in polypeptide synthesis, the average time for adding an amino acid to a growing chain, the step time of Goldstein, Goldstein, and Lowney (1964), would be approximately 60 milliseconds at 37°.

Before discussing this figure further it should be emphasized that the polysome model, now generally accepted, implies that (a) the average step time for individual amino acids must be the same, and (b) this average value cannot be subject to excessive statistical fluctuations. Unless these conditions are fulfilled it is difficult to see how a "train" of ribosomes could travel smoothly along a strand of mRNA. An important consequence of this reasoning is that all 20 amino acids must be assumed to be *equally* available, in the form of charged tRNA molecules, at the sites of protein synthesis.

It is clear that the figure of 60 milliseconds is the upper limit for the step time and, if the 70 S particles are not constantly and actively engaged with mRNA, the true step time must be shorter. In fact, the experiments of Goldstein, Goldstein, and Lowney (1964) suggest that, in *E. coli*, the true value is much less than our maximum estimate.

In these experiments leucine-starved cells were given short pulses of labeled leucine at 0°. At this temperature, incorporation is approximately 350 times slower than at 37°, and polypeptide chains can be isolated, onto which only, say, 5 or 10 amino acids were added during the labeling period. Experiments of this kind, involving treatment of the isolated proteins and peptides with carboxypeptidase under different conditions, led to three more or less independent estimates of the step time. The figures obtained for incorporation at 0° are 4.2, 5.0, and 7 seconds, which correspond to 12–20 milliseconds at 37°. The agreement between the figures is quite remarkable since the assumptions involved in interpreting the results are not the same in the three cases.

If these estimates are accepted, the true step time is considerably shorter than our maximum estimate of about 60 milliseconds. Consequently, only a minor fraction of the ribosomes may be engaged, at any given time, in the process of polypeptide synthesis. The following comment by Goldstein states the problem very clearly; he writes: "If the inactive ribosomes were truly idle, it would be difficult to understand the direct relationship between growth rate changes and ribosome content in various media. One can imagine, however, that all ribosomes pass cyclically through a phase of activity (in the polyribosomal aggregates associated with mRNA) and a phase of activation, the latter process more time-consuming than the former. Activation of a ribosome could be prerequisite for its specific combination at the 3′-OH terminus (and not elsewhere) on an mRNA strand to initiate the polypeptide assembly process" (Goldstein, Goldstein, and Lowney, 1964). In the next chapter we shall discuss experiments which strongly suggest that, whatever ribosomes do when they are not assembling amino acids, they are not idle.

The problem just presented is important, and the solution offered by Goldstein *et al.* should not be accepted without further discussion. The point is that, in cells which are opened up very carefully, about 80% of the ribosomes are in polysomes of various sizes (see, e.g., Wettstein, Staehlin, and Noll, 1963; Schaechter, 1963), and unless these structures are thought of as artifacts of preparation (cf. Section 1–7), ribosomes that are attached to mRNA must be assumed to be engaged in polypeptide synthesis. Faced with this dilemma, we shall reconsider the whole problem, and for this purpose two sets of experiments are particularly relevant: (1) those of Goldstein, Goldstein, and Lowney (1964) which we have described, and (2) the classical studies of McQuillen, Roberts, and Britten (1959). In both, the experimental evidence is very clear and only questions concerning interpretation will be discussed here.

(1) To estimate the step time, Goldstein *et al.* had to make several assumptions which so far it has not been possible to test independently. The main assumption is that during leucine

starvation all polypeptide chains stop growing at a point where leucine is required, and that chain growth starts with the addition of a leucine residue as soon as this amino acid is reintroduced. This sounds plausible, but it is not self-evident. In *E. coli*, the mole fraction of leucine is about 0.1, and Goldstein *et al.* assume that the leucine residues are randomly distributed throughout the proteins of the cell. However, proteins are known in which the mole fraction is 0.2 or more, and if such proteins occur in coli cells there must also be some that contain correspondingly less leucine. When a polypeptide chain rich in leucine is being synthesized, it is quite possible that every ribosome stops at a leucine position when this amino acid is exhausted; however, with a leucine-poor chain this need not be the case, since a ribosome which stops at a leucine position may be followed by one or more ribosomes which already have passed the preceding leucine position. The frequency with which this might happen cannot be estimated, but some of the observations of Goldstein *et al.* are in fact not easy to reconcile with the assumptions that leucine is the first amino acid to be incorporated *and* that all chains start growing almost simultaneously. These problems have been discussed in detail with Dr. Goldstein, and are brought up here because the step time is so basic and important a parameter. If his estimates prove to be too low (and they are the only ones existing today), the dilemma referred to above might disappear.

(2) In the experiments of McQuillen *et al.*, very short pulses of ^{35}S were used, and the whole cell juice was analyzed by sedimentation through sucrose gradients. In the profiles obtained after very short labeling periods, it is relatively easy to distinguish between the radioactivity associated with the ribosomes and that which has passed into the pool of soluble proteins. One can therefore estimate the average time it takes to build a polypeptide chain and to release it from the ribosome. The ribosome system can be viewed as a "pool" through which the labeled amino acids pass on their way from tRNA to the finished protein molecules. This pool is special, however, in the sense that an amino acid, once entered, must stay for a fixed time, which is determined by the position it occupies in the amino acid chain and the length of that chain. If we consider polysomes producing a given polypeptide, it is easy to see that, when the labeling period equals the time it takes to synthesize and release that particular polypeptide, the amount of radioactivity associated with the ribosomes will equal the amount that has been released

from the particles. It is also clear that when we compare these two quantities, correction should be made for the radioactivity which is carried on tRNA molecules and which, in the sedimentation analysis, will appear together with the soluble protein. The figures of Table 3–3 can be used for this purpose, and it turns out that for a labeling period of 15 seconds ($^1/_{200}$ of a generation time at $\mu = 1.2$) the correction is not insignificant.

When the data of McQuillen *et al.* (their Figures 2a and 3a) are analyzed in this way, it is found that, after 15 seconds of labeling, the radioactivity associated with the ribosomes is practically the same as that found in the soluble protein fraction. This is a crude estimate, but suggests that the average time for assembling and releasing a polypeptide chain may not be less than 15 seconds (at 37°). If we combine this figure with Goldstein's estimates of the step time, the average amino acid chain would contain 750–1500 residues. These figures are probably 3–4 times too high, and we therefore hesitate to accept the view that the true step time is much shorter than the maximum estimates of Table 3–3.

Selected numerical examples. Some interesting relationships can be derived from the numbers of the different sorts of RNA molecule, all of which we believe are synthesized by direct transcription of specific parts of the genome. First, let us consider the average number of 70 S ribosomes synthesized per nucleus and per second in rapidly growing cells ($\mu = 2.4$). This number is about 10, and we may assume that it is close to the maximum number of rRNA molecules (23 S and 16 S units) that can be produced per second at 37°.

The number of DNA regions serving as templates for, say, the 23 S RNA unit is not precisely known. First, it is conceivable that each genome has more than one such region, since reduplication of a region from which a great output may be demanded could be of selective advantage. Second, we know that a given DNA region is replicated at some specific point during the division cycle, and the average number of such regions per nucleus therefore depends on the position of the region relative to the origin of replication. If the region is replicated early a *nucleus* contains nearly twice as many of these regions as a *genome*, whereas if replication occurs late the number of regions per nucleus will be almost the same as the number per genome. These uncertainties and the limitations they impose must be kept in mind.

We have seen earlier that both 16 S and 23 S RNA anneal

specifically with DNA, and that the latter seems to account for about 0.2% of the DNA. This fraction, 0.2%, of one genome is about 6000 base pairs, as compared to some 3400 nucleotides in one 23 S unit. The effect of the position on the genome of the DNA region corresponding to the 23 S unit can be calculated as follows: if the DNA used in the annealing experiments is harvested from an exponentially growing culture, approximately 30% of the total quantity of DNA will have been synthesized during the round of replication actually in progress at the time of harvesting (cf. Chapter 6). It can now be seen that the fraction of a *genome*, with which a 23 S RNA molecule anneals, would increase over and above the observed value of 0.2% of the DNA if that specific DNA region replicates late, and vice versa if it replicates early. The limiting values are obtained by dividing the uncorrected figure of 6000 base pairs by 0.7 and by 1.4, respectively. This gives values corresponding to 2.5–1.25 times the length of the 23 S unit. When we consider further that the figure of 0.2%, reported by Yankofsky and Spiegelman (1963), probably represents a true value somewhere between 0.15% and 0.25%, it is clear that we cannot decide whether the genome has one, two, or possibly three identical "23 S" regions; higher numbers seem unlikely.

This result is somewhat disappointing, because the annealing data offer one of the few possibilities of estimating the maximum frequency with which RNA copies can be drawn from a given DNA template region. At present, all we can say is that the average yield of about ten 23 S molecules per nucleus, and per second, could be the output of a single "23 S" region, but it could also represent the joint yield from a few regions.

The copying frequency—as distinct from the copying rate—may also be estimated from the yield of certain enzymes. It can be assumed that, in a constitutive strain, mRNA is being drawn from the structural gene at the maximum frequency, and this figure could be calculated as the number of enzyme molecules produced per time unit divided by the average number of polypeptide chains made from one messenger molecule. In the case of alkaline phosphatase the first number is readily obtained, since about 5% of the amino acids are known to end up in phosphatase molecules with 385 residues per polypeptide chain. From the figures of Table 3–3, one obtains a rate of synthesis of about 50 chains per second at $\mu = 2.4$. The number of times a messenger functions has been estimated indirectly in various ways, and figures from 10 to about 70 have been suggested. The corresponding numbers of phosphatase messenger molecules produced per second, of course, are 5 and 0.7, respectively. In this range, the higher figures are quite compatible with our estimate of the maximum number of 23 S RNA molecules synthesized per nucleus per second; however, if the true figure proved to be 1 or less, it would be difficult to maintain the simple assumptions on which this comparison is based, viz., that a constitutive chain is always completely derepressed, and that one and the same DNA-dependent polymerase produces both ribosomal and messenger RNA (see also Chapter 5).

The calculations presented on the last few pages have not led, and cannot at present lead, to very precise conclusions. They have been included for two reasons: first, because they do show that no obvious contradictions result when the numbers from Table 3–3 are analyzed according to current ideas about protein and RNA synthesis; second, because some of these analyses may have heuristic value.

4

TRANSITIONS BETWEEN STEADY STATES OF GROWTH

4-1 GENERAL PRINCIPLES

Up to this point we have been concerned exclusively with steady states of growth. No specific hypothesis had been formulated beforehand and the whole survey was actually based on reasoning of the following kind: many quantitatively important syntheses in the bacterial cell are known to be governed by regulatory mechanisms; let us see if, by observing balanced growth under a variety of conditions, some general principles can be recognized. The finding of simple relationships between some of the important cell components has justified, in retrospect, the tedious process of mapping a large number of different physiological states.

Throughout these studies the experimenter essentially played the role of an observer, not interfering with the growth of the cells except to sample and carry out measurements. While reducing the element of interpretation to a minimum, this attitude of course does not reduce the errors inherent in the measurements, nor does it eliminate the problem of estimating the recovery of the quantities that are being measured. Despite these unavoidable errors and uncertainties, it has been possible to establish certain definite correlations, of which the most important indicates that the *size* of the protein-synthesizing machinery of the bacterial cell seems to be effectively and economically controlled.

We now leave the simple experiments referred to as "measurements" in the introduction. Knowing some characteristics of a number of distinct physiological states of growth, we can undertake to analyze the transition from one state to another. This kind of experiment involves interference with the growth of the culture, at a precise time and in a precise manner, in order to change the composition of the medium. This simple operation has been called a *shift* experiment, and we talk about a shift-*up* if the change of medium leads to an *in*crease in growth rate; the reverse change is called a shift-*down*. Measurements similar to those described in the two preceding chapters have been made during a large number of shift experiments involving many different pairs of media. Most of these experiments are described in two publications: Kjeldgaard, Maaløe, and Schaechter (1958) and Kjeldgaard (1961). The latter is reproduced in this volume as Appendix II.

This whole program can be looked upon as an attempt to achieve that which Henrici anticipated in his classical book "Morphological Variation and the Rate of Growth of Bacteria" (1928). Referring to the changes that bacteria could be seen to undergo between the inoculation of a culture and the time when net growth ceased, Henrici wrote: "In this work I shall show that, contrary to the orthodox teaching, the cells of bacteria are constantly changing in size and form and structure; but that instead of these changes occurring in a haphazard or meaningless fashion, or instead of being phases in a rather vague and complex life cycle, they occur with great regularity and are governed by simple laws which, after more data have been accumulated and analyzed, may probably be very precisely formulated."

The shift-up. Many experiments of this kind can be done simply by adding to, or enriching, a medium in which balanced growth has established itself. The most thoroughly investigated case is that in which, at time zero, broth is added to a steady-state culture in a glucose-minimal medium. *A priori* we know that the definitive growth rate in the enriched medium will be very nearly twice the pre-shift rate (2.4 doublings/hr, as compared to 1.2); furthermore, we know that when the new equilibrium has been reached the mass/genome will have increased by 15–20%, while the number of nuclei/cell as well as the total amount of RNA/genome will have almost doubled (see Tables 3–2 and 3–3). The detailed analyses of this transition show that (a) the changes in size and composition result from a temporary and orderly dissociation of the main synthetic activities of the cells, and (b) the *pattern* of the particular shift-up we now consider (see Figure 4–1) repeats itself in experiments with other pairs of media, and with other strains. An exception to this rule is the type of shift-up in which the situation is complicated by necessity for de novo synthesis of one or more essential enzymes whose production was repressed in the *pre*-shift medium.

The predominant feature of the shift-up is the immediate dissociation between RNA synthesis and the rest of the activities with which we are concerned, i.e., DNA and protein synthesis, on the one hand, and nuclear and cellular division, on the other. As rapidly as it is technically possible to demonstrate, and we shall see that 30–60 seconds suffice, the rate of RNA synthesis is found to have increased to a value over and above the definitive rate in the new medium. In contrast, all the other activities *initially continue at the pre-shift rates*. At different times after the shift, the rates of these other activities increase and, after relatively *short* acceleration periods, the *definitive* rates are established (cf. Figure 4–1). This dissociation pattern is in itself evidence that separate control mechanisms govern the individual activities that we now propose to discuss one by one.

4–2 THE SYNTHESIS OF RNA FOLLOWING A SHIFT-UP

In most of these experiments the orcinol color reaction has been used to determine total RNA, and fractionation has not been attempted. In this way the kinetics of RNA synthesis cannot be studied in detail, but the technique is adequate to show that a selective build-up of RNA begins very soon after the shift. This is evident from the fact that even the earliest post-shift RNA values fall on a curve displaced upward relative to the curves for mass, DNA, etc. Eventually, when the new steady state is established, the vertical distances between the RNA curve and the other three curves measure the factors by which total RNA has increased relative to mass, DNA, or cell number, respectively (see Figure 4–1).

A new shift experiment must now be introduced (Figure 4–2). It differs from the first in the sense that the definitive growth rate after the shift, the usual 2.4 doublings/hr in broth, is almost 6 times higher than the pre-shift rate. Two important features are illustrated in this experiment: first, that the general pattern

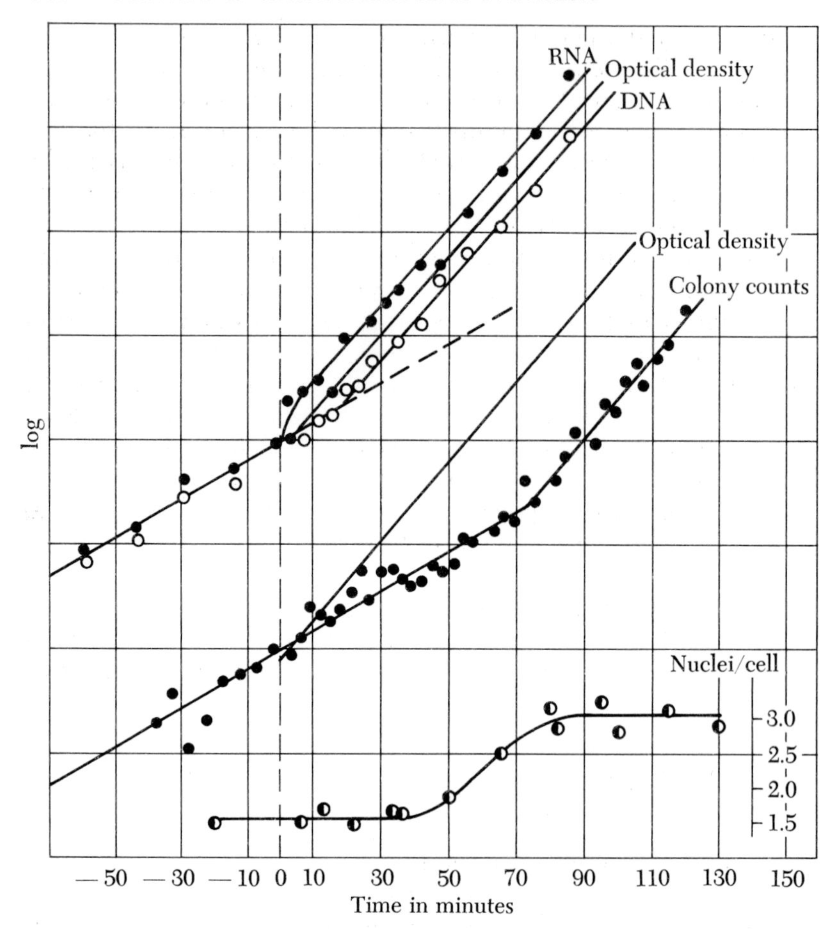

FIGURE 4–1 Shift-up experiment with *Salmonella typhimurium.* A *Salmonella typhimurium* culture was shifted, at 37°, from glucose-salt-minimal medium to broth at time 0. Optical density, viable counts, RNA, and DNA content were frequently determined. For clarity, two separate sets of curves are presented: *on top,* optical density, RNA, and DNA; and *below,* optical density and viable counts. In all cases the logarithms of the measured values are plotted against time, and all values are transposed so as to make the curves representing balanced growth in minimal medium coincide. The distance between horizontal lines corresponds to one doubling. In the lower right-hand corner, the average number of nuclei per cell that are obtained from direct counts on stained preparations are plotted against time.

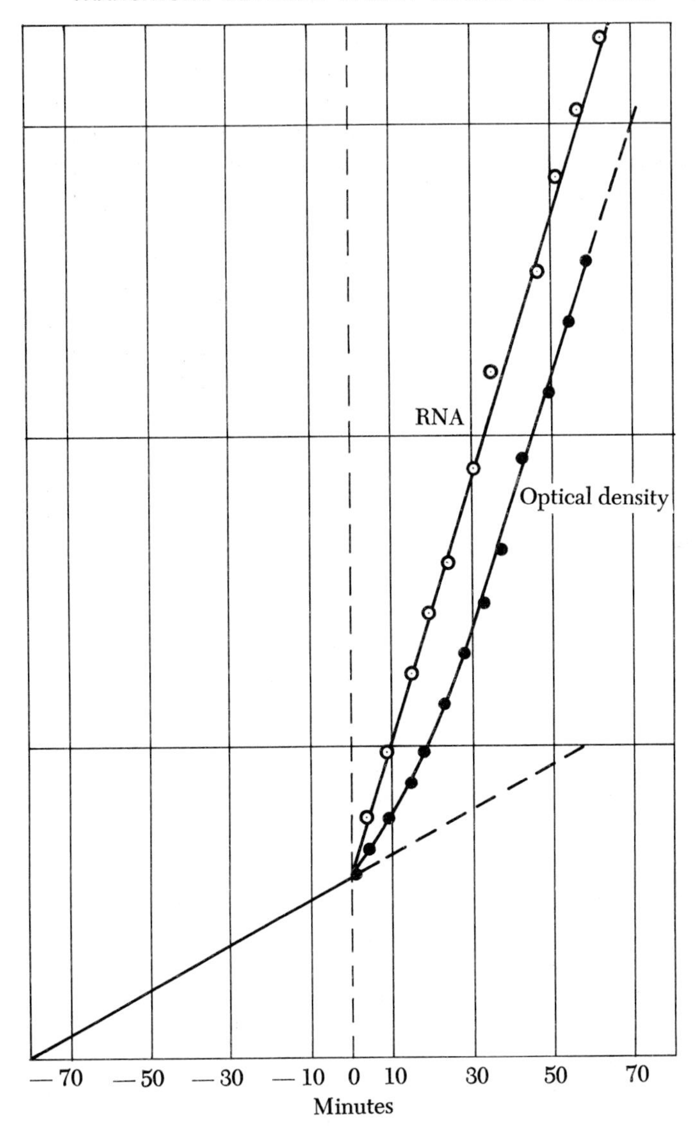

FIGURE 4–2 Shift-up experiment with *Salmonella typhimurium.* A culture of *Salmonella typhimurium* grown in glycerol-minimal medium was shifted to broth medium at time 0. Optical density and RNA content were frequently determined. The logarithms of the measured values are transposed to make the curves representing balanced growth in glycerol-minimal medium coincide.

is independent of the magnitude of the rate change; second, and more specifically, that the rate of RNA synthesis very rapidly goes up about 7-fold as compared to the 2–3-fold increase observed in the previous experiment. Thus, irrespective of the pre-shift rate of synthesis, the number of RNA units produced per second and per genome can be raised, with no apparent lag, to a value in the neighborhood of the definitive value in the broth culture. We shall look more closely at this observation, which is particularly relevant to the control of RNA synthesis.

A detailed picture of the kinetics of RNA synthesis has been obtained by following the incorporation of ^{32}P, or of ^{14}C-uracil, added to the cultures at the time of the shift. Experiments of this kind are complicated by "pool effects," i.e., the delaying effect upon incorporation of the isotope due to the presence in the cell of a pool of unlabeled precursor material. In the case of phosphorus this pool is large, as evidenced by the fact that it takes about 6–8 minutes (at 37°) before $^{32}PO_4$, added at time zero, is incorporated into RNA and DNA at the definitive differential rate. This delaying effect is illustrated in Appendix II (Figures 1 and 2). In contrast, little or no pool effect is observed with uracil incorporation into the RNA of a uracil-requiring strain.

The experiments we shall consider now were designed to show (a) to what extent and for how long the initial rate of RNA synthesis exceeds the definitive post-shift rate, and (b), how "immediate" the increase in the rate of synthesis actually is.

The most extensive study of (a) was made with $^{32}PO_4$. To eliminate as far as possible the pool effect, the following procedure was adopted: the samples withdrawn from the culture containing $^{32}PO_4$ were diluted into broth to which an excess of $^{31}PO_4$ had been added; soon after the cells were collected on a filter, washed, and assayed for radioactivity. In this way *all* ^{32}P that does not exchange with the wash medium is registered. Thus, practically all the label assimilated by the cells during exposure to ^{32}P is measured, and we assume that this equals the amount of P ($^{31}P + {}^{32}P$) which, in the same time, leaves the pools to be incorporated into RNA. The small quantities of $^{32}PO_4$ that go into DNA and into phospholipids are disregarded (for further details and discussion, see Appendix II).

Figure 4–3 illustrates the incorporation of ^{32}P during balanced growth in broth (curve I), and following a shift from glucose-minimal medium to broth (curve II). The upper right part of the graph shows the increase in RNA expressed as ^{32}P counts (scale

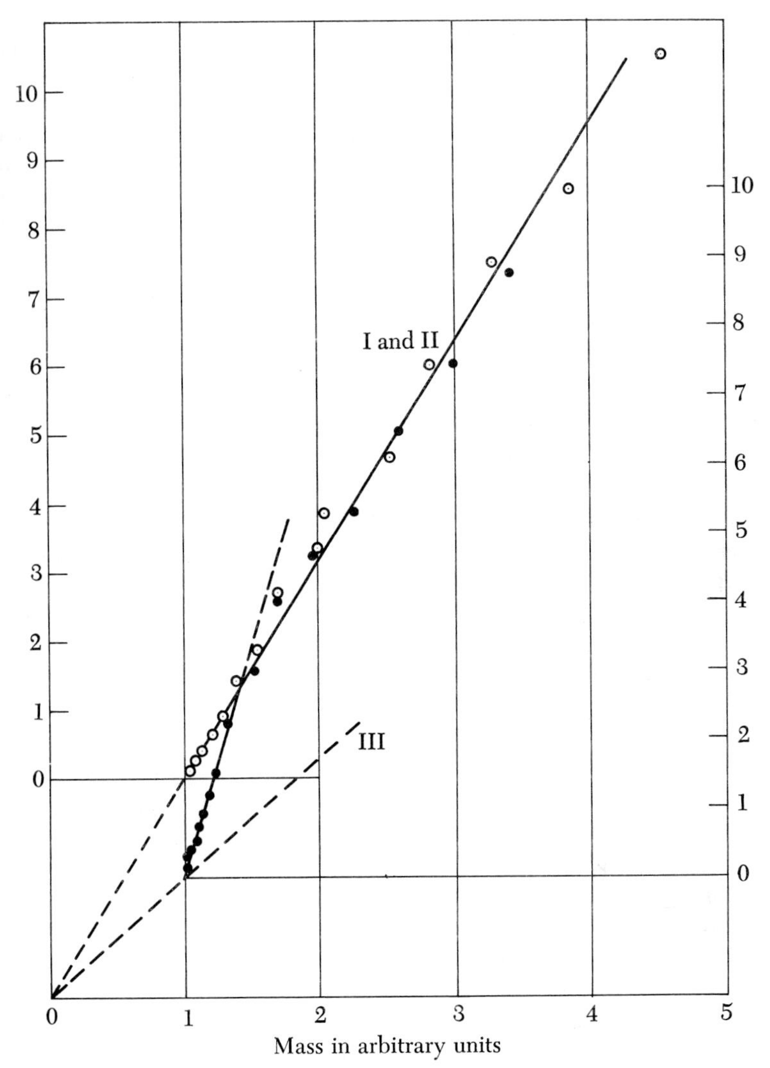

FIGURE 4–3 RNA synthesis during and after the transition period following a shift-up. Curve I (○) represents ^{32}P incorporation in a broth culture (scale on left-hand side of frame shows counts/min × 10^{-3}). The abscissa shows growth in terms of mass (mass at time of addition of the label is taken as unit). This curve has been extrapolated to zero mass (time $-\infty$), and the distance on the ordinate corresponding to the extrapolation indicates the extra amount of radioactivity that would have been incorporated had the label been present from time $-\infty$. Curve II (●) shows ^{32}P uptake after a shift from glucose-minimal medium to broth; the observed radioactivity was corrected as described in the text, and the derived values can be read on the right. Curve III shows the differential incorporation expected during balanced growth in glucose-minimal medium.

on the left-hand side of the figure), and plotted against cell mass in the control broth culture. This common differential plot has been extended by extrapolating to zero mass (time $-\infty$) in order to obtain the ordinate value corresponding to the RNA content of the culture at time zero when ^{32}P was added. The data from the shift-up experiment can be normalized to fit into this diagram, since we know that, at time zero, the RNA content per unit mass was that characteristic of a glucose-minimal culture, and that the RNA/mass ratio corresponding to balanced growth in broth has been reached after two mass doublings (see Figure 4–1). Using the figures for the RNA/mass ratio from Table 3–2, the proper correction factor was obtained and the counts from the shift experiment plotted. The resulting curve (II) is composed of an early segment with about twice the slope of the control curve (I), and a late segment that superimposes itself on the latter. In addition to the experimental curves, a theoretical curve (III) is included that shows the differential synthesis of RNA in a culture in glucose-minimal medium.

The net results of the ^{32}P experiments are: (1) very soon after the shift the differential rate of RNA synthesis increases by a factor of almost 4; (2) this excessive rate is maintained during the first 25–30 minutes (see time scale on top of the frame in Figure 4–3); (3) at this time the RNA/mass ratio characteristic of the new medium has been established; and (4) the differential rate of synthesis henceforth is that of the control broth culture, i.e., about twice the pre-shift rate.

Having answered some general questions concerning the period of excessive RNA synthesis after a shift-up, we turn to the more special problem of assessing how rapidly the high, post-shift rate of RNA synthesis is established. In order to do this without having to worry about pool effects, the experiments were done with a uracil-requiring strain of *E. coli* in which the incorporation of added ^{14}C-uracil reaches the definitive rate in less than 1 minute. Furthermore, the shift was made between a succinate-minimal medium ($\mu = 0.68$), and a defined medium containing glucose and all the common amino acids ($\mu = 1.95$), i.e., the shift did *not* involve addition of purines or pyrimidines.

Figure 4–4 shows that the rate of incorporation of uracil into RNA is constant during the first 25 minutes after the shift. Moreover, since this rate must be 5–6 times higher than the pre-shift rate, we believe that a lag of 1 minute in establishing the new high rate would have been detected in this experiment. In other words, it seems that the cells are capable of switching almost

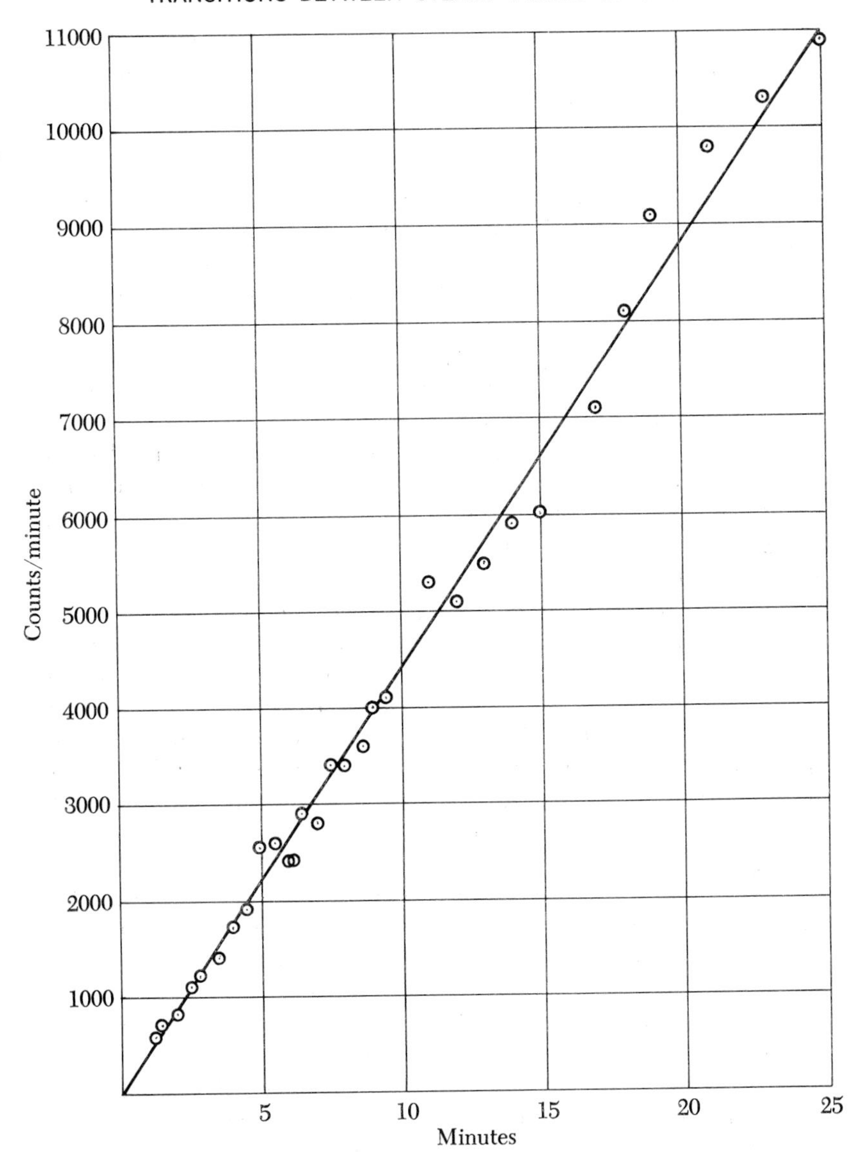

FIGURE 4–4 Incorporation of radioactive uracil during the first 25 minutes after a shift-up. This experiment was done with a uracil-requiring strain grown in a succinate-minimal medium, and shifted to a medium containing glucose and casamino acids.

instantaneously to a greatly increased rate of RNA synthesis, and to maintain this new rate for a period long enough to treble their initial RNA content. This conclusion has recently been substantiated by means of pulse experiments in which the actual rate of RNA synthesis was measured at several points during the first few minutes after a shift-up (Koch, 1965). These experiments clearly show that the rate of RNA synthesis begins to increase in less than 5 seconds, and that the full rate, which in one case was about 10 times the pre-shift rate, was established within about 90 seconds (at 37°).

Analysis of the RNA synthesized after a shift-up. The results just presented permit some interesting deductions concerning the RNA-synthesizing system in bacteria. From the fact that the transition from a low pre-shift rate to a sustained high post-shift rate is very rapid, we conclude that de novo enzyme synthesis is not involved, i.e., the slow-growing cells possess, but do not fully utilize, the enzyme systems implicated in RNA synthesis. This, in turn, means that the DNA-dependent RNA polymerase *as well as* the enzymes producing the substrates for RNA synthesis, the riboside triphosphates, must be under inhibition during slow growth. As regards the triphosphates, we shall assume that their *production* is restricted by feed-back inhibition and that their *concentrations* in the cell therefore must be high. Actually, when we postulate that one of the effects of the shift is to release this feed-back inhibition, it follows that the end-product concentrations must be somewhat *lowered* by the shift.

This argument, which is based on the large and abrupt increase in rate of RNA synthesis, derives considerable support from several independent observations. Thus experiments by Fraenkel and Neidhardt (1961) and Kurland and Maaløe (1962) (see Chapter 5 and Appendix III) show that high concentrations of chloramphenicol can produce large and instantaneous increases in the rate of RNA synthesis. Since this effect is induced in the absence of protein synthesis, it is clear that slow-growing cells possess a *latent* capacity for RNA production.

This reasoning is based on one of the general consequences of end-product, or feed-back, inhibition, viz., that the intracellular concentration of certain key products can be maintained at levels higher than those required to saturate the enzymes for which the same products serve as substrates. The only necessary condition is that the total capacity of the enzymes which remove the products be sufficiently low. In the case we have just considered, the products are the four riboside triphosphates and the enzyme removing them is the polymerase. Thus it would suffice to assume that, at low growth rates, a certain fraction of the polymerase molecules is inhibited, that the flow of triphosphates into RNA is thereby limited, and that this in turn causes the concentrations of the triphosphates to rise to levels at which feed-back inhibition sets in.

With this scheme in mind, we can now look at the conditions under which the synthesis of an individual RNA molecule is initiated. Three components are known to be required: a DNA template in the derepressed or "receptive" state, a noninhibited polymerase molecule, and a pool containing all four riboside triphosphates. For simplicity, we may assume that repression and enzyme inhibition are all-or-none phenomena, i.e., that at a given instant a template is either inaccessible or completely "open," and that a polymerase molecule is either inactive or fully active. In such a system the substrate concentration is the only factor that might limit the rate at which *a particular RNA strand* will be synthesized.[1])

Throughout this discussion we have taken for granted that the riboside triphosphates themselves, i.e., the substrates for RNA synthesis, effect feed-back inhibition (cf. Section 1–8). Since our analysis rests on this assumption and its consequences with respect to the concentrations of the triphosphates, we shall consider the possibility that even mono- or diphosphates may cause feed-back inhibition. If so, the main effect of a shift-up might be to increase ATP production and thereby raise the concentrations in the cell of all four riboside *tri*phosphates. A mechanism of this kind cannot be ruled out, but it seems unlikely since we have found that the ATP concentration in fact is the same in very slow-growing cells ($\mu =$ about 0.2) as in cells growing in glucose-minimal medium ($\mu = 1.2$) (Smith and Maaløe, 1964). It therefore seems reasonable to assume, as we have done, that the substrates for RNA synthesis are present in high concentrations even during very slow growth. If this is correct, it follows that individual RNA strands must be synthesized at a rate which, at a given temperature, is relatively independent of the growth rate. In other words, we are led to infer that the

[1] This argument, of course, is correct only if one assumes that the enzyme molecule initiating the synthesis of an RNA strand stays on until the strand is completed. *In vitro* experiments (to be discussed in Chapter 7) suggest that the DNA template and the polymerase molecule are firmly united during RNA synthesis.

overall rate of RNA synthesis, like that of protein synthesis, may be governed chiefly by the *frequency* with which new chains are being initiated, and not to any great extent by the rate at which individual chains are made.

Before leaving this subject, it should be mentioned that there is no *a priori* reason for assuming that RNA synthesis is controlled via inhibition of the polymerase. Alternatively, the overall rate of RNA synthesis might be controlled at the DNA level by a general, nonspecific repression mechanism. This model is complementary to the one just presented: it postulates that RNA synthesis is restricted by the availability, *not* of active polymerase molecules, but of "receptive" DNA sites, i.e., derepressed operons. To put it differently, it may be assumed that an operon is controlled by a common lock in addition to the specific one, or by a single lock which requires a specific as well as a general key. Formally, this second model accounts as well as the first for the kinetics of RNA synthesis in a shift-up, the only difference being that the pre-shift restriction on RNA synthesis is attributed to another, but in this respect equivalent, component of the system.

This discussion is deliberately restricted to simple models in which the same mechanism is thought to control the synthesis of messenger and of stable RNA. This idea was briefly discussed (Chapter 3), and will be considered again in the next chapter. Here attention should be drawn to a significant difference between the two alternatives presented above. Imagine that we have a constitutive mutant in which the structural gene is accessible to the polymerase at all times. If a cell always contains a more or less fixed number of polymerase molecules, and if there is no inhibitor of this enzyme in the cell, a fairly constant number of the specific mRNA molecules would be produced *per minute*, irrespective of the growth rate. Since the total quantity of protein synthesized *per generation* changes very little with the growth rates, the same probably is true of the total number of mRNA molecules. Consequently, one would expect that the longer the generation time the greater the *fraction* of the specific mRNA molecules among all messengers. This leads to the prediction that the lower the growth rate the greater the *differential* rate of synthesis of the constitutive enzyme. On the other hand, if RNA synthesis were adjusted to the growth rate through inhibition of the polymerase, as was first assumed, an accessible gene would not, automatically, give birth to a fixed number of messenger molecules per minute. In fact, on this model the specific messenger would be a *constant* fraction of all messengers, and the differential rate of synthesis of the constitutive enzyme would therefore be expected to be the same at different growth rates.

Few observations have been made that bear on this problem. The differential rate of synthesis of β-galactosidase has been shown to be the same in cultures growing at widely different rates in the chemostat (A. Novick, personal communication). This result seems clear and conclusive. However, catabolite repression, which would be expected to be stronger the lower the growth rate, may have complicated the system and masked an otherwise detectable increase in the differential rate of enzyme synthesis. The alkaline phosphatase of *E. coli* is not subject to this type of repression, and preliminary studies with constitutive mutants indicate that the differential rate of synthesis is the same in different media and at different growth rates (C. Levinthal, personal communication). If these results are confirmed, and if similar observations can be made with repressible, biosynthetic enzymes, two possibilities remain: all RNA synthesis might be controlled jointly through inhibition of the polymerase; or, if control is exerted at the DNA level, it must operate completely independently of the *specific* mechanisms controlling the activity of individual operons.

4-3 PROTEIN SYNTHESIS FOLLOWING A SHIFT-UP

In this section the main objective will be to test the validity of the hypothesis that, at a given temperature, individual ribosomes always operate with nearly the same efficiency; or, that the rate at which individual polypeptide chains grow is more or less independent of the growth rate of the cell.

As pointed out earlier, the correlation between number of ribosomes and *rate* of protein synthesis, on which this hypothesis is based, yields only information about the "average efficiency of the average ribosome." If it could be argued that the constant efficiency is also the maximum efficiency, the observed correlation would be immediately understandable. This attractively simple interpretation would imply that, in any steady state of growth, the microenvironment of a ribosome is saturated with respect to messenger and transfer RNA, various enzymes, and all the common amino acids. Rather strong evidence in favor of this view can be obtained from shift-up experiments by testing not only the general prediction, that the rate of protein synthesis per ribosome should remain unchanged during the transition period, but also the more specific implication, that no immediate increase in the overall rate of protein synthesis should be observed if the cells are suddenly flooded with amino acids.

The number of ribosomes (a), and the rate of protein synthesis (b), have been determined repeatedly during shift experiments. These measurements must be described separately:

(a) In order to decide anything about ribosomal efficiency during the transition period, it is necessary to know whether the large quantity of RNA synthesized right after the shift reflects a more or less equally large increase in *mature* ribosomes. This cannot be taken for granted, since we do not know whether slow-growing cells, that are transferred to a rich medium, can produce enough of the specific ribosomal proteins to match the dramatic increase in RNA synthesis. Thus we must consider the possibility that immature particles, like those formed in the presence of chloramphenicol, might pile up in the cells during the transition period.

To settle this question, a *S. typhimurium* culture growing in a glycerol-minimal medium ($\mu = 0.6$) was shifted to broth ($\mu = 2.4$), and at 5-minute intervals 250-ml samples were poured onto equal volumes of crushed ice. The cells were washed, resuspended (in 0.01 *M* Tris succinic acid buffer, pH 7.6, containing 5×10^{-3} *M* Mg^{++}), and disrupted by high pressure at −40°. The crude extracts were immediately analyzed in the optical ultracentrifuge. No immature particles were observed and the quantities of normal ribosomes, relative to the total amount of soluble material, can be read from Figure 4–5. This experiment shows clearly that the number of ribosomes actually increases from the low pre-shift to the high post-shift value during the first 30 minutes after the shift, i.e., during the period characterized by an excessively high rate of RNA synthesis. The rates of synthesis of RNA *and* of the ribosomal protein must therefore have been increased above the pre-shift value by roughly the same factor.

(b) We shall now consider protein synthesis in general during the period following a shift-up. The kinetics of the overall process have been studied by following the incorporation of a labeled precursor added to the medium at the time of the shift. Appendix II gives the details of experiments involving several

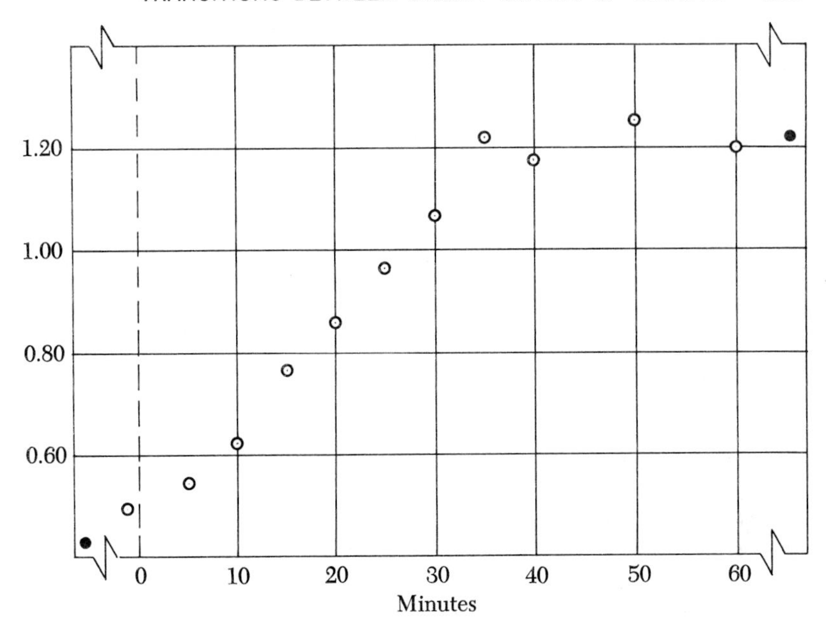

FIGURE 4–5 The relative quantities of ribosomes in *Salmonella typhimurium* before and after a shift-up. The increase in the ribosome fraction was determined during a shift of a culture of *Salmonella typhimurium* from glycerol-minimal medium to broth. Samples were withdrawn at intervals, the cells harvested, and disrupted in TSM (5×10^{-3} *M* Mg^{++}). The extracts were analyzed in the ultracentrifuge and, for each sample, the total area corresponding to ribosomes was expressed as a fraction of the area representing the soluble proteins, etc. The filled circles on the graph represent the limiting conditions, i.e., the fractions obtained from a glycerol-minimal medium culture, and from the experimental culture 2 hours after the shift, respectively.

amino acids, but one important technical point will be mentioned here: the strain of *S. typhimurium* used throughout these early studies requires none of the amino acids for growth, and to avoid competition between the externally added, labeled amino acid and internally produced, unlabeled material, the pre-shift medium always contained the amino acid unlabeled, whose incorporation was to be studied. At the time of the shift the enzymes involved in the synthesis of *this* amino acid had thus been repressed during several generations of growth, and the shift to broth medium presumably had no effect on either the uptake or the utilization of this particular acid.

The following five amino acids were used in these experiments: arginine, phenylalanine, histidine, tryptophan, and glycine. Four of these acids[2] exhibit the same incorporation pattern, with a low initial rate which, after about 20 minutes, increases to reach the definitive rate. This is illustrated in Figure 5 of Appendix II, which includes a theoretical curve calculated on the assumption that the rate of protein synthesis increases in step with the increase in number of ribosomes. The great similarity between the theoretical and the experimental curves indicates that the proportionality between the rate of protein synthesis and the number of ribosomes is maintained during the transition from low to high growth rate.

A spectacular demonstration of the dependency of protein synthesis on the number of ribosomes has been provided by McCarthy (1962). An *E. coli* culture was starved of magnesium for 24 hours, at which time it could be shown that almost all ribosomes had been lost. When magnesium was added back to the culture a considerable lag was observed before the normal growth rate was reestablished. Throughout this lag the number of ribosomes increased exponentially, and the rate of protein synthesis remained proportional to the number of particles. The autocatalytic increase in the number of particles could be explained by assuming that the synthesis of the ribosomal proteins was limited throughout by the number of ribosomes.

The differential plots used in Appendix II do not directly show how the initial rate of protein synthesis after the shift compares with the pre-shift rate. The interpretation of these diagrams is complicated by the fact that ribosome synthesis contributes excessively to the increase in mass during the transition period, when the cells enrich themselves in ribosomes. It is possible, however, from the incorporation data to construct conventional growth curves. The definitive slope of the differential plots gives a direct estimate of the radioactivity corresponding to a given increase in mass during balanced growth in broth; from this figure, and from the known values for the protein content of cells growing at the pre- and post-shift rates, respectively, one can calculate the quantity of the radioactive amino acid that the cells would have incorporated, had the pre-shift medium contained the labeled acid at the same specific activity as was

[2] For unknown reasons, the incorporation curve for glycine is different, exhibiting a constant differential rate from the time of the shift; this special case is discussed in detail in Appendix II.

used in the post-shift medium.[3] Adding this calculated activity to each of the experimental values, figures are obtained that can be plotted into a semilogarithmic diagram like that of Figure 4–1.

When the amino acid incorporation data from Appendix II are corrected in this way, the curves of Figure 4–6 are obtained, each of which may be looked upon as representing growth of the culture in terms of one particular amino acid. The common feature of these curves is that the initial post-shift rate is very nearly half the definitive rate. Since the overall growth rate also doubles after the shift, we can conclude that the pre-shift rate of protein synthesis is actually maintained for some time after the shift. The slight differences between the curves of Figure 4–6 may be attributed to the fact that the ribosomal proteins, whose amino acid composition differs somewhat from the average composition of the soluble proteins, are synthesized in large quantities immediately after the shift. Actually, during the first few minutes of the transition period, the ribosomal proteins may account for as much as 30% of all the protein produced in the cells.

As pointed out earlier, it is particularly significant that the rate of protein synthesis does not change abruptly when the shift involves transfer of the cells from a minimal medium to one rich in all the common amino acids. Indeed, the rate does not increase significantly during the first 5–10 minutes. Yet in the post-shift medium the pools of free amino acids certainly increase rapidly, as indicated by the fact that feed-back inhibition and repression become effective at once, and as shown directly by Britten and McClure (1962). Hence as far as protein synthesis is concerned, the intracellular environment is saturated with respect to amino acids both *before* and after the shift.

In summary, the experiments we have discussed here (1) show that the post-shift increase in rate of protein synthesis goes hand in hand with an increase in the number of mature ribosomes, as required by the hypothesis of constant efficiency, and (2) suggest that this constant efficiency is close to the maximum efficiency, since flooding the cells with amino acids does not in itself increase the rate of synthesis.

[3] There are two reasons for *not* including the radioactive amino acid in the pre-shift medium. First, the initial rate of incorporation after the shift would be difficult to estimate on a high background of radioactivity; second, it is very difficult to ensure that the specific activity of the amino acid does not change significantly when shifting to broth.

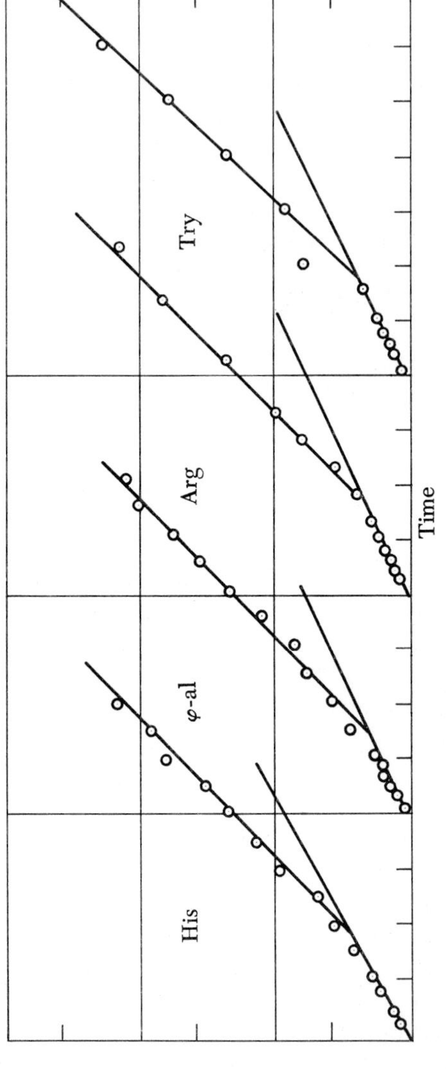

FIGURE 4–6 Incorporation of four different amino acids during the transition period following a shift-up. This graph is constructed from the data of Appendix II as described in the text. Each curve represents growth in terms of one of the amino acids, histidine, phenylalanine, arginine, and tryptophan. One interval on the abscissa is 10 minutes, and the distance between the horizontal lines corresponds to one doubling. Time zero for the individual curves is indicated by vertical lines. The growth rates represented by the two linear segments of the curves are $\mu = 1.2$ for the first 15–25 minutes after the shift, and $\mu = 2.4$ thereafter.

4–4 DNA SYNTHESIS AND CELL DIVISION FOLLOWING A SHIFT-UP

As Figure 4–1 shows, the effect of the shift on DNA synthesis is *not* immediate. As with protein synthesis, the pre-shift rate is maintained for some time; and when the post-shift rate is reached, after 20–25 minutes, the definitive RNA/DNA and protein/DNA ratios have also been established.

It is easy to argue that if DNA synthesis did not lag behind as it does, it would take a long time to reach the ratios characteristic of the rich medium. However, of the two specific models that have been considered, one can be excluded and the other has not been adequately tested.

To describe the two models, we must anticipate to some extent the discussion of DNA synthesis that follows (Chapter 6). As will be shown, DNA synthesis is more or less continuous in cultures growing at rates that exceed one doubling per hour; but, at lower rates, successive rounds of replication may be separated by a relatively long interim without DNA synthesis. At first it was thought that the maintenance of the pre-shift rate for some time after a shift-up might be due to a similar pause, intervening between the round of replication already in progress at the time of the shift and the first round to be initiated in the new medium. This model predicts that, about 20 minutes after the shift, 50–60% of the cells should be in the hypothetical, nonsynthesizing state. In the test that was carried out, a thymine-requiring strain of *E. coli* was used and autoradiograms were prepared of cells that had been exposed to ^{3}H-thymidine for short periods during the first 45 minutes after a shift-up. Of the cells that had been exposed in the interval between 18 and 21 minutes, only a small fraction remained unlabeled. Thus during this 3-minute period nearly all cells were actively synthesizing DNA and, consequently, no significant interim exists between rounds of replication.

It was then thought that the delay in DNA synthesis might be accounted for by assuming that (a) the pre-shift rate of synthesis is maintained throughout the round of replication in progress at the time of the shift, (b) the cells divide at the end of this round, and (c) the next round of replication proceeds at the broth-rate. According to this model, cell division should continue after the shift at the old rate, and during the transition period two classes of cells should exist: one synthesizing DNA at the pre-shift rate, the other at twice that rate. Both these stipulations are fulfilled, as shown in Figure 4–1 and in the series of autoradiograms just described. However, our data are not accurate enough to distinguish between this second model and a situation in which the rate of DNA synthesis increases *gradually* in each cell during the transition period. The reason is that, with a steadily increasing rate of DNA synthesis and *no* change in rate of cell division, a growing fraction of the cells might terminate their first round of replication and begin the next *before* they divide. Thus, when a cell starts on the second round of replication, it may suddenly double its overall rate of DNA synthesis, despite the fact that individual acts of replication, at a given instant, proceed at the same rate in all cells (Maaløe, 1961). We shall discuss (Chapter 6) some recent and quite unexpected findings which suggest how a "sudden doubling" of the rate of DNA synthesis in individual cells may be explained.

One important feature of the transition to a higher growth rate has not yet been touched upon. We have seen that total RNA synthesis is increased and that mature ribosomes at once begin to accumulate. However, we also know that the ratio between rRNA and tRNA is going to increase after the shift, whereas the ratio between tRNA and DNA remains more or less constant. The synthesis of tRNA during the transition period has not been analyzed separately, but it is reasonable to imagine that it follows the same kinetics as DNA synthesis, and a common explanation should be looked for. This discussion will be continued (Chapter 5).

The effects of a shift-up on cell division and on the number of nuclei per cell. Actually, the first effect of a shift-up to be registered was that it is followed by a remarkably long period during which the pre-shift division rate is maintained (see Figure 4–1). This phenomenon has long been a puzzle because whatever the actual pre-shift division rate may be it is maintained for a relatively *constant* time (60–70 minutes) after the shift. Thus, if we wanted to think about this situation in terms of a biological clock, we would have to conceive of one that, *at a fixed time* after the shift, switches to a new frequency that *may* be twice what it was before—as in the case illustrated in Figure 4–1—but which can be anything up to 8–10 times higher. This rules out any scheme according to which the first, or perhaps the first two, divisions after the shift might be triggered by a preset clock.

It now seems that the particular way in which DNA replication and nuclear division is organized in the bacterial cell may account for the rate maintenance effect. It has been shown that the rate at which DNA synthesis proceeds along the genome at a given replication site does *not* change after a shift-up and that the overall rate of synthesis is increased because extra sites are introduced (Section 6–2). This together with observations indicating that nuclear separation occurs well in advance of cell division (Section 6–7) may account for the fact that the pre-shift division rate is maintained for a more or less fixed period after the shift. The model we have in mind will be presented in a forthcoming publication.

A simple description of our observations may run as follows: the average length and thickness of the cells begin to increase immediately after the shift, and for a little more than 1 hour (at 37°) the cells grow in such a way that mass and volume *more* than double between successive cell divisions. One rather obvious result is that the number of nuclei per cell begins to increase some time after the overall rate of DNA synthesis has gone up. This time relationship is illustrated in Figure 4–1, and typical distributions of nuclei per cell were shown in Table 2–2. As mentioned earlier, it is the phenomenon of maintenance of the rate of cell division which, through its effect on the number of nuclei per cell, made us decide to express all quantities and numbers relative to DNA rather than to the number of cells.

4–5 THE SHIFT-DOWN

An experiment of this type can be done by collecting cells on a membrane filter, washing them free of the medium they grew in, and resuspending them in the new medium. Two to three liters of a culture, with 100–200 μg dry weight of cells per ml, can be manipulated in less than 2 minutes by means of a large filter (30-cm diameter). Greater quantities are difficult to handle if the cells are to be washed effectively and rapidly.

With respect to cell division and to DNA synthesis, the effects of a shift-down are, in a sense, the same as in a shift-up; in both cases the pre-shift rates are maintained for some time. Conversely, RNA and protein synthesis both stop almost completely after a shift-down. All these effects are as pronounced and easy to register as those elicited by a shift-up. However, the immediate effects are followed by slow and gradual rate changes that eventually lead to balanced growth at the reduced rate characteristic of the new medium (Figure 4–7). In this respect the two types of shift experiment are strikingly different.

The continued but limited synthesis of DNA observed after

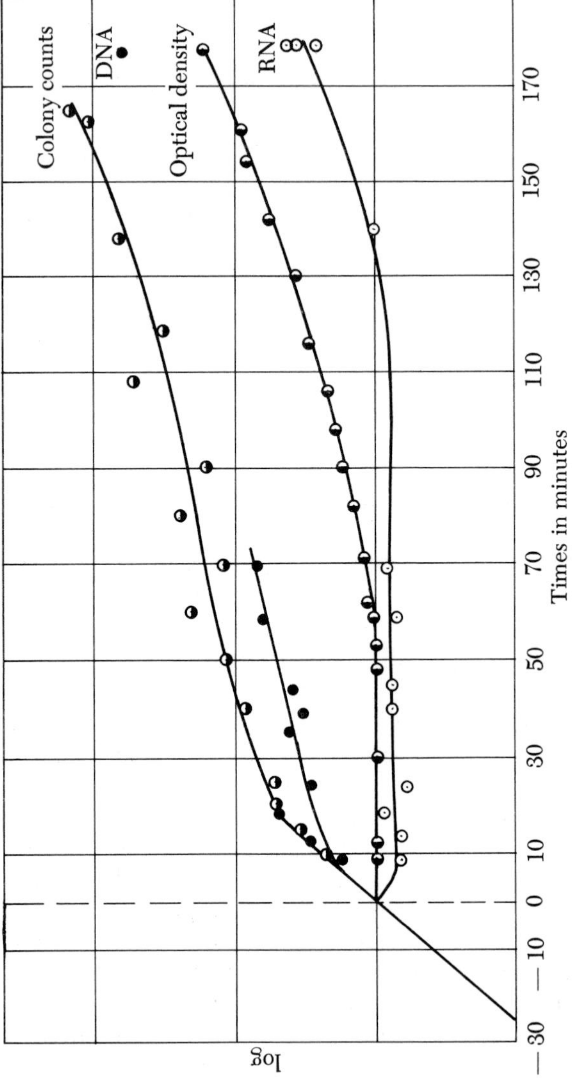

FIGURE 4–7 Shift-down experiment with *Salmonella typhimurium*. A culture was shifted, at 37°, from broth to glucose-minimal medium at time 0. Optical density, viable counts, and RNA and DNA contents were frequently determined. The logarithms of the measured values are plotted against time, and all values are transposed so as to make the curves representing balanced growth in broth coincide. The distance between horizontal lines corresponds to one doubling.

a shift-down need not be discussed in detail here. The same response is observed if protein and RNA synthesis is stopped by other means, e.g., by withdrawing a required amino acid, and the probable reason for this behavior will be discussed (Chapter 6). The rapid and "reductive" cell division that takes place during the first 20–30 minutes after the shift has not been studied in detail, and the mechanism responsible is unknown. It would be interesting to see whether the reduction in girth that eventually is observed begins in the cell that is transferred to the "slower" medium, or whether it is the result of outgrowth of new and thinner cells.

The suppression of protein and RNA synthesis that follows a shift-down is very reminiscent of the effect of removing a required amino acid from a culture. In the latter case, net protein production stops for obvious reasons but synthesis continues at a low turnover rate. After a shift from broth to minimal medium we can assume that, for some time, the cells are actually starved not of one but of all the amino acids, since the enzymes necessary for their synthesis have been repressed during growth in the rich medium. At early times after this shift, protein synthesis at a very low rate can be demonstrated if a radioactive amino acid is added to the medium (Kjeldgaard, 1963). This activity may play an important role in overcoming the apparent deadlock created when cells, which lack the enzymes with which they normally synthesize their amino acids, are to resume growth in minimal medium. Control platings on broth and minimal agar plates have shown that no loss of viability occurs during the period of readjustment.

The cessation of RNA synthesis observed in the shift-down may also be looked upon as a result of depleting the cells of free amino acids; this indirect effect will be discussed in detail in the next chapter.

Combined shift experiments. The consequences of a "collective repression" of many enzymes have been studied in *double*-shift experiments. Cells growing in glucose-minimal medium were first shifted to broth, and, at various times later, were returned to fresh minimal medium. Figure 4–8 illustrates how this regime affects growth. The steep line on the left-hand side represents growth in broth, and the times of return to minimal medium of the different samples are indicated by arrows. As the graph shows, the first 10–15 minutes in broth do not affect the ability of the cells to resume growth in minimal medium at the normal rate. Thereafter, an increasing lag is observed

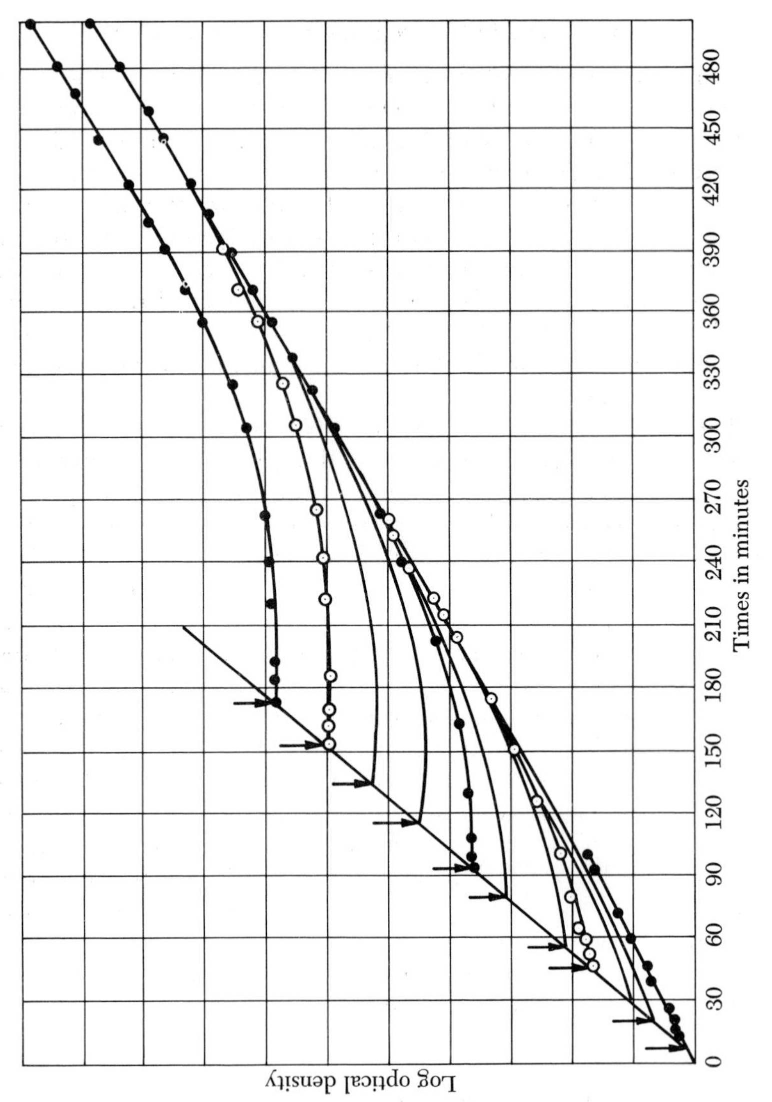

FIGURE 4–8

Double shift-up experiment with *Salmonella typhimurium.* A culture growing at 37° in a glucose-minimal medium was diluted with broth at time 0 and the optical density of the culture followed. At various times after the shift, samples of the culture were returned to minimal medium and the optical density followed. The logarithms of the optical densities are plotted against time. The steep linear curve represents the growth curve of the broth culture, and the arrows mark the time of return to minimal medium. The optical density curves of the minimal-medium cultures are transposed so as to obtain continuity with the broth curve at the time of transfer. For clarity, experimental points are not shown on all curves. The distance between horizontal lines corresponds to one doubling.

which reaches its maximum after about 6 generations of growth in broth.

Two striking features are noted in this experiment. First, all the samples that were returned to minimal medium 15–150 minutes after the shift-up ultimately follow the same growth curve. There is something very suggestive about this pattern, but we have not been able to think of a simple interpretation. The second point is illustrated in Figure 4–9, which shows the *initial* rates of growth in minimal medium in two of the samples. The first was taken after 40 minutes, i.e., one full generation time after the "indifference" period mentioned above. In this sample the initial growth rate was almost exactly $^1/_2$ the normal growth rate in minimal medium. The second sample was taken 30 minutes later, and in this case the initial growth rate was $^1/_4$ of the definitive rate in minimal medium.

The systematic reduction of the initial growth rate after the second shift may be explained by assuming that a large number of enzymes concerned with amino acid and other synthesis were present in near-limiting concentrations *before* the shift-up. The reasoning is as follows: had the enzymes been present in excess in the steady state of growth in minimal medium, their activities would have been reduced by end-product inhibition, and the release of inhibition following the shift-down would have unmasked their full synthetic capacity. If so, we would not have expected the 2-fold reduction in the initial growth rate for each generation of growth in broth, which we attribute to a "dilution" of the enzymes present in the cells at the time when mass repression sets in.

One or a few enzymes present in a near-limiting concentration in the minimal-medium cell could hardly be responsible for this effect. In many cases enzyme synthesis is partially repressed during balanced growth, and the rate of synthesis can be greatly increased if the normal, internal repression is artificially released. Thus, if only one or a few enzymes had been present in near-limiting concentrations, one would expect *their* concentrations to increase rapidly because the shift-down would cause temporary and complete derepression. To account for the fact that growth remains slow for some time after returning the cells to minimal medium, we must assume that a considerable fraction of all the enzymes of the cells is repressed during growth in broth. If all or most of the enzymes involved in this act of mass repression were originally present in near-limiting concentrations, the derepression caused by the shift-down could

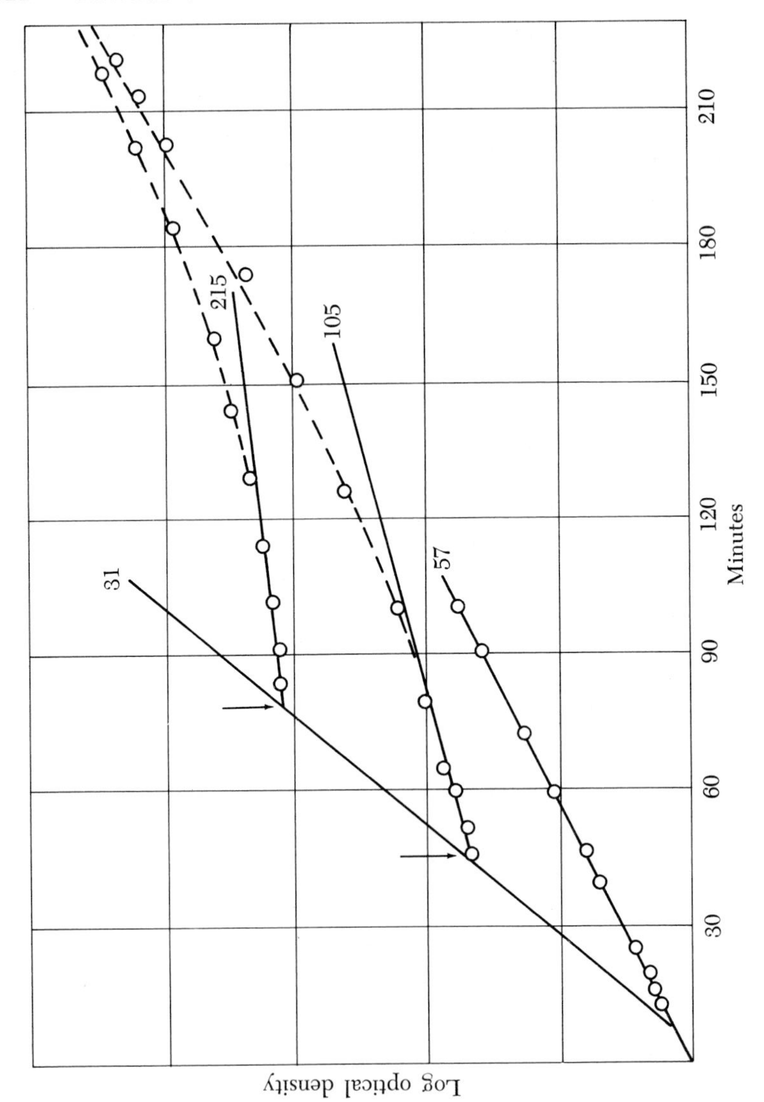

FIGURE 4–9 Double-shift experiments. A culture of *Salmonella typhimurium* in glucose-salts medium was shifted to broth at time 0, and aliquots returned to the original medium at the times indicated by arrows. Ordinate values show optical density in arbitrary units. Points show the actual readings, and the numbers indicate the steady state growth rates (doubling times in minutes) in broth (31) and in minimal medium (57), as well as the initial rates after the return to minimal medium (105 and 215, respectively).

not produce a rapid increase in the concentrations of all these enzymes (and, with that, in the rate of synthesis of the amino acids), because this would require an overall rate of protein synthesis incompatible with the reduced capacity of the cells for amino acid synthesis.

As mentioned above, the lag observed when the cells are returned to minimal medium increases until, after about 6 doublings in broth, it has reached its maximum value. By this time we may assume that the concentrations of many enzymes have been reduced to about 2% of the values characteristic of growth in the minimal medium. The reason why the lag does not increase further may well be that the concentrations of the repressed enzymes are now so low that the protein turnover observed after the shift-down is sufficient to permit them to increase *relatively* fast.

Concluding remarks. The behavior of cultures in shift experiments, and the observations pointing to an effective regulation of both RNA and protein synthesis, lead to definite ideas about the state of balanced growth. We imagine that in this state all components of the cell—nucleic acids, enzymes, metabolites, etc.—are present in concentrations which balance each other in such a way that no single component is truly limiting with respect to the overall growth rate. This is equivalent to saying that all components are under the influence of effective regulatory mechanisms, but does not imply that the concentrations of individual components in a cell cannot fluctuate. The degree of fluctuation in the concentration of a given component in a cell would depend on the sensitivity of the control mechanism concerned.

When experiments involving different growth rates are discussed, it is important to make clear exactly what is meant when the term "rate limitation" is used. If, in the state of balanced growth, no *single* component in the cell can be said to limit the growth rate, we should define what is meant by saying, e.g., that the growth rate is limited by the carbon source available in the medium. First of all, this statement implies that we know that growth with a different carbon source would be faster. Thus we are actually comparing two physiological states, characterized not only by different growth rates but also by different sets of equilibria among the components of the cell, and between them and the components of the medium. To the two carbon sources we are comparing correspond enzymes, and it is natural to assume that the rates differ at which these enzymes convert their respective substrates to supply energy and material to the cell.

A situation of this kind was analyzed in a study of balanced growth in media with glutamic acid and proline, respectively, as sole carbon sources (Maaløe and Richmond, 1962). Glutamic acid is metabolized directly via the Krebs cycle, while proline is converted to glutamic acid by a series of inducible enzymes. The experiments showed that, even in the fully induced state, the rate of conversion of proline was limiting in the sense that the cells would have grown faster had they been supplied glutamic acid in the medium. Whether, during balanced growth in the proline medium, glutamic acid was actually limiting *in the cell* is another question. At least two different situations can be envisaged: (a) complete balance between the size of all enzyme systems might be achieved with both carbon sources, and the need for synthesizing the proline-degrading enzymes, in addition to all the commonly required enzymes, might explain the low growth rate in the proline medium; and, (b) the *efficiency* of the degrading enzymes may be so low that it is impossible to establish a balanced situation in which the enzymes converting glutamic acid to cell material are saturated. Only in the latter case would it be logical to argue that the glutamic acid concentration is limiting in the proline-growing cells.

5

THE REGULATION OF RNA SYNTHESIS

5-1 THE PROBLEM IN OUTLINE

In the last chapter, some general features of RNA synthesis were discussed and arguments were presented to show that, whatever the nature of the regulatory mechanisms governing RNA synthesis, they do not involve significant changes in the concentrations of the enzymes concerned. This conclusion is unmistakable, since many different experiments show that bacteria synthesizing RNA at a low or intermediate rate can be stimulated to increase this rate greatly in the absence of protein synthesis. It was also argued, although less conclusively, that the rate at which individual RNA molecules are synthesized may well be the same at very different overall rates of synthesis (see Chapter 4).

Further to mark off the present problem, let us recall that the phenomenon of repression has been shown to reflect a special kind of control of RNA synthesis, viz., the highly specific mechanisms which decide the composition of the mRNA pool in the cell, by permitting transcripts of some and not of other operons to be produced or released. We shall not be concerned directly with this mechanism, but it is clear that we should look for similarities as well as dissimilarities between the specific control of the activity of individual operons and the more elusive mechanisms that govern the overall rates of synthesis of the three main classes of RNA.

It will be useful first to restate the general ideas about RNA synthesis in bacteria: (a) All RNA species are thought to be copies drawn from appropriate regions of the genome. This basic assumption is derived from the observation that actinomycin inhibits the synthesis of all classes of RNA (Acs, Reich, and Valanju, 1963), and from annealing experiments showing that not only mRNA, but also rRNA and tRNA, form specific hybrid structures with homologous, denatured DNA (Yankofsky and Spiegelman, 1962a,b; 1963). (b) The copying process is thought to be accomplished *in vivo* by a polymerase which is known, *in vitro*, to depend on a DNA primer and to synthesize RNA molecules of corresponding base sequences, using as substrate the four riboside triphosphates (Chamberlin and Berg, 1962; Geiduschek, Nakamoto, and Weiss, 1961). When certain biologically intact DNA molecules are used as primers, only one of the strands is copied (Hayashi, Hayashi, and Spiegelman, 1964). (c) Although not proven, it is attractive to think that all three classes of RNA are produced by the same enzyme. The best evidence in favor of this view is the transformation and methylation experiments of Hurwitz *et al.* (1963), which indicate that both mRNA and tRNA can be synthesized *in vitro* by a purified polymerase from *E. coli.* It has not been shown that the same enzyme preparation can be used to produce rRNA.

On this background one can visualize the synthesis of any of the RNA species as being regulated (1) at the DNA level, (2) at the level of the enzyme, and (3) at the substrate level. These three possibilities are not mutually exclusive.

(1) This case is in a class by itself, since it permits RNA copies to be produced from selected parts of the genome only. Two different mechanisms seem to operate, viz., the operon specific control, and the less specific control exerted by various catabolites. These two mechanisms may or may not function through separate protein intermediates (Loomis and Magasanik, 1964; Clark, 1965, respectively). An important common feature of all mechanisms that operate at the DNA level can be inferred from the fact that, to be functional *in vivo*, each species of RNA must be of a definite size. It must therefore be assumed that each specific DNA region is set off between punctuation marks that determine where the transcription process has to start and where it has to stop. It is further assumed that a starting point can exist in two different states: in the "open" state it allows attachment of the polymerase, and in the "closed" state it does not. For our present purpose it makes no difference whether, to make a

given site accessible to the enzyme, a "repressor unit" has to be removed (Jacob and Monod, 1961a), or whether a finished mRNA molecule has to be released from the DNA to make room for the synthesis of a new one (Stent, 1964). The fact that two specific control mechanisms have been accommodated at the DNA level of course does not exclude the possibility that a third mechanism, affecting the overall rate of RNA synthesis, operates at the same level.

(2) Regulation at the enzyme level is easy to visualize, and this possibility is supported by certain *in vitro* observations that will be discussed in detail later. Since it is clear from *in vivo* experiments that the number of polymerase molecules in the cell is never limiting, one has to think in terms of inhibition of the activity of this enzyme (see Section 4–2). If it is true that a single enzyme species is responsible for the synthesis of all classes of RNA, a control mechanism of this kind must be nonspecific. It should be noted, however, that this assumption is the weakest of the three listed in the beginning of this chapter, and it may turn out that more than one polymerase is involved in RNA synthesis. If so, some degree of specificity might be encountered.

(3) The concentration of one or more of the four riboside triphosphates could be under regulation, and in this way the overall rate of RNA synthesis could be adjusted to the growth rate through appropriate changes in the rate of synthesis of the individual RNA molecules. Such a mechanism, of course, would be nonspecific. We have presented certain arguments against control of RNA synthesis at the substrate level, but few of the many possible mechanisms can be definitely ruled out on the basis of existing evidence.

5–2 THE ROLE OF AMINO ACIDS IN RNA SYNTHESIS

The experiments to be described in this section all indicate that the rate of synthesis of the stable RNA species is lowered if the concentration of free amino acids in the cell is reduced in one way or another. Different and very special techniques are necessary for studying the mRNA, because it constitutes a small and unstable fraction of the total RNA. It should, however, be kept in mind that, despite its low *concentration*, the total quantity of mRNA produced in a cell is comparable to that of all the stable RNA species put together.

Removal of a required amino acid from a culture affects not only protein but also RNA synthesis. Net protein synthesis stops for obvious reasons, and at the same time net RNA synthesis is reduced to approximately 10% of the normal. At this greatly reduced rate RNA continues to be produced for long periods in the absence of the amino acid. In contrast, when protein synthesis is inhibited by chloramphenicol (CM) the rate of RNA synthesis is *not* reduced. Indeed, under certain growth conditions RNA synthesis is stimulated considerably by CM (Fraenkel and Neidhardt, 1961).

These results show that the effect of amino acid starvation cannot be attributed to exhaustion of a particular protein necessary for RNA synthesis, since at sufficiently high concentrations of CM it should be equally impossible to synthesize this hypothetical protein. (To fit the observations, the postulated compound had to be synthesized by a CM-insensitive mechanism *and* to contain many different amino acids.)

If CM is added to an amino acid-starved culture, different responses can be seen. *Low* concentrations of CM do not greatly affect the inhibition of RNA synthesis caused by starvation. In this situation, however, addition of very small quantities of the required amino acid elicits the formation of considerable quantities of RNA. It has therefore been concluded that amino acids affect RNA synthesis catalytically (Pardee and Prestidge, 1956; Gros and Gros, 1958). This effect is common to all the amino acids that have been tested, and among them phenylalanine and methionine could be replaced by the analogues *p*-fluorophenylalanine and ethionine, respectively. These and other experiments with amino acid analogues will be discussed in detail later in connection with a specific model for the control of RNA synthesis.

When CM is added to amino acid-starved cells at concentrations higher than 50–100 μg/ml, the effect of starvation is eliminated, and RNA is synthesized at the same high rate as in a nonstarved culture with CM (Aronson and Spiegelman, 1961a). We have extended this observation by studying the effect of CM at several concentrations and in different media (Kurland and Maaløe, 1962); this study is included as Appendix III, but a summary of the results and conclusions will be given here.

When cells grow in a glucose-minimal medium (i.e., without amino acids), the addition of CM produces two distinct responses. First, an apparently instantaneous doubling of the rate of RNA synthesis is observed at CM concentrations between 1 and 1000 μg/ml. This is the effect observed by Fraenkel and Neidhardt (1961), referred to above. Second, a gradual deceleration of RNA synthesis follows, and the higher the CM concentration the lower the rate of RNA synthesis at late times. At CM concentrations greater than about 100 μg/ml a constant increase in total RNA of some 60% is observed after one generation time, but RNA synthesis continues past this time at a low, constant rate (see Appendix III).

The two effects of CM are easily distinguished by the fact that the initial acceleration is independent, whereas the deceleration is strongly dependent, on the CM concentration. The fundamental difference between the two effects is evident also from experiments in which CM was added to cells growing in a glucose-amino acid medium. In this case the instantaneous acceleration of RNA synthesis is small (about 10% instead of 100%); nevertheless, the concentration-dependent deceleration of RNA synthesis was observed as before. It is therefore natural to treat the two responses to CM as separate phenomena.

The instantaneous acceleration of RNA synthesis caused by CM is reminiscent of a shift-up experiment. In both cases a state of unbalanced growth is created in which RNA synthesis is kinetically dissociated from protein synthesis, and this effect could be due, in both cases, to a rapid increase in the intracellular amino acid concentrations. Thus in the presence of CM the amino acids synthesized in the cell cannot be utilized, and after a shift to a rich medium the acids assimilated from the medium are actively concentrated in the cells. The assumption that the rate of RNA synthesis is determined in some way by the amino acid concentrations also explains why CM causes little or no stimulation of RNA synthesis when added to a broth culture, since the internal amino acid concentrations in this case would be high to begin with.

A characteristic feature of bacterial physiology makes it possible to test the notion that CM causes accumulation of amino acids in the cell. As mentioned before, cells that are starved of a required amino acid exhibit protein turnover. This proceeds at a rate of 4–5% per hour at 35°, and the degradation process is not interfered with by CM, at least during the first 45 minutes of starvation (Mandelstam, 1958). These facts suggest that RNA synthesis should proceed in the absence of a required amino acid, if CM is present at a concentration high enough to prevent recycling of the amino acids derived intracellularly by protein degradation. This prediction is borne out both in our experiments and in those of Aronson and Spiegelman cited above. Furthermore, because it would take a finite time for a starved cell to build up an internal pool of the required amino acid, when CM is added, a lag should precede the resumption of RNA synthesis. Such a lag has in fact been observed (see Appendix III, Figure 6). The late deceleration of RNA synthesis observed with CM will be discussed in Section 5–5.

The experiments just described all point to the amino acids, or derivatives thereof, as possible "inducers" of RNA synthesis. The fact that all the acids tested show the same effect indicates that they act on the same site (or a number of identical sites). This in turn makes it unlikely that the amino acids themselves are inducers, since this would require that the regulatory site, or sites, were equally sensitive to about 20 structurally different molecules. One should therefore look for a naturally occurring compound that might represent a common denominator for all the natural amino acids.

Physiological studies indicating that transfer RNA plays a role in the regulation of RNA synthesis. When an amino acid leaves the free acid pool to be built into a protein molecule, it loses some of its individuality by becoming part of a class of uniform complexes: the amino acid-charged tRNA molecules. In these complexes all amino acids are attached by the same type of linkage to the much larger tRNA molecules which, apart from their respective coding properties, show great similarity in overall structure and in function (see Section 1–4). It is therefore natural to think that the tRNA molecules might play a key role in the regulation of RNA synthesis. More specifically, we shall assume that the uncharged tRNA molecules act as repressors of RNA synthesis, and that they lose this property when they become charged.

Under this scheme the physiological regulation of the cell content of RNA would be based on the relative concentrations of charged and free tRNA molecules. In a rich medium the tendency would be to saturate the tRNA with amino acids, and RNA synthesis would thus be more or less completely derepressed. This agrees with the observation that the rate of RNA synthesis is *not* increased much when CM is added to cells growing in an amino acid medium. Similarly, the pronounced rate increase seen when CM is added to a glucose-minimal culture could be explained as the result of increasing the fraction of charged tRNA (i.e., a neutralization of repressor due to the accumulation of free amino acids brought about by CM, as described above).

As regards the number of potential repressor units, this model presents no obvious difficulties. First, we note that, irrespective of growth rate, the cells contain 250,000–300,000 tRNA molecules, of which some 10,000–20,000 presumably are specific for any one of the 20 natural amino acids. Second, we assume that in the absence of one required acid the corresponding class of tRNA molecules is left completely uncharged. Thus only about 5% of the total complement of tRNA molecules would be affected in this way by starvation, and if this is sufficient to cause *strong* inhibition of RNA synthesis it would appear that the tRNA could serve effectively as amino acid donor during normal growth and at the same time be involved in the control of RNA synthesis. This particular problem will be taken up again when we discuss possible targets for the repressor.

At this point we should consider in more detail the studies with amino acid analogues. In the last section it was mentioned that *p*-fluorophenylalanine and ethionine can substitute for the natural amino acids in experiments in which their function is to relieve the repression of RNA synthesis. This effect of the two analogues is readily understood, since it is known that they react with tRNA and subsequently become incorporated into protein. Several other phenylalanine analogues or derivatives were tested for the same function. They included glycylphenylalanine and its amide, and only one, the dipeptide, was active (Gros and Gros, 1958). These experiments indicate that the ability to derepress RNA synthesis is highly specific, and that the free carboxyl group, with which the amino acids react with tRNA, is essential.

With *p*-fluorophenylalanine an elegant experiment has been performed by Fangman and Neidhardt (1964a,b). When this analogue is incorporated by bacteria, some of the enzymes produced are devoid of activity, and, although the cells continue to increase their mass for several hours, they do not form colonies in the presence of the drug. Several resistant mutants were isolated, and one which was analyzed in detail was found to take up *p*-fluorophenylalanine from the medium without incorporating it into protein. The reason proved to be that this mutant produces a modified activating enzyme which fails to couple the analogue to tRNA. A phenylalanine-requiring derivative of the resistant mutant was then isolated and tested both with the natural amino acid and with the analogue. In this double mutant, phenylalanine derepressed RNA synthesis as usual but the analogue was inactive. This result strongly supports the idea that an amino acid has to be activated and coupled to tRNA in order to affect RNA synthesis.

Finally, a series of experiments with the analogue 5-methyltryptophan (5MT) should be considered. This compound will derepress RNA synthesis to a relatively small extent but is *not* incorporated into protein (Gros and Gros, 1958; Thang, Williams, and Grunberg-Manago, 1963). It seems that 5MT inhibits growth by interfering with enzymes of the tryptophan pathway (Cohen and Munier, 1959). To explain the derepressing effect in terms of our model, we have to assume that 5MT can replace tryptophan in the coupling reaction with tRNA, but the evidence on this point is ambiguous. Thang, Williams, and Grunberg-Manago (1963) claim that 5MT prevents the coupling of tryptophan to tRNA, but Sharon and Lipmann (1957) and Nisman and Hirsch (1958) report that it does not elicit the typical exchange reaction between ATP and pyrophosphate in the presence of a tryptophan-activating enzyme. Thus, for the time being, the 5MT experiments cannot be claimed as evidence either for or against our model. A different tryptophan analogue, α-amino-β-(3-indazole)propionic acid (Tryptazan), which is known to be incorporated into protein, completely derepresses RNA synthesis during tryptophan starvation of a requiring strain (Brawerman and Yčas, 1957). Furthermore, during inhibition of protein synthesis with 5MT, addition of Tryptazan stimulates RNA synthesis very considerably (G. Turnock and D. G. Wild, personal communication).

Genetic evidence implicating transfer RNA in the regulation of RNA synthesis. We have seen that RNA synthesis may be greatly reduced when a required amino acid is removed from the medium. This is the normal response, and strains behaving like this are said to be "stringent" with respect to the control of RNA synthesis. In contrast, strain W6 of *E. coli* K12, the methionine-requiring F^+ strain used so extensively in genetic experiments, is described as "relaxed" because it continues to synthesize RNA at a high rate when methionine is removed (Borek and Ryan, 1958).

In a study of several relaxed strains, all derived from W6, Stent and Brenner (1961) made two important observations: (a) that derivatives of the original strain respond in the relaxed manner to the removal of any amino acid for which they have become auxotrophic; and (b) that relaxedness can be transferred to other strains by conjugation. The genetic locus determining this character was called *RC* and was found to be situated near the streptomycin locus on the *E. coli* linkage map (Alföldi, Stent, and Clowes, 1962). The allelic states corresponding to the stringent and the relaxed phenotype, respectively, were designated RC^{str} (or RC^{+}), and RC^{rel} (or RC^{-}). This genetic study led Stent and Brenner to a conclusion with which we are already familiar, namely, that RNA synthesis might be controlled by the amino acids through their interaction with tRNA. It is gratifying that two quite different and independent studies suggest the same mechanism, but it is not entirely surprising since, in both cases, the proposed solution is based largely on the *need* for finding a common route through which any one of the natural amino acids might affect RNA synthesis.

The *RC* locus can be thought of as carrying the structural specification for the repressor of RNA synthesis, or for its target. In the terminology used in Section 1–9, the *RC* locus would thus be either of the *R* or of the *O* type. Consequently, a relaxed mutant would either produce a modified and less effective repressor, or its target structure would be less sensitive to repression.

(a) When we make the assumption that uncharged tRNA molecules repress RNA synthesis, it is clear that our model differs from the classical operator model by postulating *that repression is mediated not by one, but by anyone, of at least 20 different repressors with a common function.* It is also evident that relaxedness cannot be the consequence of a loss of, or a profound structural change in, the repressors, since they still serve as amino acid donors in protein synthesis. In this connection it is important to note that point mutations probably can lead to relaxedness. The evidence is that over 20 independent mutations to relaxedness have been isolated (by R. Lavallé, and in our laboratory by N. Fiil and J. D. Friesen), and revertants to the stringent type have been found (R. Lavallé, personal communication). A point mutation could affect the repressor function, as distinct from the target, in different ways; thus the mutation might be thought to affect the structure of a hypothetical unit involved in repression together with tRNA, or it might impair one of the methylating enzymes and thereby introduce a small, common modification of all the tRNA species. A third possibility would be to assume that repression is mediated by a special set of RNA molecules capable of accepting amino acids but not involved in protein synthesis, *and* that a point mutation of the O° type could eliminate this whole set of RNA molecules. This last model can probably be disregarded, since relaxed mutants are known *not* to have lost the ability to regulate RNA synthesis.

(b) As an alternative to (a), the *RC* locus can be thought to specify the structure of the target for the repressor. Theoretically, this interpretation is easy to accept as long as we think in terms of a single, modifiable target structure such as the polymerase. As mentioned earlier, this alternative is intimately associated with the problem of specificity in the control of RNA synthesis, and will be considered in detail in Section 5–4.

We have seen earlier that normally growing bacteria adjust their RNA content to the environment with great precision. When our usual, stringent *Salmonella typhimurium* strain was replaced by a relaxed *E. coli* K12 strain in a shift from minimal medium to broth, the usual transition pattern was observed (see Figure 4–1). Thus both strains respond to the shift by derepressing RNA synthesis. It was later shown by Neidhardt (1963) that stringent and relaxed strains in fact behave alike under a variety of experimental conditions including *down*-shifts between media with different carbon sources. However, if the shift is from an amino acid mixture to minimal medium, a striking difference is observed. When a culture of *S. typhimurium* (RC^+) is shifted from broth to glucose-minimal medium, it takes 2–$2^1/_2$ hours before the growth rate and the chemical composition characteristic of the new medium are established (see Figure 4–7); in a similar shift with a relaxed strain the lag is at least 5 hours, and during this time certain amino acids, notably leucine, are toxic to the cells (Alföldi *et al.*, 1963).

The original relaxed strain and some of its derivatives synthesize considerable quantities of RNA after the shift, when, effectively, the cells are starved of all the amino acids. The slowness with which the cells escape from the starvation condition has been ascribed to difficulties in reestablishing the normal RNA/protein ratio (Neidhardt, 1963). However, it is now known that transfer of the RC^- marker from the original strain to different recipients by transduction can give rise to new strains which show the usual relaxed response when a required amino acid is withdrawn, but which virtually stop RNA synthesis after a shift-down. Strains showing this behavior nevertheless pull out very slowly from the down-shift condition (R. Lavallé, personal communication). Evidently the relaxed phenotype is not defined exclusively by the state of the *RC* locus, and its physiology still presents many unsolved problems.

To account for the half-normal half-abnormal behavior of the relaxed strains, Alföldi *et al.*, (1963) introduced the concept of a general, or catholic, inducer of RNA synthesis capable of combining with all repressors irrespective of their individual amino acid specificities. It was further assumed that the efficiency of, or the sensitivity to, this auxiliary control system was greater in the relaxed than in the stringent strains. Certain consequences of this hypothesis have been tested, however, with negative results. Thus the receptor specificity of tRNA seems to be the same in relaxed as in stringent cells (Martin, Yegian, and Stent, 1963a), and no evidence could be found to indicate that the methionine-specific tRNA, isolated from a methionine-starved, relaxed culture, had had its acceptor capacity reduced, as might have been expected if it had reacted with the hypothetical inducer (Martin, Yegian, and Stent, 1963b).

Among the possible mechanisms for explaining the phenomenon of relaxedness as a repressor rather than a target effect, those just discussed seem to be the only ones that have been carefully tested. Other mechanisms should, however, be seriously considered, since it has been shown that replication of the RNA of the bacteriophage f2 in *E. coli* is strongly inhibited by amino acid starvation, provided the host cells are of the RC^+ type (Friesen, 1965). The RNA-dependent polymerase involved in this process is quite distinct from the DNA-dependent bacterial polymerase, and the inhibition observed in RC^+ but not in RC^- cells may therefore be due to a common repressor for the two enzymes, whose activity depends on the state of the *RC* locus. A mechanism involving the active participation of the ribosomes in the control of RNA synthesis along the lines suggested by Stent (1964) might be invoked to explain Friesen's results. We shall discuss this possibility in Section 5–4.

5–3 THE POSSIBLE MODE OF ACTION OF TRANSFER RNA

All three classes of RNA are synthesized during CM treatment (see Appendix III, Figure 7) and during amino acid starvation. In the latter case this is readily demonstrable with relaxed cells because large quantities of RNA are produced (Neidhardt and Eidlic, 1963), but even with stringent cells it can be shown that small amounts of all three classes of RNA are synthesized during starvation (K. Moldave, unpublished results). It is therefore quite conceivable that the amino acids affect RNA synthesis in a very general way.

The reasons for implicating tRNA in the control have been amply discussed. One further detail can be added here to strengthen the general impression that all the natural amino acids (and certain analogues possessing a free carboxyl group) act similarly on RNA synthesis. The 20 independently isolated, relaxed mutants, collected by N. Fiil and J. D. Friesen in our laboratory, *all* synthesize RNA in the typical, relaxed manner upon withdrawal of *any* of the four amino acids required by the parent strain. We shall now proceed to consider the evidence that uncharged tRNA molecules in fact may interfere with RNA synthesis.

When this special property is attributed to tRNA, it is implied that the structural change brought about by tagging an amino acid onto the molecule is sufficient to abolish its repressor activity. The primary change of course is the well-known coupling of the amino acid to the free (· · ·pCpCpA) end of the RNA chain, and it is conceivable that this terminal trinucleotide, which is common to all tRNA species, is the active part of the molecule when it is in the "repressor" state. However, at least one short internal sequence is known also to be common to all tRNA species (see Section 1–4).

Evidence that tRNA can interfere with RNA synthesis *in vitro* was first obtained by Tissières, Bourgeois, and Gros (1963). In their system the activity of the DNA-dependent polymerase from *E. coli* could be reduced 80% with uncharged tRNA, whereas charged tRNA inhibited to the extent of only 25%. Extensive work has since been done with whole extracts of bacteria (Gros *et al.*, 1965; K. Moldave, personal communication) and with purified polymerase, using T4 DNA as template (Bremer and Konrad, 1964; Stent, 1965; H. Bremer, personal communication). The general experience has been that uncharged tRNA (and various synthetic RNA preparations) are inhibitory, but also that some preparations of charged tRNA are nearly as active as the uncharged material. The lack of reproducibility in some of these experiments shows that the test system for studying this inhibition reaction has not yet been properly defined.

On the basis of kinetic data, H. Bremer and G. S. Stent (personal communication) claim that the system may be very complex with several structurally different initiation sites on the template (T4 DNA), and corresponding, specific polymerases. These observations are not easy to interpret; in particular, it is difficult to be sure that heterogeneity has not been introduced into the DNA and the enzyme preparations during isolation and purification. There is little doubt that, eventually, many of the questions discussed in this chapter will be answered by studying the inhibition reaction *in vitro;* meanwhile, we have tried to define and analyze the problem to the extent this can be done on the basis of *in vivo* experiments.

The physiological significance of inhibition of the polymerase. The importance of this reaction in the living cell is not obvious, mainly because, *in vitro*, tRNA has been used in concentrations 100 or more times lower than those encountered *in vivo*. It is therefore desirable to see how much we can deduce from *in vivo* experiments concerning the effect that uncharged tRNA may have on RNA synthesis in intact cells.

When a required amino acid is removed from a culture, the concentration of uncharged tRNA in the cells is affected in two ways: in the first place, the class of tRNA specific for that acid can be assumed to be stripped more or less completely; but, at the same time, the utilization of all the other amino acids is prevented because protein synthesis stops, and their concentrations presumably increase rapidly. The tendency would therefore be to saturate all *other* classes of tRNA with amino acids. This means that the net effect of removing a required amino acid on the concentration of uncharged tRNA will be less than might have been anticipated, and could very well be negative.

As an orientation, a crude calculation has been made on the following basis: (a) the overall rate of RNA synthesis is taken to be proportional to the concentration of active polymerase, and at maximum growth rate ($\mu = 2.8$) the enzyme is assumed to be fully active; (b) the class (or classes) of tRNA specific for a given amino acid is assumed to constitute about 5% of the total tRNA; and (c) the removal of a single, required amino acid from a culture growing in glucose-minimal medium reduces the rate of RNA synthesis about 10-fold. If the reactions between tRNA and the activated amino acids, on the one hand, and between uncharged tRNA and the polymerase, on the other, follow simple, bimolecular kinetics, we can estimate that a doubling of the amino acid concentrations in a cell would increase the rate of RNA synthesis from a value as low as that observed in an amino acid-starved culture to a value as high as that characteristic of a broth culture ($\mu = 2.4$); and a 30% increase in amino acid concentration in cells growing in a glucose-minimal medium ($\mu = 1.2$) would suffice to double the rate of RNA synthesis. However primitive, this calculation shows that rather small changes in the amino acid concentrations might have large effects on the rate of RNA synthesis. Unfortunately, this is not easy to prove, since quantitative data for the amino acid pool sizes and for the degree of saturation of the tRNA, representative of undisturbed, balanced growth, are extremely difficult to obtain.

At this point it should be emphasized that the rate of RNA synthesis need not be directly related to the fraction of tRNA molecules of all classes, left uncharged in the cell during growth in a particular medium. The role of an amino acid might be to interact with uncharged tRNA molecules already associated with and inhibiting polymerase molecules. If an inactivated enzyme molecule has to be actively freed of the inhibitor in this way, *only the amino acid matching the attached tRNA molecule could release inhibition.*

A mechanism of this kind could explain why the removal of a single, required amino acid has such a large effect on RNA synthesis, despite the fact that the removal of one amino acid will tend to increase the concentrations of all the others in the cell. During starvation, say, for leucine, the inhibition of RNA synthesis might be caused almost exclusively by leucine-specific tRNA, and the release of inhibition might require the active participation of the missing amino acid. Under this view the degree of inhibition of RNA synthesis would not necessarily reflect the total concentration in the cell of uncharged tRNA, and strong inhibition could be maintained even if the effect of starvation had been to *de*crease the sum total of uncharged tRNA molecules. This model can probably be tested *in vitro.*

The possibility that RNA synthesis is controlled by an inhibitor of the polymerase has been discussed in some detail because it is one of the most plausible mechanisms we can think of. Before proceeding to the problem of specificity, however, we must briefly consider (a) how the phenomenon of relaxedness fits into the picture, and (b) whether alternative targets for the inhibitor can be visualized.

(a) Interaction between uncharged tRNA and the polymerase, of course, would require partial structural complementarity between the two components, and we have mentioned before that a point mutation can be imagined to modify either of them. Thus, a relaxed mutant might be one in which the tRNA molecules are uniformly deficient with respect to methylation, and therefore combine less firmly with the polymerase; but the very same effect on the inhibition process could result from a mutational change in the structural gene for that enzyme. Both these possibilities could be tested experimentally but we are not aware of data relevant to this problem.

(b) The *in vitro* experiments which show that the polymerase *can* be inhibited by uncharged tRNA do not exclude a mechanism controlling bulk RNA synthesis at the DNA level. Since all the experiments we have so far discussed indicate that the synthesis of both tRNA and rRNA is under amino acid control, one could think of the *RC* locus as an operator site controlling the synthesis of all the stable RNA species. One difficulty with this concept is that the tRNA/rRNA ratio is known to vary with the growth rate. Thus, if the genetic determinants for all the stable RNA species constituted one operon, it would be necessary to introduce a mechanism acting inside the operon to regulate the relative output of the different species. Further complications arise when the synthesis of mRNA is taken into consideration, and will be discussed in the next section.

5-4 THE SUSCEPTIBILITY OF THE DIFFERENT RNA FRACTIONS TO REGULATION

The simplifying assumption that *one* polymerase species is responsible for the synthesis of all three classes of RNA, and that inhibition of this enzyme regulates the overall rate of RNA synthesis, leads to two obvious predictions: first, that the synthesis of mRNA should be inhibited together with that of the stable RNA species; second, that, in addition to the control by inhibition of the polymerase, a mechanism must exist that can modify the rate of synthesis of rRNA relative to that of tRNA. (This would also be true if the cell contained several species of polymerase, provided they were more or less equally sensitive to a common inhibitor.)

To test the first prediction, one has to compare the rates of synthesis of messenger and of stable RNA during amino acid starvation, and in the presence of CM. Unfortunately, the measurements that can be made are not easy to interpret. We argued earlier that removal of a required amino acid (or the addition of CM) causes a general increase in the amino acid concentrations in the cell. During starvation most of the amino acid-synthesizing enzymes must therefore be under repression, and many of the mRNA species produced during normal growth will not be synthesized, *irrespective of the activity of the polymerase*. We must therefore conclude that the degree of inhibition of mRNA synthesis during starvation cannot be determined accurately, for the simple reason that the rate of synthesis corresponding to *no* inhibition is not, and cannot be, accurately known. For our present purpose this aspect of the problem, however, is not too serious because an uncertainty factor of 2, which probably is a high estimate, would still allow us to decide whether the synthesis of the different classes of RNA were inhibited to *more* or *less* the same high degree during amino acid starvation.

More difficult problems are created by the instability of the

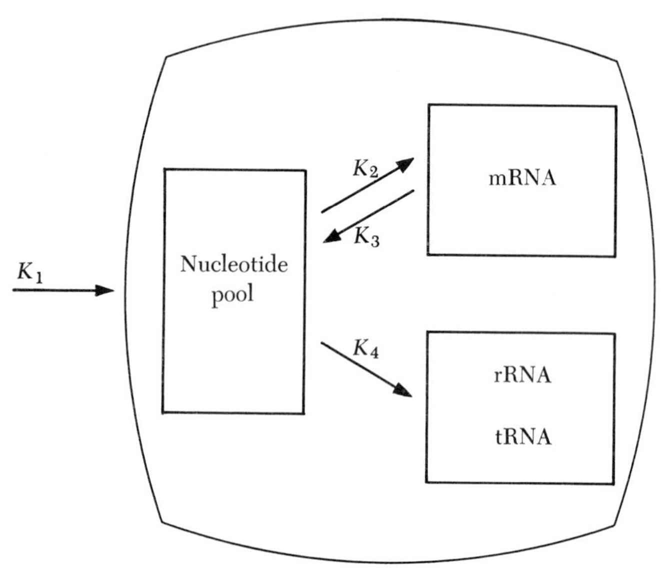

FIGURE 5-1 Flow scheme for uracil incorporation. The labeled uracil is assimilated from the medium and converted to UTP through reaction 1. Reactions 2 and 3 represent synthesis and decay of mRNA, respectively; the rate of reaction 2 is proportional to the fraction of the genome available for the synthesis of mRNA (M) under the prevailing conditions of repression [$dM/dt = K_2$(DNA)], and the rate of reaction 3 presumably is proportional to M($-dM/dt = K_3$M). During balanced growth the pool has a fixed size and is in equilibrium with the messenger fraction (M $= K_2/K_3$). Finally, reaction 4 determines the rate at which material leaves the pool definitively. At any given time *the rate of uptake of labeled uracil* (K_1) *must equal the rate of synthesis of the stable RNA fractions* (K_4). This scheme ignores the small quantity of uracil which may be converted and incorporated into DNA.

mRNA, and by the fact that existing radiochemical and biological assays estimate the mRNA according to very different criteria.

The instability problem is particularly hard to get around when the mRNA is being characterized by radiochemical means. In such experiments, RNA synthesis is often measured by the incorporation into acid-insoluble material of labeled uracil, and a flow scheme illustrating how this compound is thought to pass from the medium into the different RNA fractions is presented as Figure 5–1. The main point of this diagram is to show that the rate at which added uracil is incorporated into total RNA tells nothing direct about the rate at which nucleotides are cycled between the pool and the mRNA fraction, i.e., about the rates at which mRNA is being synthesized and broken down.

When a culture is filtered, washed, and resuspended at time zero in medium containing radioactive uracil and lacking a required amino acid, the counts per minute in acid-insoluble material (RNA) increase linearly with time for at least 2 hours at 37°. The straight line obtained in this way cuts the time axis

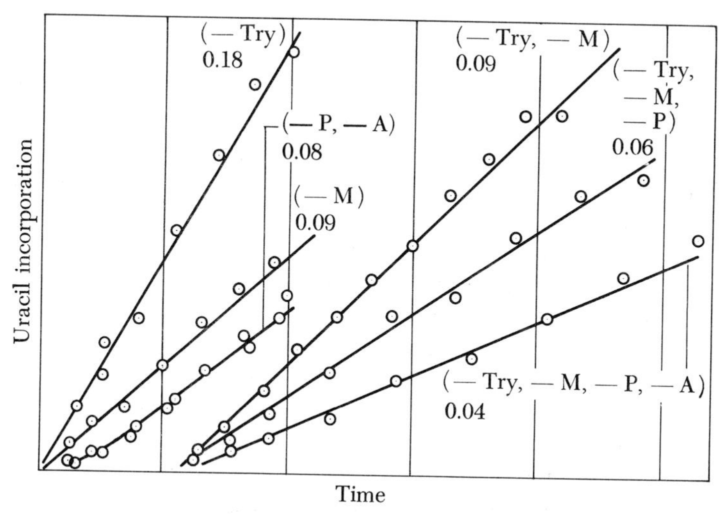

FIGURE 5–2 RNA synthesis during amino acid starvation. The stringent *E. coli* strain, TAU-bar (requiring thymine, uracil, arginine, methionine, proline, and tryptophan), was starved of one or more of the required amino acids, and the incorporation of ^{14}C-uracil was followed. The numbers on the graph indicate the rates of RNA synthesis relative to the initial rate in a fully supplemented culture. One unit on the abscissa represents 10 minutes; for clarity, the origin of one set of curves has been displaced 10 minutes to the right.

very close to the zero point, and the constant rate of incorporation is approximately $^1/_{10}$ of the *initial* rate in a control culture. If more than one required amino acid is removed the rate of RNA synthesis is reduced further, but the effects of removing individual amino acids are not additive (see Figure 5–2). This is hardly surprising, since the simultaneous removal of two or more amino acids probably causes effective starvation for only one of them, the reason being that *one and the same* process, protein synthesis, consumes all the amino acids, and when the pool of one has been emptied the drain on the other pools presumably stops.

The RNA synthesized during starvation has been characterized by sedimentation through sucrose gradients (K. Moldave and N. Fiil, unpublished results). It was found that labeling for a 10-minute period, at 36°, gave a "messenger" type of profile, whereas labeling for 60 minutes gave a pattern with distinct 23 S, 16 S, and 4 S peaks (see Figure 5–3). The appearance of these stable RNA components indicates that net quantities of RNA are being synthesized during starvation, and chemical measurements have shown that total RNA increases in a manner corresponding to the uptake of uracil.

Very similar incorporation data have been obtained with ^{14}C-adenine (Gros *et al.*, 1963a). The tentative conclusion was that mRNA is under amino acid control to the same extent as the stable RNA fractions. The evidence is, however, not quite sufficient, since the rate that is measured ($K_1 = K_4$, of Figure 5–1) is not directly related to K_2, the rate we want to know. In principle, K_2 could be estimated by first subjecting cells to uracil starvation to empty the mRNA pool (see below), and then switching to amino acid starvation and following the build-up of that pool by means of labeled uracil. Experiments of this type show a rapid initial incorporation of uracil, indicative of a high K_2 value. However, this result too is ambiguous: after uracil starvation the cells are left with little if any mRNA, but with large pools of amino acids; the rapid uptake of uracil, during the first 5–7 minutes after a shift to medium containing labeled uracil and lacking a required amino acid, is probably due to the presence of *all* the amino acids in high concentrations, and to the fact that they will be used up slowly in cells that lack mRNA at the time of the shift. We have discussed these inconclusive tracer experiments in some detail to illustrate the difficulties inherent in studies of this kind. We shall now present two alternative approaches to the same problem: one that deals with mRNA as a class, and one in which only a specific mRNA species is registered.

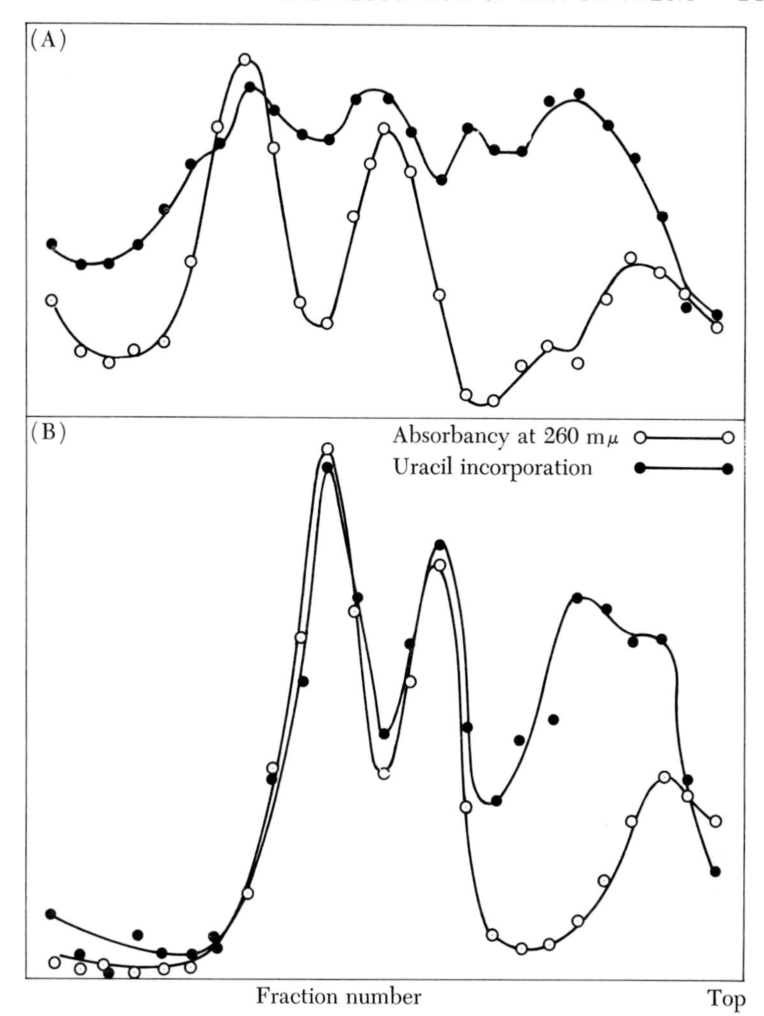

FIGURE 5-3 Analysis of the RNA produced during amino acid starvation. A stringent strain of *E. coli,* requiring methionine, was starved of this amino acid, and ^{14}C-uracil was incorporated for 10 minutes (A), and for 60 minutes (B), at 37°. These cells were mixed with a large excess of unlabeled carrier cells, and the extracted RNA was analyzed by gradient centrifugation.

Estimates of the mRNA by means of *in vitro* and *in vivo* assays. The RNA isolated from bacteria can be used to stimulate protein synthesis in an *in vitro* system, and there is good evidence that neither rRNA nor tRNA is active in this respect, provided the system is saturated beforehand with ribosomes and tRNA. When purified bacterial RNA is assayed for its stimulating

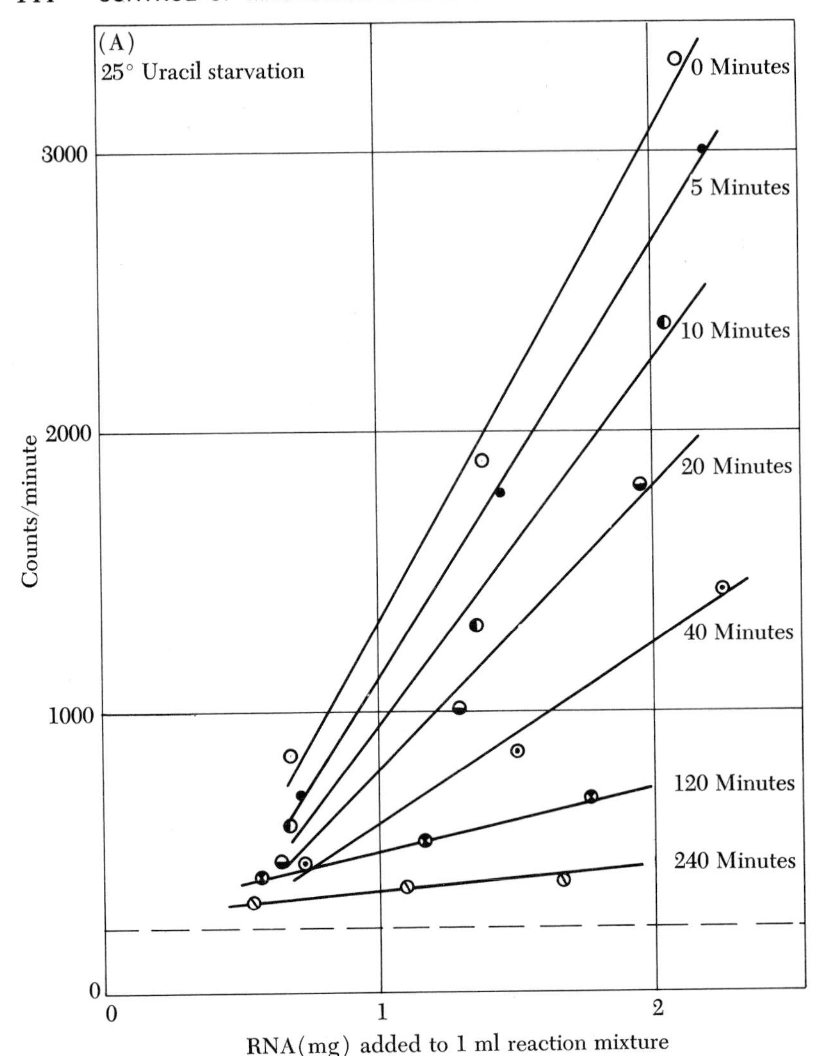

FIGURE 5–4 The stimulating activity of the RNA from uracil-starved cells on the amino acid incorporation *in vitro*. (A) The incorporation of ^{14}C-leucine. Individual curves represent the response to the addition of RNA prepared from cultures starved of uracil at 25°, as indicated. (B) The progressive loss of the stimulating activity during starvation at 25°. *Lower curve:* uracil starvation alone (several experiments); *upper curve:* uracil starvation in the presence of CM, and in the absence of required amino acids (two experiments).

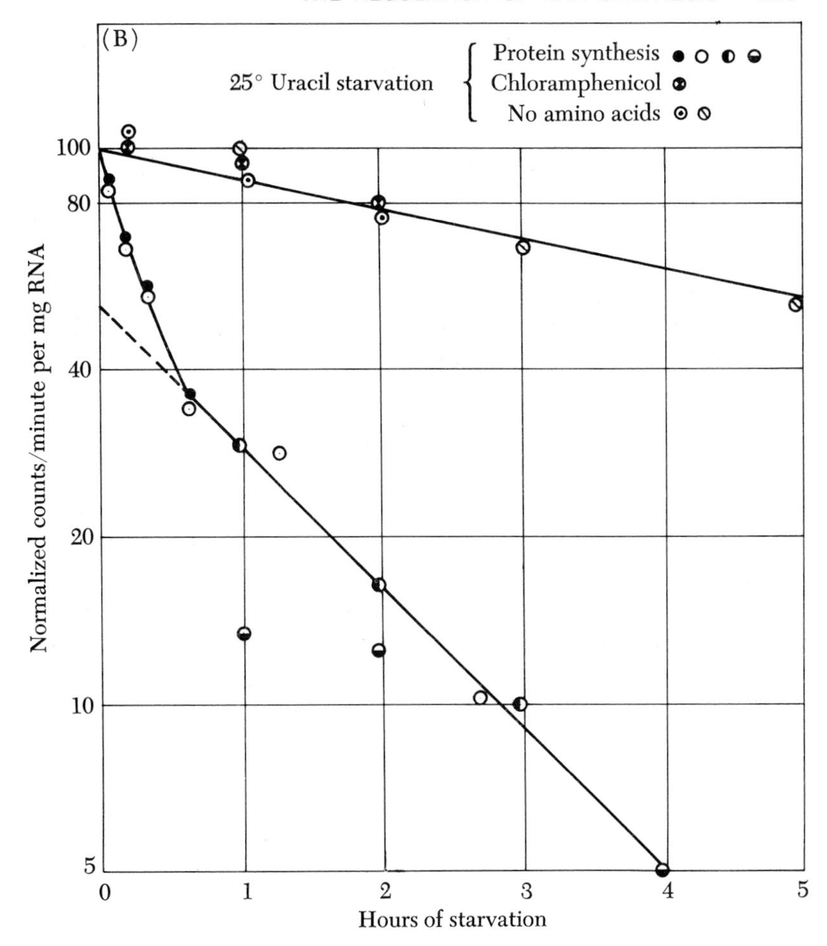

activity, the result may therefore be assumed to depend on the content of mRNA (of all kinds) of the RNA preparation (see, e.g., Willson and Gros, 1964).

The experiments to be reported here are part of an extensive study (Forchhammer, Kjeldgaard, and Moldave) of which only an abstract has been published (1965). Most of the experiments are done with RNA isolated from the stringent strain 15 of *E. coli* (a substrain requiring thymine, uracil, arginine, proline, tryptophan, and methionine). In the system used the stable RNA species do not stimulate protein synthesis significantly *in vitro*, as evidenced by the fact that, during uracil starvation, the stimulating activity per mg of the extracted RNA drops to less than 5% of the original value (see Figure 5–4). Under similar conditions Bautz (1962) has shown that the stimulating activity of the RNA isolated from T4-infected cells is due largely to an RNA fraction that anneals specifically with T4 DNA, i.e., to phage mRNA.

The following observations are relevant to our present problem: (1) During uracil starvation, the activity is lost in a manner suggesting that part of the stimulating RNA decays with a half-life of about 10 minutes at 25°, and that a fraction exists whose half-life is much longer (see Figure 5–4, A and B). (2) In the absence of the required amino acids, the stimulating activity of the RNA increases slightly during the first 20–30 minutes. (3) In the presence of CM or during amino acid starvation, removal of uracil[1] does *not* lead to a significant loss of the stimulating activity during the first hour, and after about 3 doubling times 50–60% of the original activity remains (see Figure 5–4, B). From these data the effects of (a) CM, and (b) amino acid starvation, on the rate of synthesis of mRNA may be estimated qualitatively.

(a) We first note that the nucleotides released when mRNA is broken down eventually must reach the stable RNA fraction. The rate at which this transfer takes place will depend on the breakdown rate (K_3 of Figure 5–1) and on the *relative rates* of synthesis of mRNA (K_2) and of stable RNA (K_4). In glucose-minimal medium the initial effect of CM is to increase K_4 almost 2-fold, and if K_2 and K_3 were *not* affected the net result would be that the stimulating activity would be lost about twice as fast with as without CM. Figure 5–4 shows that, instead of being reduced from about 20 to about 10 minutes by CM, the half-life of the

[1] The interpretation of these experiments obviously rests on the assumption that uracil starvation can be established under the test conditions. With CM there is little doubt that uracil starvation becomes effective very rapidly, since the presence of CM tends to increase the rate of RNA synthesis and thus speed up the exhaustion of the uracil pool. Amino acid starvation presents a different problem: We have reasoned that the removal of two required amino acids from the medium is unlikely to lead to effective starvation for more than one of them; but the argument that led to this conclusion does not apply to the present situation. The shift to medium lacking both amino acids *and* uracil was done by filtration and washing for several minutes with medium lacking only the amino acids. After one further wash with medium that also lacked uracil the cells were resuspended in this, the definitive medium. At the time of resuspension the cells may still contain uracil. However, incorporation experiments show that the uracil pool corresponds to about 1 minute of normal growth at 25°, and that RNA synthesis continues at a measurable but low rate during amino acid starvation. From these data we estimate that the uracil left in the cells when they are resuspended in the final medium would be exhausted in less than 20 minutes, at which time uracil starvation would become effective.

mRNA (as defined by this assay) is increased to 300–400 minutes. This indicates that the stability of the mRNA *molecules*, as distinguished from the mRNA *fraction*, is greatly increased in the presence of CM.[2] Alternatively one would have to assume that the drug increased K_2 30–40 times, which we consider very unlikely. In the *presence* of uracil, and the required amino acids, CM causes the stimulating activity per mg RNA to increase 3–4-fold in about half a generation time (J. Forchhammer, unpublished results). This is roughly what would be expected if K_2 and K_4 were both increased moderately by CM, as might be the case if the synthesis of all classes of RNA were regulated by the same mechanism.

This last statement is deliberately made very vague, because, as pointed out before, CM may also affect K_2 by altering the normal repression pattern of the cell. Furthermore, the increase in the stimulating activity observed with CM need not represent an accumulation of normal mRNA. The rRNA synthesized in the presence of the drug is not incorporated into mature ribosomes, and, if isolated in the "nascent" state, may possess stimulating activity (Otaka, Osawa, and Sibatani, 1964).

(b) In amino acid-starved cells, K_4 is reduced about 10-fold, and if K_2 and K_3 remained *un*changed the observed half-life of 10–20 minutes would be expected to increase to 100–200 minutes. The half-life estimated from the double-starvation experiments is about twice as long, suggesting enhanced stability of the mRNA molecules; still, the case for increased stability in the absence of protein synthesis rests largely on the results of the CM experiments. During amino acid starvation, in the *presence* of uracil, the stimulating activity increases only slightly, which means that the balance between messenger synthesis and breakdown has not been significantly altered. Thus, if we assume that the rate of breakdown, K_3, is reduced considerably when protein synthesis is inhibited, the same must be true of the rate of synthesis, K_2.

The experiments of Forchhammer, Kjeldgaard, and Moldave (1965) include determinations of the stimulating activity per milligram of the RNA isolated from steady-state cultures with growth rates in the range 0.5–2.5 doublings per hour at 37°.

[2] In this connection it must be noted that the half-life estimated from uracil-starvation experiments of course is that of the messenger fraction. This estimate could be corrected for recycling of the nucleotides between the pool and messenger fraction if we knew the ratio of K_2 to K_4. This ratio is probably not far from unity, and the true half-life of the most rapidly decaying fraction of the mRNA (Figure 5–4, B) would therefore be about 2.5 minutes at 37°.

Relative to total RNA the stimulating activity increases somewhat with the growth rate (Figure 5–5, A); however, when correction is made for the change in the proportion of tRNA at the different growth rates, the activity per milligram of rRNA is found to be constant (Figure 5–5, B); i.e., it would seem that the quantity of mRNA per ribosome is the same whether the cells contain 3000–4000 or 15,000–20,000 particles per genome (see Table 3–3). Gros *et al.* (1965) have shown that the quantity of mRNA, as defined by hybridization, is proportional to the num-

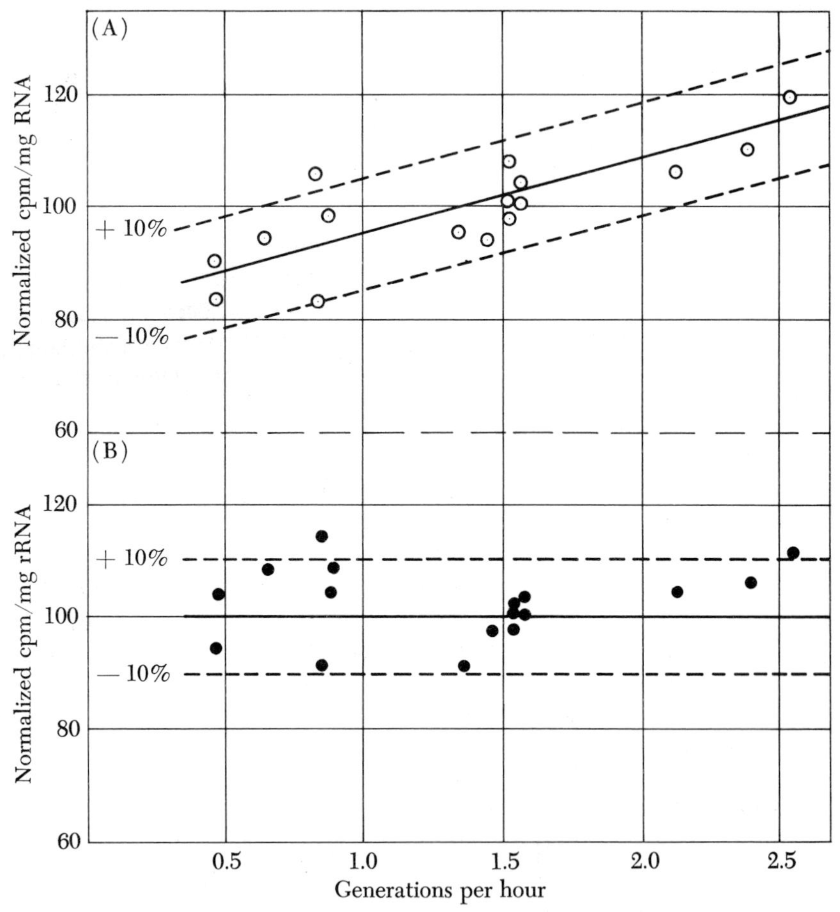

FIGURE 5–5 The stimulating activity of the RNA from cells growing at different rates on the amino acid incorporation *in vitro*. Abscissa: the growth rate (μ) at 37° in doublings/hr. (A) Uncorrected values for the stimulating activity per mg RNA in arbitrary units. (B) The same activities per mg rRNA.

ber of ribosomes even when this number has been greatly reduced by Mg^{++} starvation (see also Section 4–2). This proportionality suggests that mRNA may never be produced in excess.

It is natural to assume that, in the cytoplasm of a well-organized cell, mRNA and ribosomes are present in fixed proportions, and such a balance would automatically establish itself if, as suggested by Stent (1964), free particles were actively engaged in the release of finished mRNA molecules from their DNA templates. In this model it is necessary to account not only for a "cytoplasmic" but also for a "nuclear" messenger fraction, i.e., for the mRNA of the polysomes *and* for that associated with DNA. At the extreme growth rates represented in Figure 5–5, the mRNA of the polysomes would contain a total of about 3 and 15×10^5 nucleotides per genome, respectively (assuming that most of the ribosomes are engaged, and that neighboring particles are about 100 nucleotides apart along the messenger). The mRNA bound to DNA could amount to 3×10^6 nucleotides per genome (one per base pair), and it probably would exceed half this value if all repressed cistrons carried a bound messenger.

We shall not discuss this idea further except to point out that if 10% only of the genome carried bound mRNA (and if this fraction were isolated together with the free mRNA in our standard extraction with SDS and phenol), the stimulating activity per milligram of mRNA plus rRNA should *decrease* by a factor of almost 2 between the lowest and the highest growth rate. Figure 5–5 shows no such trend. Stent (1965) suggests that a free 70 S ribosome is necessary not only for the *release* of an mRNA molecule from its template, but also for the proper functioning of the polymerase, i.e., for the *synthesis* of the messenger. Such a scheme obviously would exclude accumulation of DNA-bound mRNA. The same would be true, however, if ribosomes and polymerase did not interact, but if the former were always present in sufficient excess to ensure that an mRNA molecule would begin to be released before synthesis had proceeded very far. This alternative seems unlikely, since Mg-starved cells with very few ribosomes exhibit a normal mRNA/rRNA ratio while in the process of building up their normal complement of 70 S particles (F. Gros, personal communication).

A few experiments have been made to test the *in vitro* stimulating activity of RNA isolated from relaxed strains before and after amino acid starvation. Willson and Gros (1964) reported that starvation for 3 hours at 37° increased the stimulating activity about 4-fold in a relaxed strain, and reduced it considerably in a control experiment with a stringent strain. In our hands, methionine starvation for 2 hours at 37° of the relaxed strain Hfr Cavalli increased the stimulating activity only slightly, and in the stringent strain 15 the activity dropped very little during the same treatment. Again no explanation can be offered for the discrepancy, and it should perhaps be looked upon as one case among many that show how closely related strains can differ in the response to an operation as "simple" as that of removing a required amino acid.

We now turn to experiments dealing with the synthesis of specific mRNA species during normal growth and under starvation conditions. Our experiments are based on the striking observation that 5-fluorouracil (FU) causes certain mutants to revert phenotypically (Champe and Benzer, 1962) (Section 1–6). There is now good evidence that the presence of the uracil analogue in the transcript makes it possible to read a certain mutated codon not as "end chain," but as "serine." Thus, given the right type of mutant and an assay for the normal product of the gene concerned, FU can be used to test for the production of the specific messenger, since only mRNA molecules that contain FU in the critical position will support the synthesis of a recognizable protein.

Garen and Siddiqi (1962) have shown that certain alkaline phosphatase mutants also respond to FU, and a particularly useful double mutant has generously been sent to us by Dr. Frank Rothman. This strain is a constitutive phosphatase mutant with an additional FU-responsive mutation in the structural gene for that enzyme. The background of alkaline phosphatase is extremely low, and an exposure to FU (10 μg/ml) for no more than 2.5 minutes at 37° produces an easily measurable burst of enzyme synthesis.

Cultures of this strain were grown for many generations in a medium containing casamino acids, then were transferred to a minimal medium containing FU, and returned 2.5 or 5 minutes later to the enriched medium to which had been added 400 μg/ml of uracil to stop further FU incorporation. The enzyme yield in this type of experiment was at least 10 times lower than in control cultures exposed to FU in the presence of the amino acids. Total RNA synthesis was reduced by a factor of 10–20 under the same shift-down conditions. An arginine auxotroph, derived from this mutant in our laboratory, behaves in the typical, stringent manner when starved of arginine, with respect to both total RNA synthesis *and* the production of the specific phosphatase messenger (G. J. Edlin, unpublished results).

The virtual absence of active phosphatase messenger in cells exposed to FU during starvation suggests that the synthesis of mRNA is inhibited under this condition. However, the lack of response is significant only to the extent that it can be assumed that FU has access to the nucleotide pool under the test conditions (cf. Figure 5–1). We have measured the free riboside triphosphates of radioactive U or FU added to the medium, and the results were that the pools of UTP and FUTP created during amino acid starvation were much smaller than those obtained during normal growth. The results of the FU experiments are thus, unfortunately, inconclusive. These and a few other experiments which failed to give clear answers have been included because they illustrate how important it is to pay attention to secondary or indirect effects of the experimental operations. This viewpoint was stressed in the introduction, when we distinguished between simple physical or chemical measurements on cells, and the less simple *in vivo* experiments in which the response to an operation, say, a shift-down, is being studied.

In this section, attempts have been made to decide whether the synthesis of mRNA and that of the stable RNA species, respectively, are affected by amino acid starvation in the same way and to similar degrees. As already emphasized, the results are far from conclusive; and, although it remains entirely possible that general RNA synthesis is controlled by uncharged tRNA, and that inhibition of the polymerase is involved, this model has to a large extent been preferred because an inhibitory effect of this type can be demonstrated *in vitro*. It is clear, however, that the conditions under which this is possible have not yet been adequately defined. Furthermore, it must be kept in mind that *in vitro* the synthesis of mRNA predominates (e.g., with T4 DNA as template, nothing but mRNA will be produced), whereas *in vivo* we have been concerned chiefly or exclusively with rRNA and tRNA. If special polymerases are involved in the synthesis of the stable RNA species, the two sets of experiments may not even be comparable.

This uncertainty is due partly to the lack of precise knowledge about the polymerase(s) and partly to the fact that the relationship between messenger synthesis and breakdown *in vivo* is unclear. Thus Képès (1963), Hartwell and Magasanik (1963), and Nakada and Magasanik (1964) find that the rate of decay of mRNA is unaffected by amino acid starvation or by CM, which is certainly not the case in the actinomycin experiments of Fan, Higa, and Levinthal (1964) and in our experiments. It is clear that assays which register the synthesis of an enzyme, i.e., the functioning of a complete and intact transcript, would be much more sensitive both to messenger turnover and to slight nuclease activities than would the actinomycin or the *in vitro* assays. However, this difference in sensitivity is hardly enough to explain why messenger breakdown seems to be independent of protein synthesis in some experiments of the former type, whereas other experiments suggest the opposite. Until something definitive is known about the way, or ways, in which mRNA is broken down, and about the susceptibility of different messenger species to breakdown, these contradictions will probably not be resolved.

5–5 THE REGULATION OF RIBOSOMAL RNA SYNTHESIS

As pointed out before, there are reasons to believe that rRNA occupies a special position as regards control. First, the fact that the rRNA/tRNA ratio is proportional to the growth rate (see Table 3–3) shows that these two RNA components are synthesized at different relative rates under different conditions. Since the DNA/tRNA ratio is constant, a doubling of the growth rate (μ) means that one and the same quantity of tRNA, but twice the quantity of rRNA, has to be produced in half the time; i.e., the rate of synthesis of tRNA is proportional to μ itself, whereas the rate of synthesis of rRNA increases as the square of μ. Second, experiments (described in Section 5–2, and in Appendix III) show that during CM inhibition the synthesis of tRNA continues at a time when no more rRNA is being produced.

A possible clue to understanding the regulation of ribosome synthesis has been found by comparing the effects of a shift-up and of CM, respectively. In both cases the immediate effects are very similar: the rate of RNA synthesis is greatly increased. However, in the shift-up this new high rate is maintained for a relatively long period, whereas in the CM experiments the high initial rate of synthesis of rRNA gradually decreases, and after some time the capacity for producing this type of RNA seems to have been exhausted. To explain these observations we assume that (a) a certain quantity of the protein which appears in the so-called CM particles is present in normal cells, (b) in some way this protein is necessary to initiate the synthesis of rRNA, or to release it from DNA. When protein synthesis is inhibited by CM, the quantity of rRNA that can be produced would thus be defined by the amount of CM-particle protein available in the cell at the time of addition of the drug (for a more detailed account of this hypothesis, see Appendix III). Under this view the initial stimulation of RNA synthesis is attributed to an amino acid-mediated release of inhibition of the polymerase, and to this effect is added a specific protein requirement for rRNA, but not for tRNA, synthesis.

If we now turn to the shift-up, it is clear that the high initial rate of rRNA synthesis could not be maintained unless the proteins consumed in the process were replaced by de novo synthesis. We know that for some time after a shift-up the rate of RNA synthesis may exceed the overall rate of protein synthesis by a considerable factor (see Figure 4–2). Maintenance of a high rate of ribosome synthesis therefore requires that the rate of synthesis of the specific proteins involved be increased correspondingly. We are therefore led to assume that the shift-up affects ribosome production in two ways: (a) it releases inhibition of RNA synthesis as described above, and (b) it derepresses the synthesis of the ribosomal proteins. To produce a balanced state after a shift-up, it would be necessary to release inhibition and to derepress the synthesis of these special proteins to the same degree. This would be achieved automatically if inhibition and repression both were linear functions of the concentration of the same repressor substance. Such a 2-fold effect of the repressor would also, in a simple manner, account for the fact that the rate of ribosome synthesis is proportional to the square of the growth rate.

A word of caution is in order here, because at least two problems need to be looked into before our model can be said to have been examined adequately. First, the protein assumed to be necessary for the synthesis of rRNA should be characterized, and it should be shown that its synthesis is derepressed to the proper extent in a shift-up; second, the relationship between rRNA and tRNA synthesis during the transition period following the shift must be investigated. As was mentioned (Chapter 4), it is not at all clear how the shift produces the observed change in the rRNA/tRNA ratio.

6

THE REGULATION OF DNA SYNTHESIS

6–1 INTRODUCTORY REMARKS

The replication of the bacterial genome is easier to discuss than RNA synthesis since only one molecular species is involved. On the other hand, the problem is complicated by the fact that the genome probably forms a continuous covalently linked structure about 1000 times larger than any protein or RNA molecule in the cell. *One* of these giant structures seems to be sufficient for a bacterium to begin to grow and divide normally. In this chapter, we propose to discuss problems concerning the initiation of replication and its rate of progression along the DNA double helix. In the next and last chapter, certain topological problems connected with the size of the genome will be examined.

It will be useful first to recapitulate and comment briefly on some important facts:

(1) It has long been known that bacteria contain a single genetic linkage group, and that they are haploid organisms. When it was demonstrated that long DNA molecules are easily broken by hydrodynamic shear, it became customary to think that even a structure as large as the bacterial genome (about 3×10^6 base pairs) might in fact constitute a single DNA molecule (Levinthal and Davison, 1961b). This is an attractively simple assumption from the point of view of the chemistry of replication. Moreover, if non-DNA "linkers" exist they seem to be at least as resistant

to shear as the DNA double helix itself. A "link" would therefore have to consist of more than a single covalent bond and could not, as has been thought, facilitate replication by providing a point of free rotation. Cairns' autoradiograms convincingly show that the genome of *E. coli* replicates as a single unit, but the resolution obtainable with his technique is quite insufficient to demonstrate possible non-DNA "linkers" (see Section 2–3).

Two further comments should be made about Cairns' important contribution: (a) As was discussed (Section 2–3), autoradiograms have been obtained in which complete; circularized DNA structures can be traced. These pictures indicate that replication takes place at a single site, the "growing point" (g.p.), through which the entire genome can be imagined to pass in a continuous manner (see Figure 6–1). It should be realized, however, that the isolation of a bacterial genome is an extremely delicate process and that, to date, only a handful of pictures exists which seem to show the intact unit. Structures with more than one g.p. could have been missed either by chance or because of excessive fragility. (b) With DNA labeled for 3 minutes, out of a generation time of 30 minutes, Cairns recorded several tracks about 60–70μ long. These tracks occurred in pairs joined at one end (presumably the g.p.). At this rate a single g.p. could not travel more than 600–700μ between successive cell divisions; still, measurements of whole "circles" indicate that the genome is 1000–1200μ long. This apparent discrepancy will be discussed in the next section.

(2) With density labeling techniques, Meselson and Stahl (1958) showed that the DNA of *E. coli* replicates semiconservatively *in vivo* (see Section 1–2). Their experiments reveal nothing about the number of g.p. or about the rate of progression of the replication process proper. However, they show that, after one generation of growth, at least 90% of the DNA in the culture has replicated once, and once only. This important observation implies that, as a rule, successive rounds of replication are initiated at the same point on the genome. Only in this way is it possible in a continuous process to replicate *all parts* of the genome during a period characterized by an exact doubling of the total quantity of DNA (see Figure 6–1). It is also clear that in the *individual cells*, the time interval between the initiation of successive rounds of replication cannot be subject to the same large fluctuations as the cell division time, whose coefficient of variation is about 0.2 (see, e.g., Schaechter *et al.*, 1962). If it were, the "fast" cells after the lapse of one *average* division time would have yielded significant quantities of DNA

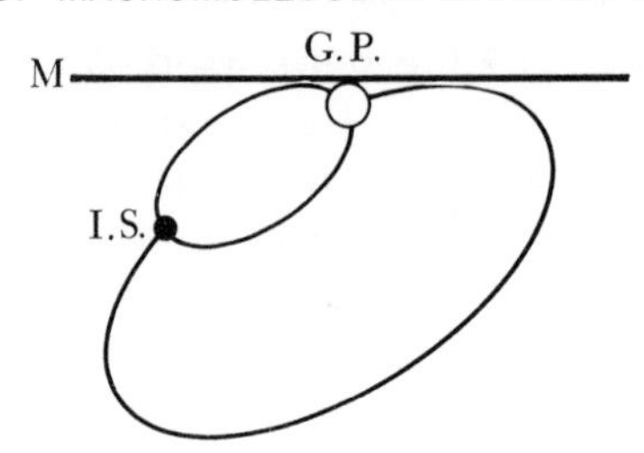

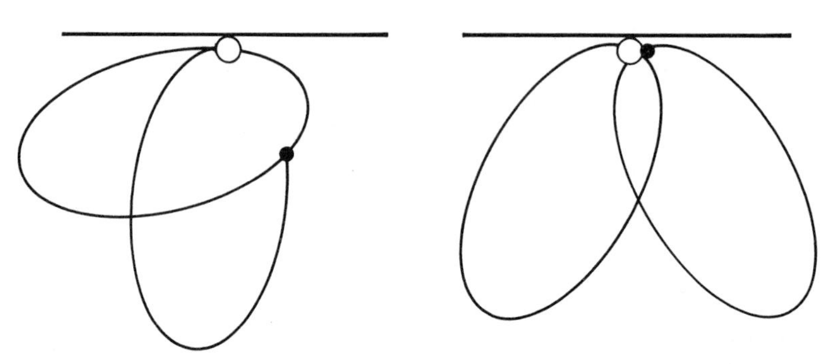

FIGURE 6–1 Replication of the bacterial genome. Diagrammatic presentation of the replication cycle as reconstructed by Cairns (1963). M is the cell membrane with which the growing point, G.P., is thought to be associated (Jacob and Brenner, 1963; cf. Section 6–5). The site on the genome at which replication is initiated is marked I.S.; for mechanical reasons this structure is referred to by Cairns as the "swivel point." As discussed (Section 6–7), each of the three stages presented here probably stains as a single body; cytologically, nuclear division is thought to take place when two new and separate growing points have been synthesized and a new round of replication initiated.

that had replicated twice (i.e., had become "light"), and the "slow" cells would have yielded corresponding quantities of "heavy" material (i.e., DNA that had not yet replicated). This argument is important for understanding the results of the synchronization experiments to be presented later.

(3) DNA replication has also been studied extensively *in vitro* (see Section 1–2). The results obtained have revealed intimate details about the process that could not have been obtained otherwise. Let us just recall that the polymerase studied by Kornberg and his colleagues requires a DNA primer, preferably in a slightly denatured state, as well as all four deoxyriboside triphosphates, and that the product is an exact copy of the primer.

In the present context, however, we are concerned less with the refined enzymology of the *in vitro* reaction than with some obvious differences between this process and replication *in vivo*. With bacterial DNA as primer the many free ends produced by shearing forces in the course of preparation serve as starting points for DNA synthesis, and it has been shown that branched molecules and "hairpin structures" which probably never occur *in vivo* are formed (Schildkraut, Richardson, and Kornberg, 1964). The fact that *in vivo* replication always seems to proceed linearly along the entire genome indicates that the initiation site is distinguished by a structural element, whose function it is to establish "primer condition" in the right place and at the right time. Considerable indirect evidence for the existence of such a mechanism will be presented in this chapter, but much remains to be done before *in vitro* systems can be set up in which the biochemistry of the "natural" initiation process can be studied.

It should finally be mentioned that the two antiparallel DNA strands need not replicate from opposite ends of the molecule. This was once thought to be a necessary consequence of the structure of the double helix, but a plausible mechanism by which both strands could be copied in the *same* direction has been suggested (Levinthal and Davison, 1961b). There is thus no obvious inconsistency between *in vivo* and *in vitro* observations in this respect.

6-2 THE DURATION OF THE REPLICATION CYCLE

In cells with a proper nucleus and mitotic division, the DNA content doubles during a relatively small fraction of the cell cycle. When techniques were first developed for synchronizing division in bacterial cultures, one of the immediate objectives was to find out when DNA synthesis takes place relative to cell division. One way of obtaining synchrony is to alternate between short periods of growth at 37° and longer periods at 25°. A series of well-synchronized divisions can be produced in this way, and it was found that the DNA content of the cells doubled during the first $^1/_3$–$^1/_2$ of the division cycle (Lark and Maaløe, 1954). It was obvious, however, that the temperature regimen employed might upset the normal sequence of events in the cells, and control experiments were therefore set up to see whether DNA synthesis also was discontinuous in nonsynchronized cells.

This can be tested by exposing the cells of an exponentially growing culture to tritiated thymine, or thymidine, for, say, 10% of a generation time. After extraction of the acid-soluble material, whole cell autoradiograms are prepared. Since nearly all the tritium is retained in thymine, only cells that synthesized DNA during the exposure will remain labeled and produce grains in the photographic emulsion. Thus the *fraction* of the cells that have incorporated thymine is an estimate of the *fraction* of the generation time during which DNA is synthesized. In experiments of this type it was found that DNA was produced during 80% or more of the generation time (Schaechter, Bentzon, and Maaløe, 1959). This result, of course, shows that cultures synchronized by means of temperature shifts cannot be used to study the normal pattern of replication. Data obtained with a more satisfactory synchronization technique are presented (Section 6–7).

The fact that DNA synthesis can be almost continuous in bacteria has been confirmed by several workers. Nevertheless, in slow-growing cells replication is distinctly discontinuous, and in cultures with generation times of about 100 minutes some 50% of the cells have been found not to incorporate thymine in pulse-labeling experiments; the other half of the cells became uniformly labeled (N. O. Kjeldgaard and D. M. Freifelder, unpublished results). Exactly what the corresponding replication time is cannot be calculated without taking the age distribution into account. Thus, if replication took place during the first half of the division period, more cells would become labeled than if it occurred during the second half (about 60 and 40% of the cells, respectively, would be scored as actively synthesizing). All we can conclude from the autoradiographic experiments is therefore that the duration of the replication cycle seems to be *approximately* the same whether the generation time is 40–50 minutes or about 100 minutes, as in minimal media with glucose or acetate, respectively, as carbon source.[1]

With these results it is tempting to draw a parallel to protein

[1] A new paper by Lark and Lark (1965) appeared too late to be discussed in the text (Section 6–6). With one of the 15T⁻ strains of *E. coli* (see Section 6–4) they show that DNA synthesis takes place during most of the division cycle, even in relatively slow-growing cells. From further experiments a very interesting model is developed which suggests that a cell always contains at least two genomes which tend to replicate sequentially rather than simultaneously during slow growth. A comparison between some of our autoradiographic experiments and those of Lark and Lark indicates that strains may differ in this respect. It is particularly interesting, however, that the notion of slow-growing cells containing two replicating genomes has been derived independently and from entirely different experiments by D. J. Clark and ourselves (Section 6–7).

synthesis. We have discussed (Sections 3–4, 3–5, and 4–3) the evidence that, once initiated, the synthesis of a polypeptide chain proceeds at a rate which, like any chemical reaction, depends on temperature but *not* on the growth rate at a *fixed* temperature. The same might be true of DNA replication, and it would in fact be the natural consequence of having a single, immutable g.p. and no substrate limitation. Until recently, the main argument against this idea was that cells growing in a rich medium are known to double their DNA content in 20–25 minutes at 37°. With *one* g.p., replication obviously would have to proceed twice as fast along the genome during growth in broth as compared to growth in glucose-minimal medium.

Genetic studies by Sueoka and his colleagues have thrown new light on this problem:

Their experiments were designed primarily to provide genetic evidence that replication is initiated at one particular site on the genome (Yoshikawa and Sueoka, 1963). The approach was based on the fact that, in an exponentially growing culture, continuous, linear replication beginning at a fixed point implies that practically all the time two copies of an early replicating marker are present for each copy of a late replicating one. It was assumed that resting cells and spores contain finished genomes only, i.e., that in these states all markers are present in the *same* number. DNA from *B. subtilis* was used and the transforming activity determined for each of 11 characters. To eliminate differences between the absolute transformation efficiencies, the ratios between pairs of markers were used, and the data were normalized by assigning unit value to all ratios obtained with DNA from resting cells or spores. With DNA isolated from cells growing exponentially in glucose-minimal medium, the corresponding transformation ratios ranged from 1 to 2. A consistent genetic map could be constructed from these figures, on which the markers should be arranged *in the order in which they are replicated*. The validity of the assumptions on which this mapping procedure is based was greatly strengthened when it was found, in two cases, that markers close together on the map could be co-transformed, i.e., that they were in fact near neighbors on a DNA molecule.

The data just described fit the familiar model of a genome with an obligatory initiation site and a single g.p. It should be noted, however, that this is strictly true only if replication is continuous. With slow-growing cells, the relative abundance of the outside markers and hence their transformation ratio would be expected to be significantly less than 2, because the DNA would be a *mixture* of replicating and nonreplicating genomes.

With rapidly growing cells very striking results have been obtained. Spores of *B. subtilis* were germinated in a rich medium (generation time about 20 minutes at 37°), the DNA was isolated at various times, and the ratio between the transforming activities for the outside markers was determined. As a function of time this ratio remained constant (unity by definition) for about 1 hour, then increased in two steps to reach a value close to 4. The same high value was found when analyzing the DNA isolated from cells during balanced growth in the rich medium (see Figure 6–2). To explain these observations the authors postulate that rapidly growing cells normally have *three* growing points per nucleus, two of which are created simultaneously at the time when the preceding one has traveled about halfway through the genome (Yoshikawa, O'Sullivan, and Sueoka, 1964). This logical conclusion has recently been confirmed by germinating heavy (D_2O) spores in light medium and analyzing the marker distribution in heavy, hybrid, and light DNA molecules (Oishi, Yoshikawa, and Sueoka, 1964). With an entirely different technique, to be described later, Pritchard and Lark (1964) have shown that extra growing points also can be established in the nuclei of *E. coli*.

The dichotomous, or multifork, replication pattern characteristic of rapidly growing cells implies that the *rate* of the elementary replication process is more or less the same whether the generation time is 40–50 minutes as in glucose-minimal medium, or 20–25 minutes as in broth (see Figure 6–3). It is interesting to note that the seemingly complex experiments of Yoshikawa *et al.* actually involve nothing but the characterization of the DNA isolated from cells in well-defined growth states. This is the type of experiment described in the introduction as a "measurement."

Cairns' autoradiographic analyses are also of this type and we shall now look back to see how the two types of experiment agree. With a 3-minute labeling period Cairns observed tracks 60–70μ long. This replication rate was measured on DNA from *E. coli* growing in a casamino acid medium. The doubling time was 30 minutes, during which a single g.p. could thus travel 600–700μ (possibly 700–800μ, since a slight lag in the uptake of the labeled thymidine may have reduced the effective incorporation time from 3 to about 2.5 minutes). These figures

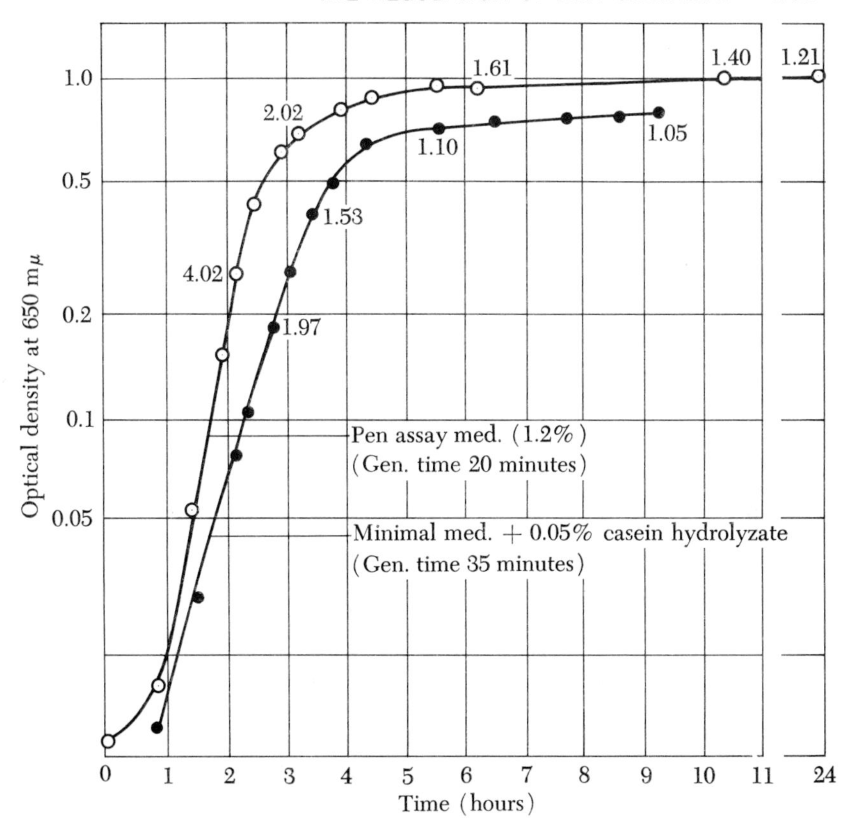

FIGURE 6–2 Growth rates and transformation ratios for outside markers. With strain W23 of *B. subtilis,* the growth rate and the transformation ratio for the outside markers (adenine and methionine, respectively) were compared in standard medium and in Penassay broth. The adenine/methionine ratios shown on the graph were obtained by normalizing against a standard stationary DNA of strain W23 (Yoshikawa, O'Sullivan, and Sueoka, *Proc. Natl. Acad. Sci. Wash.,* **52,** 973; their Figure 3).

indicate that, with a single g.p., a genome of 1000–1200μ could not replicate itself in 30 minutes.

Figure 6–3 is constructed on the assumption that the rate of DNA synthesis is constant per g.p., and shows the patterns corresponding to (a) one initiation, and (b) two equally spaced initiations per round of replication (r.o.r.). The time it takes for a g.p. to travel through the length of the genome, i.e., the duration of one r.o.r., has been chosen as a natural unit, and it is easy to see that the DNA doubling times are 1 and 0.5 in (a) and (b), re-

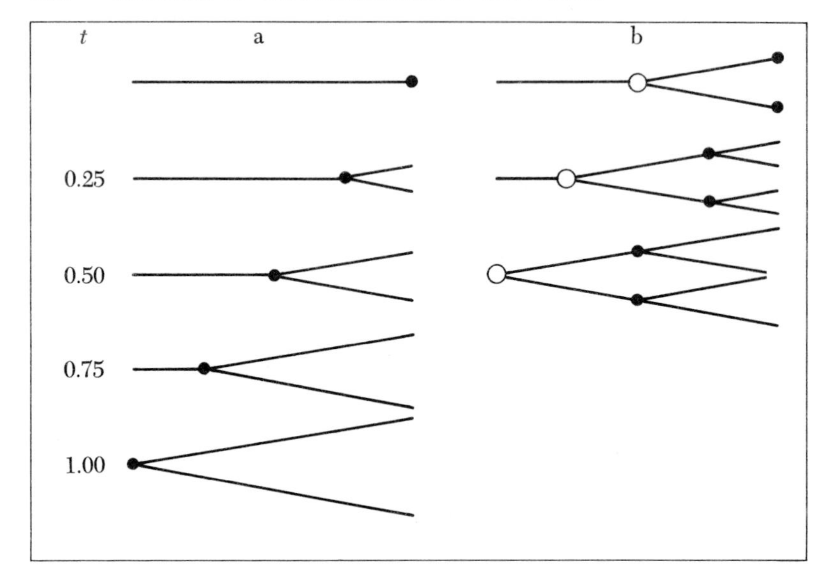

FIGURE 6–3 Replication with single and multiple growing points. A formal presentation of replication with (a) a single g.p., and (b) multiple g.p. Each g.p. is thought to move at a constant rate along the genome. Time (t) is indicated on the left-hand side, and the unit is the time it takes for a g.p. to move from the beginning to the end of the genome. The *filled circles* represent the most recently established g.p.; in series (b) the *open circles* represent a g.p. that had moved halfway through the genome at the time when replication was reinitiated at both ends of the fork.

spectively. These figures would correspond to growth in glucose-minimal medium and in a rich broth, respectively. If the time between successive initiations were intermediate between 1 and 0.5, corresponding doubling times would be obtained. The case studied by Cairns would seem to fall into this category.

6–3 A GENERAL PRINCIPLE OF REGULATION

The experiments discussed above are interpreted as follows: (a) Replication is normally initiated at a specific site, and proceeds continuously through the entire length of the genome; at a given temperature, this unit process takes approximately the same time whatever the growth rate. (b) During slow growth, DNA synthesis is discontinuous, and a full r.o.r. takes less than one division time. (c) At the growth rate characteristic of glucose-minimal medium, synthesis is almost continuous, and one r.o.r. can just be completed during the division cycle. (d) At higher growth rates, synthesis is also continuous, but *less* than one r.o.r. is accomplished between successive divisions; the necessary doubling of the total DNA content of the cell is achieved by having more than one growing point per nucleus.

This description brings out an important feature common to DNA and protein synthesis *in vivo*. With both types of molecule the rate at which individual chains grow is more or less independent of the growth rate of the cells (at a given temperature). It was argued (Section 4–2) that the same principle may apply to RNA synthesis. We are therefore led to believe that *the overall production of DNA, RNA, and protein is regulated by mechanisms that control the frequencies with which the synthesis of individual nucleotide and amino acid chains are initiated.*

This new dogma implies that the substrates involved are never limiting in normally growing cells, and a case in point was presented (Section 4–3) where it was shown that a sudden increase in the intracellular concentrations of amino acids does not, in itself, accelerate protein synthesis.

The "frequency" mechanisms thought to govern nucleic acid and protein synthesis, and the feed-back inhibitions regulating nucleotide and amino acid production, together seem to constitute a well-balanced overall system of regulation. As pointed out repeatedly, feed-back inhibition implies that the *concentration* of an end product is inversely related to its *flow rate*, which in turn depends on the capacity of the enzymes for which the particular end product serves as substrate. Thus, in a shift-up the capacity for RNA synthesis is suddenly increased and the demand for more substrate is thought to be satisfied by *lowering* the nucleotide concentrations, thereby releasing feed-back inhibition and *increasing* the flow rate. If the various components of this system are properly matched, individual RNA chains may be synthesized at very nearly the same rate before and after the shift (although the tendency, of course, would be for the chains to grow fastest *before*). This in turn means that the low overall rate of synthesis characteristic of the pre-shift medium could not be maintained except by limiting the frequency with which the syntheses of new RNA molecules were initiated. As was discussed in Chapter 5, limitation at this level could be introduced in several ways, e.g., by partial inhibition of the RNA-synthesizing enzyme(s). With such a mechanism the frequency with which an "open" DNA site would be transcribed might adjust itself to the growth conditions, and thereby to the growth rate.

6-4 THYMINELESS DEATH AND THE INITIATION OF REPLICATION

The great importance we attach to the initiation of chain growth makes it highly desirable to study this event separately. With RNA and protein synthesis, this cannot be done under physiological growth conditions because the individual events cannot be recognized. Very likely the conditions necessary for starting the transcription of a DNA template, or the translation of a message, will have to be analyzed *in vitro* first. Replication, however, is different since this process seems to be initiated only once, or twice, per nucleus and per division cycle; attempts can therefore be made to define (a) the conditions under which initiation can take place, and (b) the time at which it normally occurs. These two problems will be discussed below and in Section 6–7, respectively.

Several cases have been described in which DNA synthesis is dissociated from protein and RNA synthesis. With suitable doses of ultraviolet light the synthesis of DNA, but not that of protein and RNA, will be inhibited (see, e.g., Kanazir and Errera, 1956), and chloramphenicol can cause the opposite effect (see e.g., Billen, 1959). From our viewpoint it is more important, however, that similar dissociations are regularly produced in a *normal* cell during the period of adjustment to growth in a new medium; thus, in a shift-down, total DNA increases by 40–60% in the absence of net protein or RNA synthesis and, in a shift-up, DNA synthesis is retarded, and the new and higher rate is established only after a lag during which the old, pre-shift rate is maintained (see Chapter 4).

Our present interpretation of these phenomena is based mainly on experiments with the stringent strain $15T^-$ of *E. coli*. This strain requires thymine (T) for DNA synthesis and responds in a characteristic way when deprived of T. In a (−T)-medium the colony count remains constant for about 30 minutes at 37°, after which viability is lost exponentially with a half-time of 10–12 minutes. This is the phenomenon of thymineless death (t.l.d.), and it normally proceeds as described until less than 10^{-4} of the cells survive (Cohen and Barner, 1954).

In most of the experiments to be discussed below, substrains with additional requirements were used. They all behave like

$15T^-$ when starved of T and, in particular, exhibit t.l.d. to a considerable extent in media lacking T *and* one or more of the required amino acids.[2]

We shall now describe a series of experiments with the TAU strain. Unless specifically mentioned the cells were grown in glucose-minimal medium supplemented with T, A, and U. Partially supplemented media are designated, e.g., (−T,+AU)g, which stands for glucose medium without T, but with A and U, i.e., a medium in which nearly all cells suffer t.l.d.

When cells growing exponentially in glucose medium are transferred to (+T,−AU)g, protein and RNA synthesis virtually stop but DNA synthesis continues. Initially the rate is the same as before the transfer, but gradually decreases and after 60–90 minutes at 37° no further synthesis is observed. At this time total DNA has increased about 40%. Altogether, the cells respond much as they do to a shift-down, except of course that they do not start growing again.

A culture that has been transferred to (+T,−AU)g may be tested for its susceptibility to t.l.d. by also removing T from the medium. If the three required compounds are withdrawn simultaneously, t.l.d. begins after the usual 30-minute lag, the half-life is 15–20 rather than 10–12 minutes, and more significantly a few percent of the cells remain practically unaffected (Figure 6–4, curve II). During incubation in (+T,−AU)g the "immune" fraction gradually increases and, at about the time when DNA synthesis stops, *the entire cell population is immune to t.l.d.* in the (−T,−AU)g test medium (Figure 6–4, curves III–V). Other auxotrophs derived from strain $15T^-$ behave in the same way during amino acid starvation.

We have seen that practically all cells suffer t.l.d. when T alone is removed, i.e., every cell is potentially susceptible. The effect of removing T *and* a required amino acid indicates that, at a given moment, a small fraction of the cells are in a particular state, characterized by immunity to t.l.d., and that they cannot leave this state while starved of amino acids. Furthermore, the experiment shows that all the cells become immune in the course of amino acid starvation, and that they pass into this state at very different times.

[2] The strain TAU requires T, arginine (A), and uracil (U); TAU-bar requires T, A, U, methionine (M), proline (P), and tryptophan (Try); and TMTry requires T, M, and Try. The $15T^-$ family of strains differs from the T^- strains isolated by the method of Okada, Yanagisawa, and Ryan (1960); thus, some K12 strains of the latter type do not suffer t.l.d. at all if deprived of both T and a required amino acid. (See also Section 6–5.)

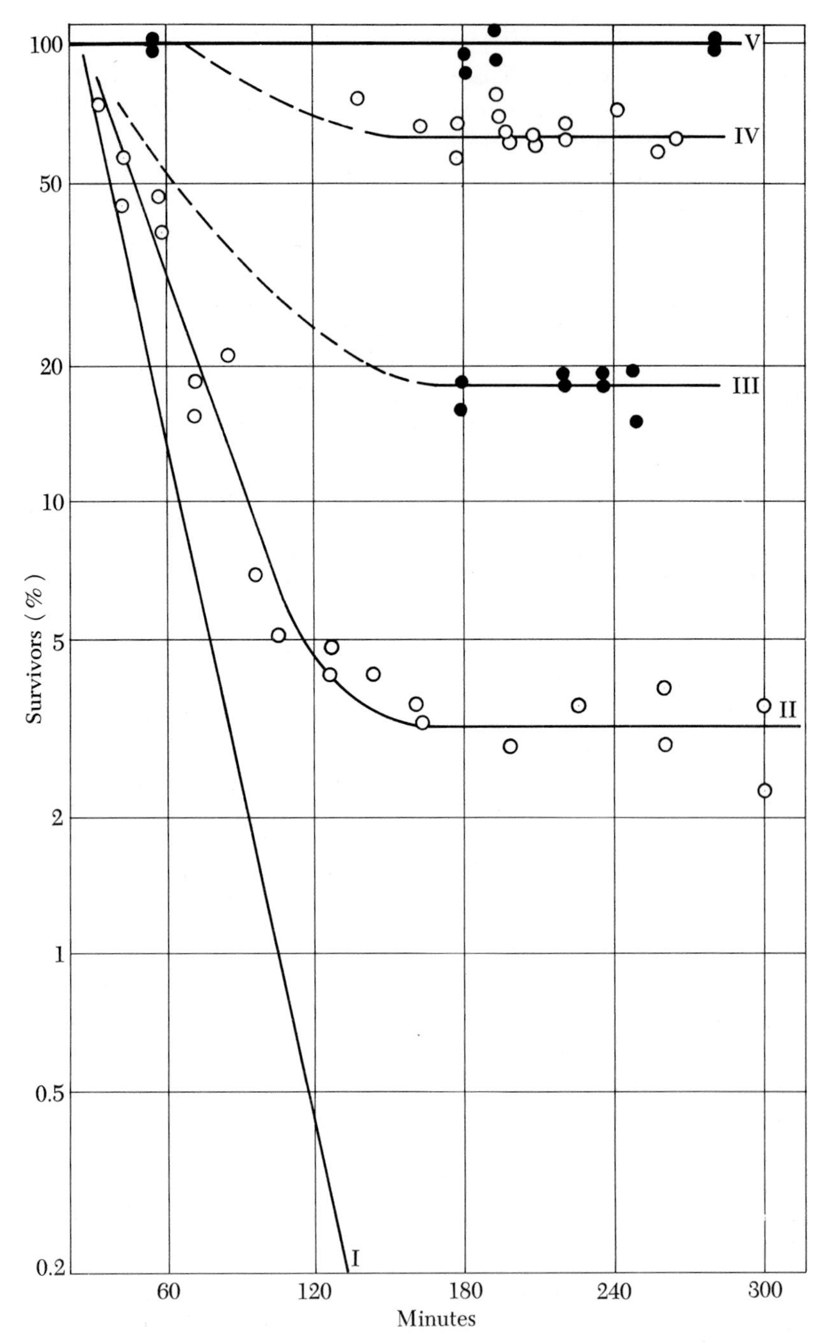

FIGURE 6–4 Acquisition of immunity to thymineless death. The individual curves show the effect of preincubation in (+T,–AU)g for various times on survival during subsequent incubation in (–T,–AU)g. Curves II–V, compiled from several experiments, correspond to 0, 30, 60, and 90 min. preincubation, respectively; for comparison, curve I is included to show the course of thymineless death in (–T,+AU)g (Maaløe and Hanawalt, 1961).

The gradual accumulation of immune cells indicates that the activities leading into this state can continue during starvation, and, since protein and RNA synthesis are blocked, we assume that the process involved is replication itself which is known to continue. The hypothesis therefore is that (a) cells deprived of T during active replication suffer t.l.d., whereas cells that have terminated one r.o.r. and not initiated a new one are immune, and (b) the act of initiation requires protein synthesis.

This model predicts that DNA should be produced during amino acid starvation in exactly the quantity necessary to complete already initiated replication. We have calculated that, with cultures growing in glucose-minimal medium, the expected DNA increment is close to 40% (Maaløe and Hanawalt, 1961). With several substrains of 15T⁻, and in several laboratories, values of 40–50% have been regularly obtained (see, e.g., Schaechter, 1961; Lark and Lark, 1964). Experimental values somewhat in excess of the theoretical are attributed to leakiness in the system, permitting cells that terminate an r.o.r. early in the starvation period to initiate and complete a second round. By means of density labeling, it has been shown that normal, hybrid DNA molecules are synthesized during starvation (see Appendix IV).

When a *broth* culture is starved the DNA increment is about 80% instead of 40–50% (Schaechter, 1961). This high value was difficult to explain at the time, but would have been predicted had it been known that rapidly growing cells contain several growing points per nucleus (see Figure 6–3).

Our model further implies that (a) the number of cells that continue to synthesize DNA should decrease as starvation progresses, and (b) the quantity produced *per cell* should vary greatly. These expectations have been verified by Schaechter (see p. 158 of Appendix IV) and Lark, Repko, and Hoffman (1963), respectively.

Finally, a comment on the postulate that it is *protein* synthesis that is required to initiate replication. Since the strains discussed above all are stringent, it is clear that starvation of one or more amino acids (and in some cases of U as well) affects both protein and RNA synthesis. There are, however, two reasons for dismissing RNA synthesis per se as an initiation factor: (a) amino acid starvation in the presence of a high concentration of chloramphenicol produces the same effects as starvation alone, despite the fact that the inhibition of RNA synthesis is reversed by the drug (Friesen and Maaløe, 1965), and (b) a temperature mutant has been isolated which grows normally at 30°, but at 40° fails to initiate properly; i.e., when shifted to the high temperature, it shows the same pattern of DNA synthesis as normal strains do under amino acid starvation, or in the presence of CM (F. Jacob, personal communication).

Loss of immunity and resumption of DNA synthesis. Let us first consider the cells that exhibit immunity when a normal culture is transferred to (–T,–AU)g. If immunity indicates absence of DNA synthesis, it is clear that these cells survive because they were transferred during the interim between two r.o.r. This selected population would be expected to represent a particular phase in the normal division cycle, and two experiments support this view: (a) a culture was held in (–T,–AU)g at 37° until only the immune cells survived (140 min); T, A, and U were then added back and during subsequent growth moderately good division synchrony was observed; (b) after the same pretreatment in (–T,–AU)g, A and U were added but withdrawn again after 2–3 minutes; during this short period of growth the majority (about 70%) of the survivors lost their immunity to t.l.d. (see Figure 6–5).

If succinate is substituted for glucose as the sole C source, the doubling time increases from 42–44 to about 65 minutes at 37°. When TAU cells are transferred from complete succinate medium to (–T,–AU)suc, the "natural" immune fraction is 20–30% as compared to 2–5% in a glucose culture (Maaløe, 1961). In general, the immune fraction *in*creases with *de*creasing growth rate, and in the resting state all the cells are immune (D. M. Freifelder, unpublished results). As shown earlier, this also applies to the fraction of the cells which, at a given moment, do *not* synthesize DNA.

We now turn to populations that have attained full immunity as a result of starvation, e.g., in (+T,–AU)g. In this case we obviously deal with cells representing all phases of the division cycle, and it must be emphasized *that such a population remains heterogeneous despite the fact that all cells become immune to t.l.d.* In the course of starvation, the individual cells increase their DNA content by factors ranging from 1 to 2, but the cell mass remains nearly constant. The net result is that some cells hardly change the DNA/mass ratio with which they entered the period of starvation, while others double their initial ratio. When such a population resumes growth in complete medium, this acquired heterogeneity must somehow resolve itself and give place to a normal age distribution with respect to replication.

This problem has been studied by following the loss of immunity, on the one hand, and the resumption of DNA synthesis in whole cultures and in single cells, on the other. Figure 6–5 shows that the acquired immunity is lost *gradually* during the

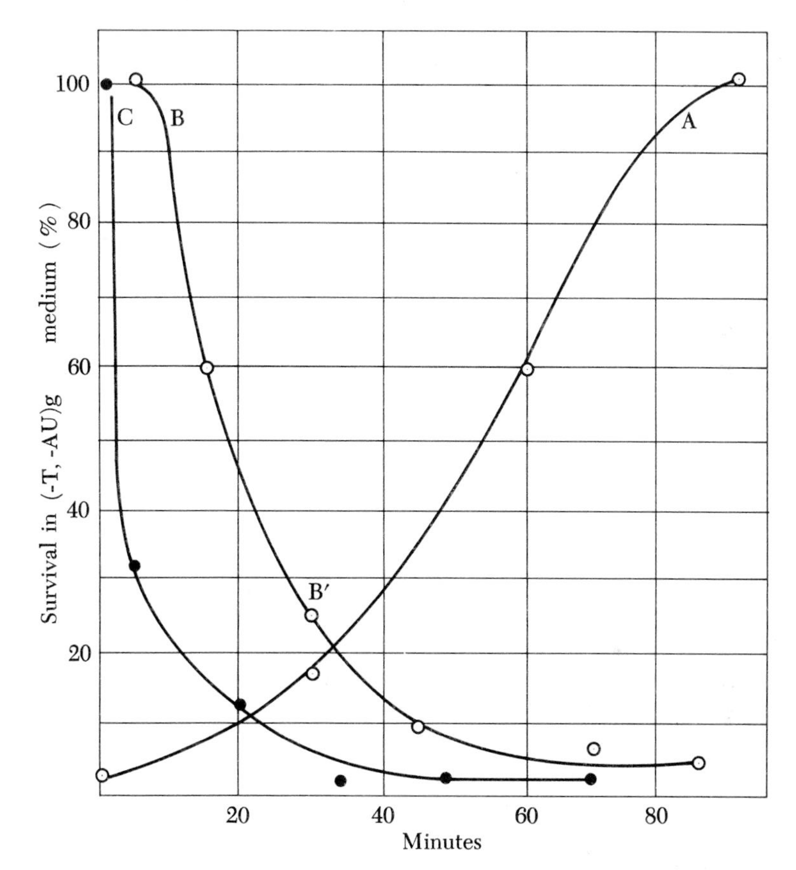

FIGURE 6–5 Loss of acquired immunity to thymineless death. All points show survival levels after incubation for 3–4 hours at 37° in (–T,–AU)g. Curve A: Preincubation in (+T,–AU)g for times indicated on the abscissa; the gradual build-up of immunity is illustrated (cf. Figure 6–4). Curve B: 90 minutes in (+T,–AU)g, followed by incubation in (+T,+AU)g for times indicated. This curve shows the loss of acquired immunity. The single point marked B′ corresponds to 90 minutes in (+T,–AU)g followed by 35 minutes in (–T,+AU)g, and shows that loss of immunity is independent of the presence of thymine. Curve C: 140 minutes in (–T,–AU)g followed by incubation in (+T,+AU)g for times indicated; shows loss of immunity in the "naturally" immune cell class (Maaløe and Hanawalt, 1961).

first generation time after returning the cells to complete medium; thus it takes about 20 minutes before half the cells have become susceptible to t.l.d., as contrasted to the 70% conversion in 2–3 minutes observed with the "natural" survivors. Hand in hand with the loss of immunity the differential rate of DNA synthesis increases (Figure 6–6), and at about the time when 90% of the cells have become susceptible to t.l.d. the definitive rate has been reached. Except for a lag of a few minutes, cell mass increases at the prestarvation rate throughout this time, and the net result is that the normal DNA/mass ratio is reestablished in the culture as a whole.

If immune cells are allowed to grow for about one generation time in (–T,+AU)g, and if T is then added, DNA synthesis at once resumes at the definitive differential rate (see Figure 6–6).

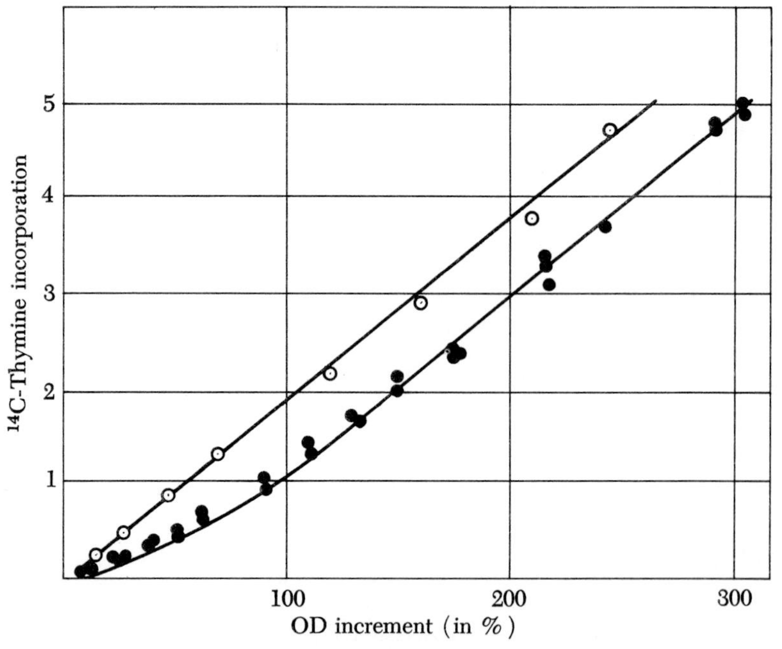

FIGURE 6–6 Resumption of DNA synthesis after starvation. Incorporation of ^{14}C-thymine added to cultures of the TAU strain after different pretreatments. *Lower curve:* 90 minutes (+T,–AU)g, then growth in complete medium containing ^{14}C-thymine. *Upper curve:* 90 minutes in (+T,–AU)g followed by 50 minutes in (–T,+AU)g before addition of labeled thymine. The activities on the ordinate are in arbitrary units, since the *lower curve* represents two independent experiments (Maaløe and Hanawalt, 1961).

It is clear therefore that the processes necessary to restore the full capacity for DNA synthesis can proceed in the absence of T.

This phenomenon has been studied at the cellular level with the autoradiographic technique (as described in Appendix IV). The main experiment involved the following operations: (a) transfer of the cells from balanced growth in glucose-minimal medium to (+T,–AU)g, (b) at 90 minutes, transfer to (–T,+AU)g, and (c) after 15 and 45 minutes, respectively, return to (+T,–AU)g containing ^{3}HT. From this final suspension samples were taken at intervals to prepare whole-cell autoradiograms. The variable in this experiment, of course, is the period of growth in (–T,+AU)g, and the main purpose was to see whether some cells regained their capacity to synthesize DNA earlier than others. Second, we wanted to see how much DNA an active cell would produce under conditions that excluded further initiation. The results were that (1) the longer the growth period in (–T,+AU)g, the greater the *fraction* of the cells that synthesized any DNA at all in the test medium, and (2) the *active* cells began synthesizing at once and produced a quantity of DNA corresponding roughly to one r.o.r. (see Figure 1 in Appendix IV).

This experiment shows that the synthesis of the specific proteins necessary for replication, on the one hand, and the onset of replication, on the other, can be separated in time. These proteins can therefore (a) be made, and (b) remain functional for a long time, in the absence of net DNA synthesis. Such "initiation in advance" apparently is sufficient to make an immune cell become susceptible to t.l.d., despite the fact that no net *DNA* synthesis will occur until the cells eventually are plated for colony counts. The significance of this observation will be discussed in the next section.

We assume that growth and replication are linked in such a way that cells with excess DNA are *prevented,* in some unknown manner, from initiating a new r.o.r. until the DNA/mass ratio has reached a more normal value. The gradual increase in the overall rate of DNA synthesis, observed when prestarved cells resume growth in complete medium, thus is thought to reflect the heterogeneity caused by replication in the absence of mass increase. Once reinitiated, replication is assumed to proceed at its usual rate in the individual cells. We shall discuss this hypothesis again in connection with Lark's experiments (Section 6–6).

Finally, it has to be emphasized that the procedure described here for aligning cells with respect to replication is *not* a general method of "synchronization." During amino acid starvation the cells almost certainly complete an r.o.r. before they stop DNA synthesis; but this pretreatment does not in itself produce synchrony, since the cells do not start the next r.o.r. simultaneously. The two-cycle experiment with a (+T,–amino acid) period followed by (–T,+amino acid) is also inadequate. In this case nearly all cells may resume replication when T is added back to the culture, but during the second period of the pretreatment the heterogeneity introduced during the first is reversed; thus the general increase in cell mass during the second period will reduce the abnormally high DNA/mass ratios, created in some of the cells during the first; however, at the same time abnormally *low* ratios will develop in other cells. Upon readdition of T, cells with very low ratios may be expected to initiate a second r.o.r. before the first is finished.

6–5 THYMINELESS DEATH

We have emphasized the suggestive correlation between susceptibility to t.l.d. and active DNA synthesis, respectively. In the absence of direct proof that these two characteristics always go together in a cell, we have assumed that an immune cell is one that has finished an r.o.r. and not yet initiated a new one at the time of transfer to the (–T,–amino acid) test medium. In other words, we believe that a critical event takes place at the *end* of an r.o.r., which makes the cell immune until the next act of "initiation" has taken place. If this is correct, the mechanism of t.l.d. is of obvious interest.

The phenomenon of t.l.d. has been demonstrated in several strains that require T because of a genetic block, and it can be induced by means of thymine analogues. However, it seems that the mechanism is not always the same. Thus, inhibition of T synthesis causes death in *B. subtilis,* and Mennigmann and Szybalski (1962) have suggested that this is due to single-strand breaks in the DNA. With the technique of Freifelder and Davison (1963), however, no single-strand breaks could be demonstrated in the DNA from TAU cells that had been starved of T for several hours (see Freifelder and Maaløe, 1964).

In some strains, phage or colicin production can be induced by removing T (Melechen and Skaar, 1962; Sicard and Devoret, 1962). In such cases the starved cultures eventually lyse. The fact that t.l.d. in the TAU and related strains is not accompanied by lysis might be due to lack of lysogeny or colicinogeny. Because of these differences no further comparison will be made between t.l.d. in different bacteria; what follows concerns only the 15T⁻ family of strains.

The kinetics of t.l.d. are illustrated in Figure 6–3. After a very "solid" lag of about 30 minutes, at 37°, a strictly exponential loss of viability is observed that extends over 4–5 decades. Examination of many survival curves shows that the transition between the lag and the exponential phase is very abrupt, and t.l.d. is therefore not a typical multihit phenomenon. Nevertheless, the cells that survive after, say, 1 hour are not unaffected by T starvation (in the sense of a particle exposed to x-rays and not yet hit). Thus, if T is added back and again withdrawn some time later, the further course of t.l.d. depends on the length of the "recovery" period in complete medium. If this period is as short as 20 minutes, the lag before t.l.d. begins again is reduced from the usual 30 to about 15 minutes and a recovery period of about 1 hour is necessary before the cells react as if they had not previously been starved of T. This memory effect shows that the survivors after the first starvation period had been affected and that this condition lasts a considerable time (Maaløe, 1963).

It has long been known that t.l.d. requires active metabolism (Cohen and Barner, 1954). The strict dependency on energy has been demonstrated with the TAU strain by Freifelder and Maaløe, 1964. With succinic acid as the sole C source, the energy flow can be effectively turned off by bubbling with N_2 instead of air. We observed that, at any time after removing T from the medium, the processes leading to t.l.d. could be stopped immediately by N_2, and that they continued as if nothing had happened when air was reintroduced. This shows that (a) the conditioning for t.l.d. that builds up during T starvation is *not* lost if the energy flow is blocked, even for hours, and (b) in this respect there is no difference between the 30-minute lag and the subsequent killing phase. We interpret this to mean that the "build-up" is continuous. The nature of this hypothetical process is discussed below.

When cells are exposed to very low T concentrations, other aspects of the phenomenon of t.l.d. are revealed. With sufficiently diluted cultures it was found that, at 0.2 μg T/ml, the growth rate is just perceptibly reduced, i.e., the diffusion into the cells of T begins to be limiting. At 0.05 μg T/ml the rate of DNA synthesis is reduced to about one third its normal value and cell division continues but only for about an hour. After

4–5 hours the cells are greatly enlarged and half of them no longer form colonies. This late and slow loss of viability may or may not be t.l.d. proper.

The response to low T concentrations is drastically altered if the cells are first starved of T. When TAU cells are given T at 0.05 μg/ml after 40 minutes in (−T,+AU)g, at 37°, most of the cells that survived at 40 minutes (i.e., produced colonies on agar with 2 μg T/ml) suffer t.l.d. However, in the absence of A and U the low T concentration completely prevents further loss of viability; it makes no difference whether A and U are present during the first 40 minutes.

To interpret these results, we first recall that normally growing cells transferred directly to complete medium with only 0.05 μg T/ml continue to divide and only begin to die after 1–2 hours. The rapid loss of viability observed in (low T,+AU)g *after* incubation in (−T,±AU)g must therefore be due to the pretreatment, and the absence of killing in (low T,−AU)g shows that this "conditioning" is effective only in complete medium. This suggests that t.l.d. involves (a) the build-up of a potential for killing, which begins as soon as the cells are suspended in a (−T)-medium, and (b) the expression of this potential, which requires a complete medium and therefore normally takes place on the agar plate (Maaløe, 1963). As was shown (Section 6–4), this potential is *not* built up in cells that have completed replication and not yet synthesized the specific proteins necessary for a new r.o.r.

After removal of T practically no net DNA synthesis is observed (see, e.g., Lark and Lark, 1964), and the adenine-, guanine-, and cytosine-deoxyriboside 5′-triphosphates (deATP, deGTP, and deCTP, respectively) might therefore be expected to accumulate in the cells. This question has been extensively studied by our colleagues, A. Munch-Petersen and J. Neuhard (1964). Instead of a "passive" accumulation of all three nucleotides, they observed that (a) the deATP concentration increased about 5-fold during the first 30 minutes and then remained constant for at least 1 hour, (b) the deGTP concentration did not change at all, and (c) deCTP increased even more than deATP but only after a lag of about 30 minutes *and* in the presence of A and U. In (−T,−AU)g the same early increase in deATP was observed, but deCTP remained constant (Neuhard and Munch-Petersen, 1965). It is clear therefore that only the accumulation of deATP can be thought to reflect the processes that lead to t.l.d.

In their studies Munch-Petersen and Neuhard (1964) also

examined the pool of deoxythymidine phosphates. In normally growing cells this pool contains approximately 0.5 μmole of T per g dry weight of cells, and after transfer to (–T,±AU)g it decreases with a half-time of 1–2 minutes at 37°. The total quantity of T in the pool amounts to 1–2% of that contained in DNA (cf. Table 3–2), and the rapid disappearance of this material during starvation indicates that some but, as mentioned before, very little DNA is synthesized in the absence of T. In (+T,–AU)g the pool increases, and after 90 minutes when full immunity has been attained it contained about 1.3 μmoles of T per g dry weight. When T is now removed the pool decreases slowly, as shown in Figure 6–7, and no significant increase in deATP is observed during the first hour. The early deATP accumulation seen after direct transfer to (–T,±AU)g could therefore be a response to rapid decrease in the concentration of the T-nucleotides.

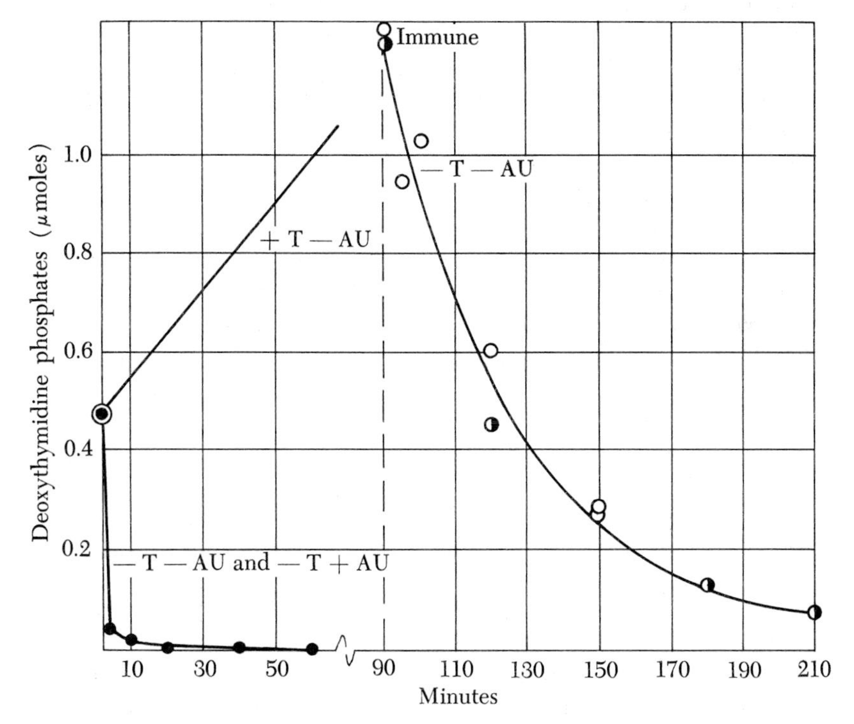

FIGURE 6–7 Changes in the pool of deoxythymidine phosphates during starvation. The figures represent the sum of the mono-, di-, and triphosphates as determined by thin-layer chromatography (Munch-Petersen and Neuhard, 1964). Strain TAU was used and the starvation program is shown on the graph.

The slow drain on the pool of T-nucleotides in immune cells, i.e., in the absence of net DNA synthesis, has not been explained. It is interesting, however, that after about 2 hours the concentration of T-nucleotides is at least 5 times less than in normal cells (see Figure 6–7). At this low level the processes leading to t.l.d. might be expected to be induced, yet no death occurs for at least another 3 hours (see Figure 6–3). Since t.l.d. normally is accompanied by an accumulation of deATP, the enzymes involved in the overall process of t.l.d. would seem to be absent, or at least not functional, in immune cells. We favor a model which postulates that (a) these enzymes are part of a complex structure, the g.p., (b) this structure is unstable unless in association with DNA, and (c) it disintegrates when an r.o.r. is finished because the stabilizing effect is lost (Maaløe, 1963). A new r.o.r. would then be initiated by a stimulus causing one g.p. to be assembled for each of the *two* complete genomes present. At least one of the new g.p. *must* be synthesized de novo, and for reasons of symmetry we assume that both genomes are stimulated and that each directs the synthesis of a new g.p.

This description contains essentially the same elements as the generalized replicon model of Jacob and Brenner (1963), except for the important notion that the g.p. is intimately associated with the cell membrane (see also Ryter and Jacob, 1964).

One particular aspect of their model will be discussed in detail here. The synthesis of the new g.p. is thought to occur in response to the production and release into the cytoplasm of a specific protein, the "initiator." The temperature mutant of Jacob, which fails to initiate at high temperatures, may produce an abnormally labile initiator (cf. Section 6–4). It must be remembered, however, that successive r.o.r. are initiated at very different time intervals, depending on the overall growth rate. This cannot be explained by assuming that the initiator is produced at a particular time during an r.o.r. (e.g., at the time when the relevant cistron is about to be, or has just been, replicated). With such a scheme the initiator would appear too early or too late, respectively, in slow- and in fast-growing cells.

It is not attractive to invoke, *ad hoc*, a control mechanism whose function would be to time the production of the initiator. Instead, one could imagine a mechanism involving (a) constant, "derepressed" production of initiator, (b) a high affinity of this product for double-stranded DNA, and (c) initiation supervening when the DNA is saturated with the hypothetical (basic) protein. Such a mechanism would explain the delayed initiation in slow-growing cells, as well as the "premature" initiation in fast-growing cells, if a fixed and appropriate quantity of the initiator were produced *per generation time*, irrespective of growth rate. This last assumption is perhaps the least arbitrary part of the model, and a case in point was discussed (Section 4–2) when we considered the production of mRNA and of protein from a completely derepressed cistron.

One reason for presenting this speculative scheme is to show that growth, in terms of protein synthesis, might conceivably be "measured" with the DNA as the tape. However, it should also be noted that a coupling between protein synthesis and initiation, of the type suggested above, could explain various transition phenomena; e.g., why cells with an abnormally high DNA/mass ratio seem not to initiate replication until they have grown for some time, and why the *rate* of DNA synthesis does not increase immediately after a shift-up. In the latter case the rate increase, of course, is thought to reflect the initiation of the "extra" g.p. characteristic of rapidly growing cells, and it would not be expected to take place until the overall rate of protein synthesis, including the synthesis of the initiator, eventually increased (cf. Section 4–4).

After this digression, let us return briefly to the mechanism of t.l.d. With the TAU strain, death is observed in both the presence and absence of A and/or U. However, the requirements for A and U are due to a single, revertible mutation, and, in order to study separately the effect of U starvation, Hanawalt isolated the TAU-bar strain in which the requirements are independently derived. With this strain, he observed the following survival percentages after 1, 2, 3, 5, and 6 hours, respectively (Hanawalt, 1963):

In (−T,+U,+amino acid)g:	15	1	0.01	—	—
In (−T,+U,−amino acid)g:	20	5	4	4	—
In (−T,−U,+amino acid)g:	90	81	68	58	30
In (−T,−U,−amino acid)g:	73	12	3	3	3

The surprising finding here is that t.l.d. is practically absent when starving for T *and* U in the presence of amino acids; when all the required compounds are withdrawn, t.l.d. proceeds slowly but to more or less the same extent as when the TAU strain is starved in (−T,−AU)g. Hanawalt suggests that the synthesis of mRNA may be involved in t.l.d., and that the TAU strain is sufficiently "leaky" to permit this synthesis to take place in the absence of U. However, it is also conceivable that TAU and

TAU-bar accumulate different intermediary metabolites in the absence of U, and therefore do not respond in the same way when starved of both U and T (compare the complex pattern of accumulation observed by Neuhard and Munch-Petersen, 1965).

It should finally be noted that the T requirement in *E. coli* strain 15 probably involves *two* mutational steps (Breitman and Bradford, 1964). Current studies with T^- strains derived from *E. coli* K 12 indicate that two steps are necessary in order to obtain strains that utilize T effectively at the same low concentrations as $15T^-$. To improve our understanding of the enzymatic processes leading to t.l.d., these mutants are being analyzed both genetically and biochemically (R. H. Pritchard, personal communication).

6–6 STUDIES OF REPLICATION BY DOUBLE LABELING TECHNIQUES

In a series of experiments by Lark and his colleagues, density labeling of the DNA has been combined with the use of radioactive T, and several aspects of the replication process have been illustrated by this elegant method.

First, replication in normally growing cells was studied (Lark, Repko, and Hoffman, 1963). A culture of the TMTry strain was labeled with ^{3}HT for about $^1/_{10}$ of a generation time, and quickly transferred to medium in which 5-bromouracil (Bu) was substituted for T. DNA was prepared at intervals from this culture, and the distribution of the radioactivity between the normal and the Bu-substituted material was determined by centrifugation in CsCl gradients. The appearance of radioactivity in the "half-heavy" hybrid DNA shows that the labeled segment has been replicated. It was found that growth and replication in the Bu medium had to continue for most of a generation time before the label began to appear in hybrid DNA. Like the data of Sueoka and his colleagues (see Section 6–2), these new results fit the model of a genome with an obligatory initiation site and a single, continuously moving g.p.[3]

In the next series of experiments, starvation in (+T,−MTry)g was introduced between the pulse labeling with ^{3}HT and the growth period in complete Bu medium. Figure 6–8 shows the expected distribution of radioactivity before and after starvation.

[3] Strictly speaking, none of these results eliminates the possibility of several, synchronously replicating "chromosomes." This, however, is ruled out by genetic evidence (a single linkage group) and by Cairns' autoradiograms.

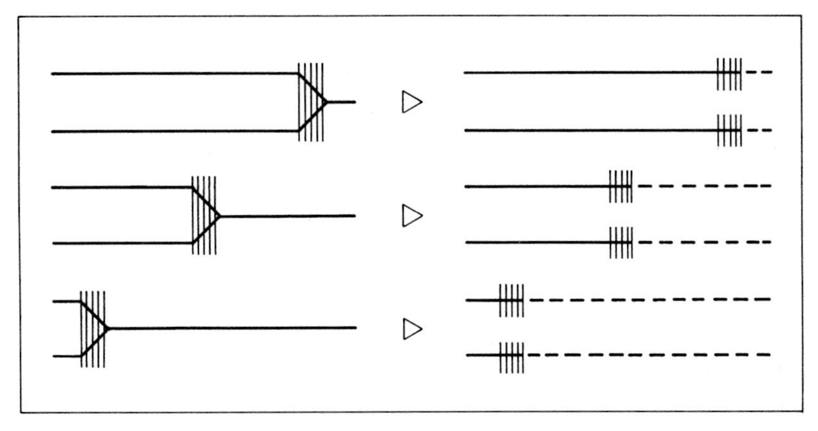

FIGURE 6–8 Pulse labeling of DNA. *Left:* three genomes in different states of replication. The *shaded areas* indicate that, during the last 1/10 of the replication period, ^{3}H-thymine has been incorporated. *Right:* the same genomes are drawn in the states assumed to be reached during amino acid starvation. The parts of the genome which are distal to the labeled regions, and which would have replicated during starvation, are indicated by *broken lines.*

On the right-hand side of the diagram are the genomes of cells that have finished replication during amino acid starvation. The transfer of their radioactivity into hybrid DNA during growth in Bu medium was followed in the experiments. It should be possible to predict the time course of this transfer from the model presented earlier, which says that cells with excessive DNA/mass ratios initiate replication only when their mass has increased appropriately. Thus the class of cells whose genomes are labeled near the end (Figure 6–8, top row) would be expected to initiate *soon* after transfer to the Bu medium and to replicate the labeled segment *late* during the first r.o.r., whereas cells labeled at the opposite end (Figure 6–8, bottom row) would be expected to initiate *late* and replicate the labeled segment soon thereafter. The prediction would therefore be that about 40% of all the DNA would have been replicated *before* any label appeared in hybrid material, and that all the label would have been transferred by the time about 60% of the DNA had replicated. The result obtained by Lark *et al.* is strikingly different. They found that transfer of label began as soon as hybrid material appeared, and that it continued at a constant rate throughout the first r.o.r. in the Bu medium. *This* is the result to be expected if all the cells started replicating at the *same* time.

Clearly, it is difficult to reconcile the data of Lark *et al.* with our model. It is therefore important to recognize that (a) this model is based on clear-cut evidence that after amino acid starvation the cells start replicating at different times (see Appendix IV), and (b) it is *assumed* that the time of initiation is correlated with the DNA/mass ratio. If we were to abandon this assumption there would be no obvious discrepancy between Lark's and our own observations.

There are two reasons for not doing so right away:

(1) Without the postulated correlation, the heterogeneity with respect to the DNA/mass ratio developing during amino acid starvation would be exaggerated instead of being resolved during subsequent growth. Thus, when all cells eventually had resumed replication, the DNA/mass ratio would vary from twice to half the normal value (see discussion at the end of Section 6–4). Unless a mechanism exists for preventing such a drift, the heterogeneity might persist indefinitely and it would be meaningless to speak of a "normal" DNA/mass ratio. We find this unlikely, though without being able to disprove it.

(2) However elegant in design, Lark's experiments are complicated by the fact that Bu is toxic. Thus exposure to Bu for 140 minutes at 37° kills about 90% of the cells and markedly reduces their overall synthetic capacity (see Appendix IV, pp. 162–163). In most of Lark's experiments the physiological conditions must have changed greatly during growth in the Bu medium. To account for the gradual increase in the rate of DNA synthesis after the starvation period, Lark assumes that a structural element, possibly a protein, is lacking in the part of the genome that replicated in the absence of M and Try, and that the deficient DNA subsequently replicates more slowly than the rest. This seems unlikely since only about 60% of the label had appeared in hybrid material by the time total DNA had doubled in the Bu medium. If all the cells started replication at the same time, and if the material synthesized during starvation replicated slowly, *all* the label should have been transferred *before* total DNA had doubled (this can be seen from Figure 6–8, where the broken lines represent the parts assumed to replicate slowly). Also, the distribution between light, hybrid, and heavy material at the end of the experiment is not in agreement with the chemical measurements of the total DNA increment.

Finally, DNA synthesis in the Bu medium is usually preceded

by a lag of 20 minutes or more. This is different from the pattern of Figure 6–6, and suggests that the cells may have grown for a considerable time in the Bu medium *before* replication began. The effect of this might be similar to that observed if amino acid starvation is followed by a period in (–T,+amino acid) before replication is allowed to begin (cf. Figure 6–6). In summary, we think that some of the discrepancies between Lark's and our results may be ascribed to "toxic" effects of Bu; new and different experiments are needed to clear up this ambiguity.

In a second paper, Pritchard and Lark (1964) analyzed replication after a period of T starvation. The striking result was that growth in (–T,+MTry)g induced the formation of new g.p. at the normal site of initiation, and that subsequent replication occurred at the old as well as at the new g.p. Induction did *not* take place in (–T,–MTry)g. This very significant observation shows that multiple g.p. (of normal occurrence in rapidly growing cells) are induced when replication is artifically prevented while growth of the cells continues. The same mechanism probably accounts for the results we obtained with low, rate-limiting T concentrations (Maaløe and Rasmussen, 1963). A detailed analysis of the experiments of Pritchard and Lark is difficult, because the processes leading to t.l.d. proceed together with the observed initiation of new g.p. The authors believe that the absence of T has a direct inducing effect. This may be true, but it may be argued against their assumption that the concentration of the T-nucleotides falls very rapidly in the absence of T (see Figure 6–7), whereas the new g.p. seems to be created gradually during the first 30–50 minutes of growth in the (–T)-medium.

A third paper, by Lark and Lark (1964), deals with the requirements for initiation. They assume that during T starvation most cells initiate a new g.p. at the end of only *one* of the two arms of the growing chromosome. (The results would probably be the same if about half the cells went through a completely normal initiation process, each creating *two* new g.p.) From this assumption it is argued that two different components are synthesized in a complete initiation process, and that only one of them, the initiator, needs to be synthesized when an "extra" g.p. is created during T starvation. The additional compound is viewed as a structural element whose synthesis is insensitive to chloramphenicol (CM). This is based on experiments in which CM is introduced together with the required amino acids after the usual pretreatment in (+T,–MTry)g. With 12.5 μg CM/ml, bulk protein synthesis was inhibited about 90%, and a quantity of DNA corresponding to one r.o.r. in about half the cells was synthesized; with 25 μg CM/ml, this quantity was reduced and, with 50 or 100 μg CM/ml, no synthesis was observed. Considering that sufficiently high CM concentrations blocked all reinitiation, it is difficult to accept these data as evidence for a structural component whose synthesis is more or less insensitive to CM.[4]

Since multiple g.p. seem to be nothing abnormal, we are inclined to think that those produced under T starvation are "normal" in the sense that they are created in response to a mass increase. This, of course, does not imply that initiation does *not* involve the synthesis of compounds other than proteins; we just do not know.

6-7 DNA REPLICATION AND THE NORMAL DIVISION CYCLE

The relationship between replication and cell division in bacteria has long been a puzzle. Thus, the fact that slow-growing cells may complete an r.o.r. in, say, half a division time does not tell when initiation takes place relative to cell division. It is a curious fact that, from the time it was observed that an r.o.r. takes practically a whole division time (in a glucose medium), it has been tacitly assumed that initiation occurred immediately after cell division. This anticipation turns out to be wrong.

To study this relationship with cells as small as most bacteria, it is necessary to provide cultures in which (a) the cells divide synchronously, and (b) the division cycle is truly "normal." As emphasized before, synchronous division may be obtained in various ways, some of which are known to produce artifacts (Maaløe, 1962). The present study was undertaken because, finally, a physiologically satisfactory synchronization method seemed to be available. This new technique was developed by Helmstetter and Cummings (1963)[5], and involves the following two steps: (a) cells from an exponentially growing culture are allowed "spontaneously" to adsorb onto a millipore filter with

[4] The study of Thang, Williams, and Grunberg-Manago (1963) is quoted as evidence that the synthesis of some enzymes is relatively insensitive to CM. *A priori* this seems unlikely, since CM does not interfere with the charging of tRNA with amino acids, and therefore should not in its action discriminate between proteins with different amino acid compositions. The observation, that low concentrations of CM affect the synthesis of certain enzymes to different degrees, probably reflects changes in the repression pattern caused by the drug.

[5] We are indebted to Dr. Helmstetter for introducing this technique during the time he spent as a postdoctoral fellow in our laboratory.

an average pore size of 0.22μ, (b) the filter is inverted and fresh, prewarmed medium is passed through, first rapidly to dislodge loosely attached cells and then at a constant rate of approximately 10 ml/min/100 cm^2. A steady state can be reached and maintained for several hours during which nearly all the cells that pass into the stream of fresh medium are derived from adsorbed ones that divide *in situ*. The apparatus therefore continues to deliver "new-born" cells which during subsequent growth divide synchronously (see Figure 6–9).

This remarkably simple arrangement, of course, has its limitations: up to now, only a few strains, notably *E. coli* B/r, have given reproducible results; furthermore, the concentration in the effluent is at most $1–2 \times 10^7$ cells/ml. However, the all-

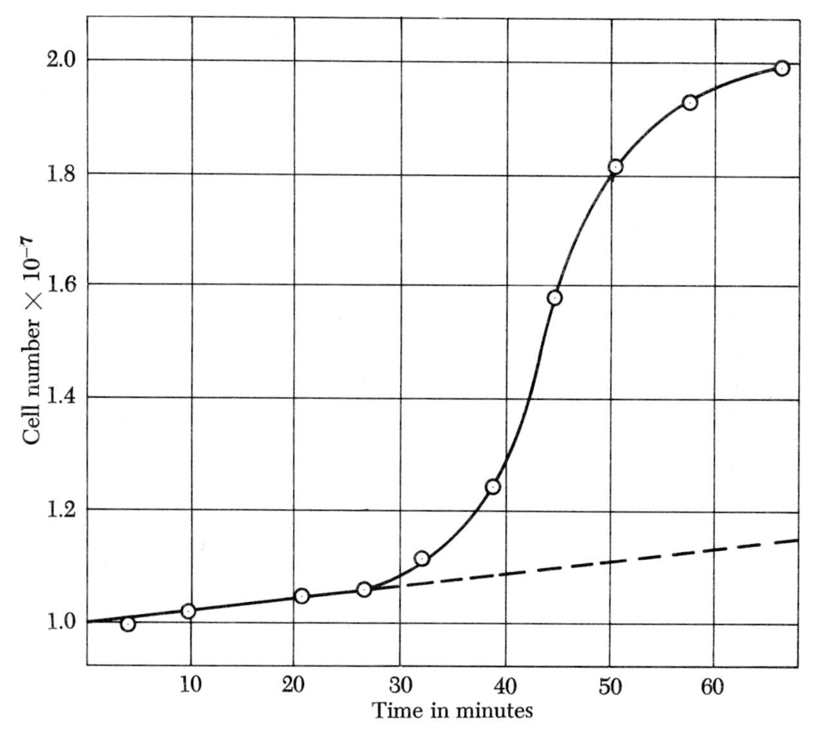

FIGURE 6–9 Synchronous division in *E. coli* strain B/r. Total cell counts plotted against the time after collecting the effluent from the filter. The cells were grown in glucose-minimal medium with an average division time close to 45 minutes. The first segment of the curve has been extrapolated to show that, probably, about 10% of the cells were *not* in phase with the rest of the population.

important fact is that *the adsorbed cells reach a steady state of growth with the same doubling time as in a well-aerated batch culture.* This indicates that the samples collected consist of normally growing cells. Of course, attempts are being made in several laboratories to improve the technique, but at present experiments must be designed bearing the limitations in mind.

The study to be described here was made by Dr. David J. Clark in our laboratory and the aim was to see whether replication is initiated at a defined time relative to cell division, and if so at which point in the division cycle this event takes place. A full account including a description of the apparatus used to obtain samples of 50–100 ml/min will be published elsewhere.

With *E. coli* B/r, two sets of measurements were made: (1) the rate of DNA synthesis was determined by adding labeled thymidine to samples representing different times in the division cycle, and following the incorporation for about 5 minutes, (2) labeled thymidine *and* 150 μg/ml of CM were added to representative samples, and the total incorporation at 60–100 minutes was measured. In set (1) the scope of the experiments is limited by the fact that, in strain B/r, thymidine induces the synthesis of an enzyme which splits off the deoxyribose moiety; the rate measurement therefore cannot be extended beyond 6–7 minutes. The validity of the measurements of type (2) depends on the assumption that a sufficiently high concentration of CM is equivalent to amino acid starvation. This is probably correct, since control experiments with exponentially growing cells show that incorporation has reached a well-defined maximum after about 60 min.[6] In addition, CM of course prevents the formation of the thymidine-splitting enzyme.

The incorporation obtained in the presence of CM thus estimates how much DNA has to be synthesized to complete already initiated replication. High counts indicate that label and CM were added at a time when replication had recently been initiated in many cells; conversely, low counts indicate that most cells were near the end of an r.o.r. at the time of addition. Figure 6–10 illustrates two experiments of this type; in (A) the doubling time was 45 minutes (glucose-minimal medium), and

[6] This indicates that the 150 μg/ml of CM used here are adequate to prevent the prolonged and excessive incorporation observed by Lark and Lark (1964) in strain TMTry with 25 μg/ml. Chemical measurements by K. V. Rasmussen (unpublished) have shown that, in the presence of 150 μg/ml of CM, a B/r culture in glucose minimal medium increases its total DNA by about 40%. The time course is similar to that observed with the 15T⁻ strains; see e.g., Appendix IV, Figs. 4a and 7.

in (B) 75 minutes (succinate-minimal medium). In both, the counts increase from a minimum to a well-defined maximum which is reached shortly before cell division begins; this pattern repeats itself in the second division cycle.

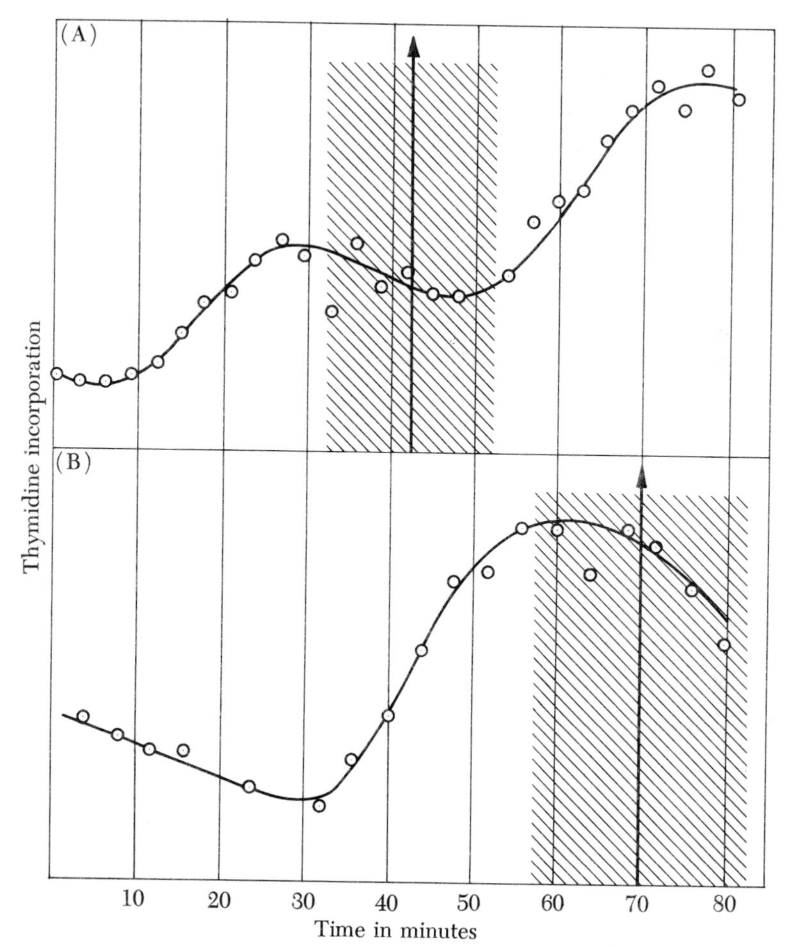

FIGURE 6–10 Residual DNA synthesis at various times during synchronous division. (A) Strain B/r growing in glucose-minimal medium at 37°; the average division time is shown by a *vertical arrow* and the division period is *hatched.* The counts on the ordinate represent the thymidine incorporation attained at 60 minutes after adding the label plus 150 μg/ml of CM. (B) Same strain growing in succinate-minimal medium at 37°; the average division time and period are indicated as above. Counts after 100 minutes with label and CM. In both (A) and (B) the abscissa shows the time of addition of label + CM.

To analyze this experiment let us first consider the shortcomings of the technique, viz., the imperfection of the synchrony (a), and the unavoidable background of irrelevant counts (b).

(a) Total cell counts were obtained with an electronic counter (Coulter, Model B), and a typical curve is shown in Figure 6–9. The well-defined period of cell division always occupies 20–30% of the whole cycle, and a slight but continuous increase in the counts during the first 30 minutes indicates that the population may contain about 10% of nonsynchronized cells (see below). The great spread in the division time is somewhat puzzling, since we know from the experiments of Meselson and Stahl (1958) that the time it takes to go through an r.o.r. varies little from cell to cell (see Section 6–1). To understand how replication can be almost continuous *and* more accurately timed than cell division, we assume that division in the physiological sense, i.e., the completion of a septum between sister cells, occurs at regular intervals, and that the time between this event and cell separation varies considerably (see Schaechter *et al.*, 1962). If so, the "newborn" cells collected from the filter are not of exactly the same physiological age, and the relatively "old" ones would tend to divide early in our samples, and vice versa.

(b) For several reasons we expect a more or less constant background of radioactivity in our samples: (1) as mentioned above, a small but not insignificant fraction of the cells are not synchronized; (2) in the presence of CM, excessive amounts of RNA are synthesized and some of the label may end up in this fraction; (3) as shown by H. Yoshikawa (personal communication), "repair" synthesis may account for a small amount of uptake. It is difficult and so far we are not able to account quantitatively for these sources of incorporation. No importance can therefore be attached to the size of the "step" between the lowest and highest counts observed during the division cycle, and without knowing the true ratio between these levels the data cannot be analyzed quantitatively.

These reservations leave us with the reproducible patterns of Figure 6–10. The first cells to initiate the new r.o.r. are thought to do so at the time when the counts begin to increase, and we assume that these cells also divide early. With the more or less symmetrical distribution according to division time as the norm, it is possible to construct a theoretical incorporation curve with nearly the same shape and time course as the experimental curve. This numerical reconstruction indicates that the cells with average division time (the largest class) initiate their rep-

lication 5–10 minutes before maximum incorporation is reached. This conclusion is supported by measurements of the rates of DNA synthesis carried out under comparable experimental conditions by D. A. Glaser (personal communication) and by D. J. Clark; in both series of experiments the rate of synthesis seems to double somewhere around the middle of the division period in glucose medium.

When A and B in Figure 6–10 are compared, it will be noted that the time interval between initiation and the subsequent cell division is very similar. This has been observed with division periods as long as 100 minutes at 37°. *Such a relationship between replication and division suggests that cell division is triggered at the time of initiation or soon after, say, when a particular cistron is replicated.*

A direct consequence of the time relation between replication and cell division is that *two* complete genomes must always start replicating simultaneously in the same cell. This is so because an r.o.r. which is initiated about 25 minutes before division cannot be completed until *after* the cell has divided. Thus, unless two identical units were present at the time of initiation the nuclear material could not be equally partitioned between the daughter cells.[7]

Finally, let us consider the old observation that the average number of cytologically distinct nuclei approaches unity as the growth rate goes toward zero. Since two nuclei *must* be present at the time of division, this means that visible separation occurs the later in the division cycle the slower the cells grow. This in turn indicates that the two genomes present throughout the interim between successive r.o.r. stain as one body, and that the nucleus does not divide cytologically until, or shortly after, the onset of replication (see Figure 6–1). Direct observations on synchronized cells (D. J. Clark, to be published) support this deduction, to which reference was made (Section 2–3) when we tried to estimate the quantity of DNA per nucleus.

[7] This reasoning leads to the same general conclusion regarding the average number of genomes per cell as has been advanced by Lark and Lark (1965). As pointed out (see footnote to Section 6–2) their assumption about sequential replication of the two genomes in slow-growing cells may not be valid in all cases; thus, if the data of Figure 6–10 are correctly interpreted it would seem that, in strain B/r of *E. coli*, replication of *both* genomes is initiated more or less simultaneously even during slow growth.

7

THE BACTERIAL NUCLEUS

7–1 THE DISTRIBUTION OF MACROMOLECULES IN THE CELL

As in the last chapter we shall be concerned mainly with DNA. The reason for taking this subject up again is that we now want to discuss specific questions arising because the DNA is packed into a small volume in the bacterial cell where it forms a highly concentrated gel. We believe that the topological problems of the bacterial nucleus are important in themselves, and that it makes sense to try to clarify them even if the ideas that emerge cannot be tested right away.

It was emphasized earlier that the concentrations of the nucleic acids, and of many enzymes, are much higher in the living cell than in the test tubes in which we study the synthesis of DNA, RNA, and protein. There are obvious practical reasons for this; thus, the viscosity alone would make it impossible to work with macroscopic systems having DNA concentrations approaching those of the bacterial nucleus. Figures for the number of cells per g dry weight, and for DNA, RNA, and protein in mg/g, have been given for several growth rates, as have the numbers of ribosomes, etc., per unit DNA (Tables 3–2, and 3–3, respectively). With this information and a cell volume calculated to be approximately $2.5 \times 10^{12}\mu^3$ per g dry weight (see Figure 2–3, and Section 3–5), we can begin to construct a realistic picture of the cell.

The total volumes, derived by dividing $2.5 \times 10^{12}\mu^3$ by the number of cells per g, are $1.9\mu^3$ and about $0.4\mu^3$ for fast- and slow-growing cells (2.4 and 0.2 doublings/hr, respectively). These figures agree well with the direct measurements made by Ecker and Schaechter (1963), which gave mean cell volumes of 1.2 and $0.39\mu^3$ for 2.0 and 0.13 doublings/hr, respectively (see Figure 2–3). The cells are composed of three major parts: (a) an outer "shell" comprising the wall and the cytoplasmic membrane; (b) the nuclear space containing all, or nearly all, the DNA; and (c) the cytoplasm with all the ribosomes and most of the soluble proteins.

Assuming that the outer shell (a) is 100 Å thick, it accounts for about 5% of the total volume in large cells and nearly 10% in small cells. The volume of the nucleus (b) is difficult to estimate accurately. However, the "nuclear vacuoles" seen in living cells with the phase-contrast microscope are very similar in size and position to the nuclei as they appear in reconstruction pictures made from electron micrographs of serial sections (Birch-Andersen, 1955). We therefore assume that estimates of the nuclear volume obtained from such micrographs are valid, and that, in the living cell, the DNA occupies 8–10% of the total volume. We are confident that the true volume is *not* twice as large. In the following the figure of 10% will be used, but critical estimates will also be calculated for a nuclear volume of 20%. Subtracting (a) and (b) we are left with a cytoplasmic volume of 80–85% of the total.

In fast-growing cells a large number of ribosomes are distributed throughout the cytoplasm (see Figure 3–8). The volume of a 70 S particle is about 2×10^6 Å^3, and it is not too different from a sphere with a diameter of 160 Å; at very high growth rates, the total mass of the ribosomes is about equal to that of all the proteins in the cytoplasm, in the wall and in the membrane. If they are distributed evenly, the mean free distance between two 70 S ribosomes is not more than 150–200 Å, i.e., about the same as the diameter of the particles themselves. In slow-growing cells, the packing is much less dense, and the soluble proteins make up a large fraction of the cytoplasmic macromolecules. Among the soluble proteins some very large species can be visualized as spheres with diameters around 100 Å.

It is quite clear from electron micrographs that ribosomes never diffuse into the nuclear region which, in turn, contains most, if not all, the DNA. We thus deal with a two-phase system. This is a remarkable fact and we know nothing about the forces that cause the DNA to condense and form its own "compartment" in the cell without apparently being separated from the cytoplasm by a membrane. However, this makes it possible to calculate the spacing between neighboring segments of the genome if we assume that, in small regions of the nucleus, the long, coiled genome takes the shape of a multistranded cable composed of parallel DNA "molecules." This is actually the orientation observed by Luzzati and Nicolaïeff (1963), who write: ". . . At high concentrations the DNA rods are aligned with their axes parallel and organized in hexagonal arrays, each molecule being separated from the others by the solvent. The molecules are effectively independent, the distance between them depending only on the concentration."

With the nuclei accounting for 10% of the total cell volume, the mean distance between the axes of neighboring DNA duplexes is close to 50 Å and, if they are viewed as cylinders, 22 Å in diameter; this leaves only about 30 Å of free space between them. (If the DNA occupied 20% instead of 10% of the cell volume, these distances would increase to about 70 and 50 Å, respectively.) Figure 7–1 shows an imagined cross section through a region in which the DNA duplexes are cut at right angles to the axis; the regular hexagonal packing used to illustrate the spacing must not be construed to mean that the nucleus is a rigid, crystal-like body. Outside the nucleus two circles indicate the dimensions of a 70 S ribosome and of a spherical protein molecule with molecular weight about 10^6.

It is in a physical system of this description that replication and transcription take place. Two questions should therefore be examined, neither of which applies to dilute *in vitro* systems: (a) are all parts of the genome accessible to transcription at a given instant, and (b) how does a newly synthesized RNA molecule disengage itself from the DNA template?

(a) As has been mentioned, the nuclear region is *not* accessible to ribosomes. Thus, a model like that proposed by Stent (1965), in which a 70 S ribosome is closely associated with the polymerase at the site of transcription, implies that this process can occur only at the interface between nucleus and cytoplasm. In this connection it is significant that the DNA-dependent RNA polymerase appears to be a more or less spherical molecule of the size indicated in Figure 7–1. It seems unlikely that such a large molecule can penetrate freely into the nucleus and we assume that, like the 70 S particle, the polymerase can associate only with DNA strands exposed at the interface. The size and shape of the polymerase as presented here are quoted from

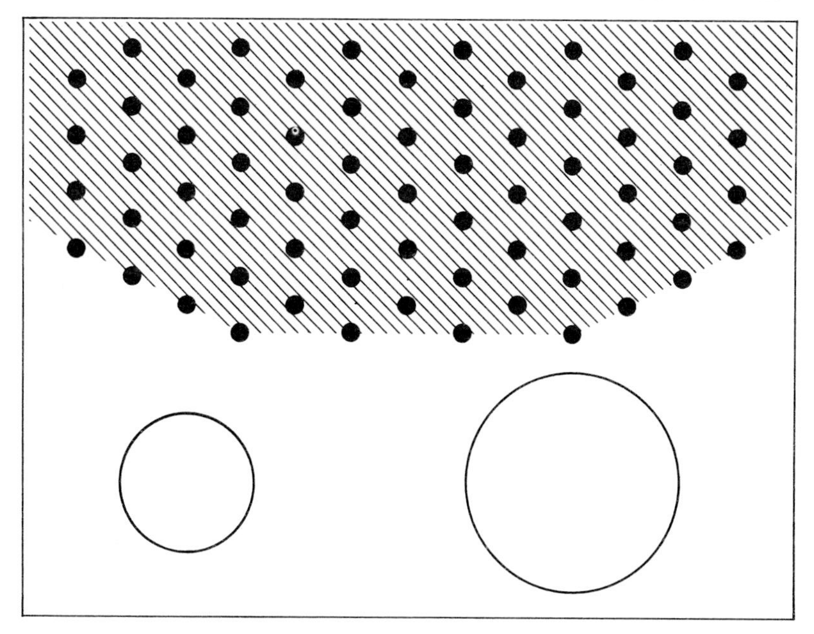

FIGURE 7–1 Spacing of the DNA in the bacterial nucleus. The *upper, hatched portion* of the diagram represents the nuclear area. The *black circles* illustrate cross sections through DNA rods, 22 Å in diameter and arranged in a hexagonal pattern with 50 Å between centers. The *two circles* outside the "nucleus" illustrate the dimensions of a 70 S ribosome (reduced to a sphere with diameter of 160 Å), and a spherical protein 100 Å in diameter.

Fuchs *et al.* (1964); we shall later discuss the suggested structure of this enzyme.

It must be emphasized that the arguments presented here do *not* imply that a large part of the genome is more or less permanently inaccessible to transcription. At a given instant most of the strands in a bundle of, say, 150 are obviously "internal" [1]; however, we visualize the DNA of the nucleus as being in constant thermal motion such that any part of the genome would expose itself at the interface at relatively short intervals (probably seconds). With the synchronization technique described (Section 6–7), Cummings (1965) has actually demonstrated that

[1] The number of duplexes in a bundle can be roughly estimated from the irregularities of the nuclear space, as seen in electron micrographs. In sections through the nucleus it is not rare to see circular areas 500–1000 Å in diameter. If such an area represents a "bundle," it would contain between one and two hundred duplexes, of which 20–30% would form the outer layer.

the lactose operon is accessible to transcription throughout the normal division cycle.

Note that accessibility is not a problem as far as replication is concerned, since this process takes place at a special site, the growing point, through which the whole genome is thought to be threaded.

(b) The unwinding problem involved in replication has been discussed several times. It is easy to see that the two sister strands can be separated by rotating the DNA molecule around its axis, and Levinthal and Crane (1956) have calculated that the energy liberated by the triphosphates in the course of replication might generate the force necessary to spin the entire bacterial genome. Alternatives to this model, involving breaks and reunion of covalent bonds in the DNA backbone, have also been discussed (see Delbrück and Stent, 1957). We believe that the bacterial DNA must spin, not only to unwind the DNA duplex, and rewind the two new ones in the course of replication, but also in order to disengage the RNA molecules constantly being produced by copying various regions of the genome. It is this second problem we particularly want to discuss.

When RNA is synthesized *in vitro* with DNA as template, the reaction proceeds in a dilute and homogeneous system. Thus template and product can diffuse free of each other, and the problem of transferring the RNA from where it is produced to where it is to function does not exist. In addition, two direct observations indicate that the *in vitro* system is incomplete: first, the new RNA chains remain attached to the DNA when synthesis stops, presumably because the complexes between DNA, polymerase, and RNA do not dissociate spontaneously; second, the chains grow very slowly (Bremer and Konrad, 1964).

7–2 DYNAMIC ASPECTS OF THE TRANSCRIPTION PROCESS

We propose a formally simple, mechanical model according to which RNA synthesis takes place at the interface between nucleus and cytoplasm and causes the DNA with which the polymerase is engaged to spin. The way in which this is thought to occur is illustrated in Figure 7–2, which again shows a cross section of a bundle of DNA duplexes. In this graph the individual double strands are presented "in motion," i.e., they are displaced randomly from the positions representing rigid hex-

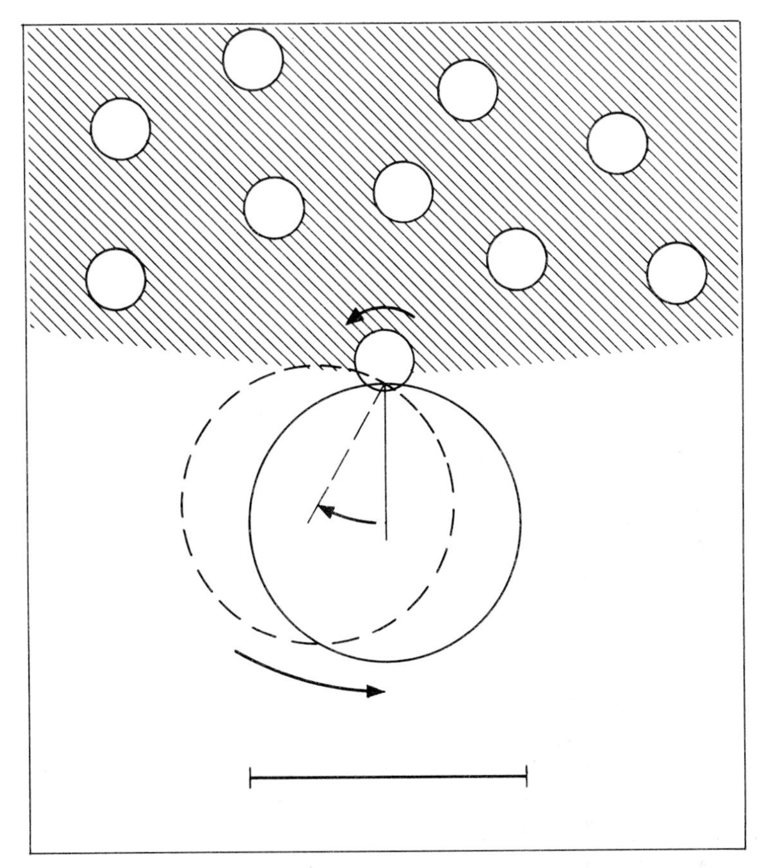

FIGURE 7–2 Interaction between DNA and polymerases at the interface. The diagram shows a section at right angles to the interface between nucleus (*upper, hatched area*) and cytoplasm. The average distance between the centers of the cross-sectional DNA rods is 50 Å, but the rods have been displaced relative to each other to indicate thermal motion. The *large circles* represent a polymerase molecule interacting with two successive sites on a DNA template. To get from position 1 (*the fully drawn circle*) to position 2, the enzyme must turn 36° in the clockwise direction and move 3.4 Å out of the plane of the graph; this is shown by the *middle arrow*. The return movement to "neutral" position is indicated by the *big arrow*, and the concomitant rotation of the template is illustrated by the *top arrow*. The *horizontal bar* at the foot of the diagram indicates 100 Å.

agonal packing, to illustrate the effect of thermal agitation. One interface duplex is shown with a polymerase molecule attached eccentrically. Two positions are indicated, corresponding to successive specific interactions between enzyme and template. In each position a new nucleotide is added to the growing RNA chain as the enzyme "faces" successive bases on the DNA strand that is being transcribed. Between these interactions the enzyme thus has to move 36° over, and 3.4 Å out of the plane of the graph (this is indicated by the smaller arrow). We now assume that the enzyme which cannot cross the interface always tends to be pushed back to a neutral position by the thermal movement of adjacent DNA duplexes (this reverse movement is indicated by the large arrow). In order to impart rotation to the DNA, it is of course necessary to assume that enzyme and template interact firmly and for sufficient time to permit the "ratchet" movement to occur. The required binding energy is thought to be supplied by the triphosphates consumed in the process of RNA synthesis.

This simple model is essentially based on the postulate that the enzyme must engage with successive sites disposed at regular intervals along one of the DNA strands *without penetrating the interface*. With a spinning template, the enzyme would be able to move (actually wriggle) along a line parallel to the axis of the DNA. The RNA chain being synthesized could therefore pass directly into the cytoplasm, and the part of the template that had been transcribed would always be free. On the other hand, if the *enzyme* could move freely relative to the template, the latter might remain stationary; in this case the enzyme would have to trace a spiral around the DNA and the new RNA chain would eventually have to disentangle itself. We shall discuss this possibility later.

The unwinding problems in DNA and in RNA synthesis are analogous, and it might therefore be argued that both would be overcome if the replication process itself generated spin. This solution is not acceptable, however, because mRNA and protein synthesis are known sometimes to proceed for long periods in the absence of DNA synthesis. With the TAU strain it has actually been shown that, after starvation in (+T,−AU)-medium (with succinate as C source) and transfer to (−T,+AU)-medium, the cells can be induced to form β-galactosidase or tryptophanase at high rates (K. V. Rasmussen, unpublished results). Since RNA is always synthesized at many points along the genome of a growing cell, we prefer to think that this is the process which causes the DNA to spin, and that this spin (a) keeps the new RNA chains free of the template, and (b) is utilized, at the appropriate times, to unwind the DNA for replication. Under this view, the speed of rotation would be defined by the physical constants characteristic of the interaction between the polymerase and the DNA template.

In this unifying but very speculative model, replication is coupled mechanically to transcription, and it is therefore implied that DNA and RNA chains would have to grow at the same rate. As regards DNA, we know that a genome with about 3×10^6 base pairs and a single g.p. can be replicated in 2500–3000 seconds, i.e., that the process covers about 100 full turns of the double helix per second at 37°. It would thus be predicted that an RNA chain would grow at a rate of about 1000 nucleotides per second. The actual rate is unknown and very difficult to measure. However, a rough estimate can be derived from the fact that, in rapidly growing cells, about 10 ribosomes are produced per genome and per second. This indicates that 5–10 copies must be drawn per second from the DNA site specifying, say, the 23 S RNA (cf. Section 3–5). Thus, in 0.1–0.2 second a polymerase molecule must displace itself sufficiently along the template to make room for a new one. At the predicated rate of synthesis the displacement would be 300–400 Å in 0.1 second, which seems quite adequate. Rates corresponding to a displacement of less than about 100 Å would be difficult to accept.

At this point we shall also consider the rate of *translation*. Unfortunately, the number of amino acids added to a growing polypeptide chain per second is not precisely known, and existing estimates range from a fairly well-defined minimum of 15–20 to figures as high as 50–75 (see Section 3–5). The corresponding number of nucleotides on the mRNA is of the order of 100. The rate of translation is thus about 10 times lower than the rate of replication, which in turn may be equal to the rate of transcription. If this proves to be correct, transcription and translation could not be coupled in the way envisaged by Stent (1965).

Up to now, it has been assumed that the genome behaves as a single double-stranded DNA molecule. However, it is by no means excluded that points exist along the genome (e.g., single-strand breaks) at which free rotation is permitted. The DNA segment between two such points, of course, would be independent of the rest of the genome as far as rotation is concerned.

This possibility is emphasized because it has been suggested that closely related Hfr strains *replicate their DNA in opposite directions.*

Experiments by Nagata (1963) and W. Vielmetter (personal communication) seem to support this notion, as does the fact that the transfer of genetic material to an F^- cell can occur in both directions. Furthermore, genetic studies suggest that the leucine and tryptophane operons in *S. typhimurium* may be transcribed in opposite directions (Margolin, 1965).

As we have presented the situation, replication *as well as* transcription requires that the DNA spins, and since only one of the two sister strands serves as template it is clear that the *direction* of the spin is important. If cases exist in which replication and transcription require spin in opposite directions, it would be necessary to assume that different DNA segments can rotate independently of each other. Esthetically, this model is not attractive.

Finally, we shall examine the possibility that all problems connected with replication are solved at or near the g.p. (e.g., by spinning and unwinding successive, short DNA segments, or by breaking and reforming bonds), and that the rest of the genome does not spin. In this situation, transcription would require that the polymerase moved around the DNA template and, since we do not believe that a protein molecule about 100 Å in diameter can do so inside the nucleus, two alternatives have been envisaged: first, that a DNA duplex loops out into the cytoplasm to allow the polymerase to interact with it on all sides; second, that the enzyme actually forms a ring, or short cylinder, *around* the DNA molecule. This latter possibility is suggested by the electron micrographs of Fuchs *et al.* (1964), according to which the enzyme may consist of 5 or 6 rod-like subunits arranged symmetrically around a central hole.

In both cases the RNA chain produced in the act of transcription would, initially, be added as a third strand, parallel to those of the DNA double helix. Since many RNA molecules contain several thousand nucleotides, corresponding to as many hundred turns around the template, the unwinding problem is not trivial. To disentangle an RNA chain, say, 10,000 Å long and to transfer it to the cytoplasm by simple diffusion probably would take a very long time, because the chain would diffuse into a space traversed by a large number of parallel DNA duplexes. Furthermore, the time it would take to clear a template for a new act of transcription would be expected to vary enormously.

It has been suggested that the free end of a growing mRNA molecule might engage with a ribosome and that the rest of the messenger might be "pulled" away from the template as translation proceeds. This is conceivable, but a mechanism of this kind would be very inefficient from the point of view of clearing the template. First, the RNA chain would have to be finished before it would be free to be pulled away from the DNA; second, with a pull exerted near the end of the template at which transcription begins, the entire messenger would have to be released before the synthesis of a new one could begin. (If the rate of translation is of the order of 100 nucleotides per second, it might thus take about 1 minute to release a long mRNA molecule.)

The discussion in this chapter has been less "serious" than in earlier ones, in the sense that no critical experiments have come up for examination. Still, we hope to have achieved two things: first, to demonstrate the great difference between the physical conditions in the living cell and those under which transcription and translation are being studied *in vitro;* second, to show that the interface between nucleus and cytoplasm has some of the properties of a surface, or membrane, to which specific proteins can attach, and that it may be the site of a novel type of mechanical interaction between macromolecules.

REFERENCES[1]

Acs, G., Reich, E., and Valanju, S. (1963), "RNA metabolism of *B. subtilis.* Effects of actinomycin." *Biochim. Biophys. Acta,* **76,** 68. (5–1)

Adler, J., and Kaiser, A. D. (1963), "Mapping of the galactose genes in *E. coli* by transduction with phage Pl." *Virology,* **19,** 117. (1–8)

Alföldi, L., Stent, G. S., and Clowes, R. C. (1962), "The chromosomal site of the RNA control (RC) locus in *E. coli.*" *J. Mol. Biol.,* **5,** 348. (5–2)

Alföldi, L., Stent, G. S., Hoogs, M., and Hill, R. (1963), "Physiological effects of the RNA control (RC) gene in *E. coli.*" *Z. Vererbungslehre,* **94,** 285. (5–2)

Allen, D. W., and Zamecnik, P. C. (1962), "The effect of puromycin on rabbit reticulocyte ribosomes." *Biochim. Biophys. Acta,* **55,** 865. (1–5, 1–7)

Ames, B. N., and Garry, B. (1959), "Coordinate repression of the synthesis of four histidine biosynthetic enzymes by histidine." *Proc. Natl. Acad. Sci. U.S.,* **45,** 1453. (1–8)

Ames, B. N., Garry, B., and Herzenberg, L. A. (1960), "The genetic control of the enzymes of histidine biosynthesis in *Salmonella typhimurium.*" *J. Gen. Microbiol.,* **22,** 369. (1–8)

Ames, B. N., and Hartman, P. E. (1962), "Genes, enzymes, and control mechanisms in histidine biosynthesis," in "The Molecular Basis of Neoplasia," Texas University Press, Austin, p. 322. (1–8)

Ames, B. N., and Hartman, P. E. (1963), "The histidine operon." *Cold Spring Harbor Symp. Quant. Biol.,* **28,** 349. (1–8, 1–9)

Ames, B. N., Hartman, P. E., and Jacob, F. (1963), "Chromosomal alterations affecting the regulation of histidine biosynthetic enzymes in *Salmonella.*" *J. Mol. Biol.,* **7,** 23. (1–8)

Ames, B. N., Martin, R. G., and Garry, B. J. (1961), "The first step of histidine biosynthesis." *J. Biol. Chem.,* **236,** 2019. (1–8)

Anfinsen, C. B., Haber, E., Sela, M., and White, F. H. (1961), "The kinetics of formation of native ribonuclease during oxidation of the reduced polypeptide chain." *Proc. Natl. Acad. Sci. U.S.,* **47,** 1309. (1–7)

Aposhian, H. V., and Kornberg, A. (1962), "Enzymatic synthesis of DNA, IX. The polymerase formed after T2 bacteriophage infection of *Escherichia coli.* A new enzyme." *J. Biol. Chem.,* **237,** 519. (1–2)

Appel, S. H., Alpers, D. H., and Tomkins, G. M. (1965), "Multiple molecular forms of β-galactosidase." *J. Mol. Biol.,* **11,** 12. (3–5)

Aronson, A. I., and Spiegelman, S. (1961a), "Protein and ribonucleic acid synthesis in a chloramphenicol-inhibited system." *Biochim. Biophys. Acta,* **53,** 70. (5–2)

[1] Each reference is followed by indications, in parentheses, of the relevant sections in the text.

Aronson, A. I., and Spiegelman, S. (1961b), "On the nature of the ribonucleic acid synthesized in the presence of chloramphenicol." *Biochim. Biophys. Acta,* **53,** 84. (1–3)

Astrachan, L., and Fischer, T. N. (1961), "Resemblance of bacterial RNA and DNA." *Federation. Proc.,* **20,** 359. (1–5)

Astrachan, L., and Volkin, E. (1958), "Properties of ribonucleic acid turnover in T2 infected *Escherichia coli.*" *Biochim. Biophys. Acta,* **29,** 536. (1–5)

Attardi, G., Naono, S., Gros, F., Buttin, G., and Jacob, F. (1963a), "Régulation de la transcription DNA-RNA messager intervenant dans la biosynthèse d'enzymes bactériens et l'expression des fonctions virales du phage." *Compt. Rend.,* **256,** 805. (1–8)

Attardi, G., Naono, S., Rouvière, I., Jacob, F., and Gros, F. (1963b), "Production of messenger RNA and regulation of protein synthesis." *Cold Spring Harbor Symp. Quant. Biol.,* **28,** 363. (1–5, 1–8, 1–9)

August, J. T., Ortiz, P. J., and Hurwitz, J. (1962), "Ribonucleic acid-dependent ribonucleotide incorporation." *J. Biol. Chem.,* **237,** 3786. (1–3)

Avery, O. T., MacLeod, C. M., and McCarty, M. (1944), "Studies on the chemical nature of the substance inducing transformation of pneumococcal types." *J. Exptl. Med.,* **79,** 137. (1–2)

Barondes, S. H., and Nirenberg, M. W. (1962), "Fate of a synthetic polynucleotide directing cell-free protein synthesis. II. Association with ribosomes." *Science,* **138,** 813. (1–7)

Bautz, E. K. F. (1962), "The role of phage specific RNA as messenger." *Biochem. Biophys. Res. Commun.,* **9,** 192. (5–4)

Bautz, E. K. F. (1963a), "Purification and properties of messenger RNA from bacteriophage T4," in "Informational Macromolecules," eds. Vogel, H. J., Bryson, V., and Lampen, J. O., Academic Press, New York, p. 409. (1–5)

Bautz, E. K. F. (1963b), "The structure of T4 messenger RNA in relation to messenger function." *Cold Spring Harbor Symp. Quant. Biol.,* **28,** 205. (1–5)

Bautz, E. K. F. (1963c), "Physical properties of messenger RNA of bacteriophage T4." *Proc. Natl. Acad. Sci. U.S.,* **49,** 68. (1–5)

Beckwith, J. R. (1963), "Restoration of operon activity by suppressors." *Biochim. Biophys. Acta,* **76,** 162. (1–8)

Beckwith, J. R. (1964), "A deletion analysis of the Lac operator region in *E. coli.*" *J. Mol. Biol.,* **8,** 427. (1–8)

Beckwith, J. R., Pardee, A. B., Austrian, B., and Jacob, F. (1962), "Coordination of the synthesis of the enzymes in the pyrimidine pathway of *E. Coli.*" *J. Mol. Biol.,* **5,** 618. (1–8)

Belozersky, A. N., and Spirin, A. S. (1958), "A correlation between the composition of deoxyribonucleic and ribonucleic acid." *Nature,* **182,** 111. (1–2)

Benzer, S. (1961), "On the topography of the genetic fine structure." *Proc. Natl. Acad. Sci. U.S.,* **47,** 403. (1–6)

Benzer, S., and Champe, S. P. (1961), "Ambivalent rII mutants of phage T4." *Proc. Natl. Acad. Sci. U.S.,* **47,** 1025. (1–9)

Bergmann, F. H., Berg, P., and Dieckmann, M. (1961), "The enzymic synthesis of amino acyl derivatives of ribonucleic acid. II. The preparation of leucyl-, valyl-, isoleucyl- and methionyl ribonucleic acid synthetases from *Escherichia coli.*" *J. Biol. Chem.,* **236,** 1735. (1–4)

Bessman, M. J., Lehman, I. R., Simms, E. S., and Kornberg, A. (1958), "Enzymatic synthesis of deoxyribonucleic acid. II. General properties of the reaction." *J. Biol. Chem.,* **233,** 171. (1–2)

Billen, D. (1959), "Alterations in the radiosensitivity of *Escherichia coli* through modification of cellular macromolecular components." *Biochim. Biophys. Acta,* **34**, 110. (6–4)

Birch-Andersen, A. (1955), "Reconstruction of the nuclear sites of *Salmonella typhimurium* from electron micrographs of serial section." *J. Gen. Microbiol.,* **13**, 327. (2–3, 7–1)

Bishop, J., Leahy, I., and Schweet, R. (1960), "Formation of the peptide chain of hemoglobin." *Proc. Natl. Acad. Sci. U.S.,* **46**, 1030. (1–5)

Boezi, J. A., and Cowie, D. B. (1961), "Kinetic studies of β-galactosidase induction." *Biophys. J.,* **1**, 639. (1–8)

Bolton, E. T., Britten, R. J., Cowie, D. B., McCarthy, B. J., McQuillen, K., and Roberts, R. B. (1959), in *Carnegie Inst. Yr. Bk.,* 58, p. 259. (1–3)

Bolton, E. T., and McCarthy, B. (1962), "A general method for the isolation of RNA complementary to DNA." *Proc. Natl. Acad. Sci. U.S.,* **48**, 1390. (1–5)

Boman, H. G., Boman, I. A., and Maas, W. K. (1961), "Studies on the incorporation of arginine into acceptor RNA of *Escherichia coli,*" in "Biological Structure and Function," eds. Goodwin, T. W., and Lindberg, O., Academic Press, New York, Vol. I, p. 297. (1–8)

Bonhoeffer, F., and Gierer, A. (1963), "On the growth mechanism of the bacterial chromosome." *J. Mol. Biol.,* **7**, 534. (1–2)

Borek, E., and Ryan, A. (1958), "Studies on a mutant of *Escherichia coli* with unbalanced ribonucleic acid synthesis." *J. Bacteriol.,* **75**, 72. (5–2)

Brachet, J. (1942), "La localisation des acides pentose-nucléiques dans les tissus animaux et les œufs d'amphibiens en voie de développement." *Arch. Biol. (Liège),* **53**, 207. (3–2)

Brawerman, G., and Yčas, M. (1957), "Incorporation of the amino acid analog tryptazan into the protein of *Escherichia coli.*" *Arch. Biochem. Biophys.,* **68**, 112. (5–2)

Breitman, T. R., and Bradford, R. M. (1964), "The induction of thymidine phosphorylase and excretion of deoxyribose during thymine starvation." *Biochem. Biophys. Res. Commun.,* **17**, 786. (6–5)

Bremer, H., and Konrad, M. W. (1964), "A complex of enzymatically synthesized RNA and template DNA." *Proc. Natl. Acad. Sci. U.S.,* **51**, 807. (5–3, 7–1)

Brenner, S., Jacob, F., and Meselson, M. (1961), "An unstable intermediate carrying information from genes to ribosomes for protein synthesis." *Nature,* **190**, 576. (1–3, 1–5)

Brenner, S., Stretton, A. O. W., and Kaplan, S. (1965), "Genetic code: The 'nonsense' triplets for chain termination and their suppression." *Nature,* **206**, 994. (1–9)

Britten, R. J., and McClure, F. T. (1962), "The amino acid pool in *E. coli.*" *Bacteriol. Rev.,* **26**, 292. (4–3)

Britten, R. J., and Roberts, R. B. (1960), "High-resolution density gradient sedimentation analysis." *Science,* **131**, 32. (1–5)

Brown, D. D. (1961), in *Cold Spring Harbor Symp. Quant. Biol.,* **26**, 254. (1–9)

Burstein, C., Cohn, M., Képès, A., and Monod, J. (1965), "Rôle du lactose et ses produits métaboliques dans l'induction de l'opéron lactose chez *Escherichia coli.*" *Biochim. Biophys. Acta,* **95**, 634. (1–8)

Buttin, G. (1961), "Some aspects of regulation in the synthesis of the enzymes governing galactose metabolism." *Cold Spring Harbor Symp. Quant. Biol.,* **26**, 213. (1–8, 1–9)

Buttin, G. (1963), "Répression et dérépression de la biosynthèse des enzymes du métabolisme du galactose chez *Escherichia coli* K 12." *Colloq. Intern. Centre Natl. Rech. Sci. (Paris),* No. 124, 185. (1–8)

Cairns, J. (1963), "The bacterial chromosome and its manner of replication as seen by autoradiography." *J. Mol. Biol.*, **6**, 208. (1–2, 2–3, 6–1)

Campbell, A. (1957), "Synchronization of cell division." *Bacteriol. Rev.*, **21**, 263. (2–3)

Canon, M., Krug, R., and Gilbert, W. (1963), "The binding of s-RNA by *Escherichia coli* ribosomes." *J. Mol. Biol.*, **7**, 360. (1–7)

Cantoni, G. L., Ishikura, H., Richards, H. H., and Tanaka, K. (1963), "Studies on soluble ribonucleic acid. XI. A model for the base sequence of serine s-RNA." *Cold Spring Harbor Symp. Quant. Biol.*, **28**, 123. (1–4)

Caspersson, T. O. (1950), "Cell Growth and Cell Function. A Cytochemical Study," W. W. Norton, New York. (3–2)

Chamberlin, M., and Berg, P. (1962), "Deoxyribonucleic acid directed synthesis of ribonucleic acid by an enzyme from *Escherichia coli.*" *Proc. Natl. Acad. Sci. U.S.*, **48**, 81. (1–6, 5–1)

Champe, S. P., and Benzer, S. (1962), "Reversal of mutant phenotypes by 5-fluorouracil: an approach to nucleotide sequences in messenger-RNA. "*Proc. Natl. Acad. Sci. U.S.*, **48**, 532. (1–6, 5–4)

Changeux, J.-P. (1963), "Allosteric interaction on biosynthetic l-threonine deaminase from *E. coli* K12." *Cold Spring Harbor Symp. Quant. Biol.*, **28**, 497. (1–8)

Chapeville, F., Lipmann, F., von Ehrenstein, G., Weisblum, B., Ray, W. J., Jr., and Benzer, S. (1962), "On the role of soluble ribonucleic acid in coding for amino acids." *Proc. Natl. Acad. Sci. U.S.*, **48**, 1086. (1–4)

Chargaff, E. (1955), "Isolation and composition of the deoxypentose nucleic acid and of the corresponding nucleoproteins," in "The Nucleic Acids," eds. Chargaff, E., and Davidson, J. N., Academic Press, New York, Vol. I, p. 307. (1–2)

Chun, E. H. L., and Littlefield, J. W. (1961), "The separation of the light and heavy strands of bromouracil-substituted mammalian DNA." *J. Mol. Biol.*, **3**, 668. (1–2)

Clark, D. J. (1965), "Unstable inducer-specific repressor for β-galactosidase in *Escherichia coli.*" In preparation. (5–1)

Clark, D. J., and Marr, A. G. (1964), "Studies on the repression of β-galactosidase in *Escherichia coli.*" *Biochim. Biophys. Acta*, **92**, 85. (1–9)

Cohen, G. N., and Munier, R. (1959), "Effets des analogues structuraux d'amino-acides sur la croissance, la synthèse de protéines et la synthèse d'enzymes chez *E. coli.*" *Biochim. Biophys. Acta*, **31**, 347. (5–2)

Cohen, G. N., and Patte, J. C. (1963), "Some aspects of the regulation of amino acid biosynthesis in a branched pathway." *Cold Spring Harbor Symp. Quant. Biol.*, **28**, 513. (1–8)

Cohen, S. S. (1948), "The synthesis of bacterial viruses. I. The synthesis of nucleic acid and protein in *E. coli* B infected with $T2r^+$ bacteriophages." *J. Biol. Chem.*, **174**, 281. (1–3, 1–5)

Cohen, S. S., and Barner, H. D. (1954), "Studies on unbalanced growth in *Escherichia coli.*" *Proc. Natl. Acad. Sci. U.S.*, **40**, 885. (6–4, 6–5)

Cohen, S. S., and Lichtenstein, J. (1960), "Polyamines and ribosome structure." *J. Biol. Chem.*, **235**, 2112. (1–3)

Cohn, M. (1957), "Contributions of studies on the β-galactosidase of *Escherichia coli* to our understanding of enzyme synthesis." *Bacteriol. Rev.*, **21**, 140. (1–8)

Cohn, M., Cohen, G. N., and Monod, J. (1953), "L'effet inhibiteur spécifique de la méthionine dans la formation de la méthionine-synthétase chez *Escherichia coli.*" *Compt. Rend.*, **236**, 746. (1–8)

Cohn, M., and Horibata, K. (1959a), "Inhibition by glucose of the induced synthesis of the β-galactoside-enzyme system of *Escherichia coli*. Analysis of maintenance." *J. Bacteriol.*, **78**, 601. (1–9)

Cohn, M., and Horibata, K. (1959b), "Physiology of the inhibition by glucose of the induced synthesis of the β-galactoside-enzyme system of *Escherichia coli*." *J. Bacteriol.*, **78**, 624. (1–9)

Cowie, D. B., Spiegelman, S., Roberts, R. B., and Duerksen, J. D. (1961), "Ribosome-bound β-galactosidase." *Proc. Natl. Acad. Sci. U.S.*, **47**, 114. (1–3)

Craven, G. R., Steers, E., and Anfinsen, C. (1965), "Purification, composition and molecular weight of the β-galactosidase of *Escherichia coli* K12." *J. Biol. Chem.*, **240**, 2468. (1–8)

Crick, F. H. C. (1958), "On protein synthesis." *Symp. Soc. Exp. Biol.*, **12**, 138. (1–1, 1–4, 1–7)

Crick, F. H. C., Barnett, L., Brenner, S., and Watts-Tobin, R. J. (1961), "The general nature of the genetic code for proteins." *Nature*, **192**, 1227. (1–2)

Cummings, D. J. (1965), "Macromolecular synthesis during synchronous growth of *Escherichia coli* B/r." *Biochim. Biophys. Acta*, **85**, 341. (7–1)

Dagley, S., Turnock, C., and Wild, D. G. (1963), "The accumulation of ribonucleic acid by a mutant of *E. coli*." *Biochem. J.*, **88**, 555. (1–3)

Dagley, S., White, A. E., Wild, D. G., and Sykes, J. (1962), "Synthesis of protein and ribosomes by bacteria." *Nature*, **194**, 25. (1–3)

Davern, C. I., and Meselson, M. (1960), "The molecular conservation of ribonucleic acid during bacterial growth." *J. Mol. Biol.*, **2**, 153. (1–3)

Davies, J., Gilbert, W., and Gorini, L. (1964), "Streptomycin, suppression and the code." *Proc. Natl. Acad. Sci. U.S.*, **51**, 883. (1–7)

Delbrück, M., and Stent, G. S. (1957), "On the mechanism of DNA replication," in "The Chemical Basis of Heredity," eds. McElroy, W. D., and Glass, B., Johns Hopkins Press, Baltimore, p. 699. (7–1)

De Voe, H., and Tinoco, I. (1962), "The stability of helical polynucleotides: base contributions." *J. Mol. Biol.*, **4**, 500. (1–2)

Dintzis, H. M. (1961), "Assembly of the peptide chains of hemoglobin." *Proc. Natl. Acad. Sci. U.S.*, **47**, 247. (1–5)

Dintzis, H. M., and Knopf, P. M. (1963), "Cell-free synthesis of hemoglobin," in "Informational Macromolecules," eds. Vogel, H. J., Bryson, V., and Lampen, J. O., Academic Press, New York, p. 375. (1–7)

Djordjevic, B., and Szybalski, W. (1960), "Genetics of human cell lines. III. Incorporation of 5-bromo- and 5-iododeoxyuridine into the DNA of human cells and its effects on radiation sensitivity." *J. Exptl. Med.*, **112**, 509. (1–2)

Doerfler, W., Zillig, W., Fuchs, E., and Albers, M. (1962), "Untersuchungen zur Biosynthese der Proteine. V. Die Funktion von Nucleinsäuren beim Einbau von Aminosäuren in Proteine in einem zellfreien System aus *Escherichia coli*." *Z. Physiol. Chem.*, **330**, 96. (1–6)

Dubin, D. T. (1964), "Some effects of streptomycin on RNA metabolism in *E. coli*." *J. Mol. Biol.*, **8**, 749. (1–3)

Duerksen, J. D., and O'Connor, M. L. (1963), "The demonstration of ribosome-bound penicillinase in *Bacillus cereus*." *Biochem. Biophys. Res. Commun.* **10**, 34. (1–3)

Dunn, D. B., Smith, J. D., and Spahr, P. F. (1960), "Nucleotide composition of soluble ribonucleic acid from *Escherichia coli*." *J. Mol. Biol.*, **2**, 113. (1–4)

Echols, H., Garen, A., Garen, S., and Torriani, A. (1961), "Genetic control of repression of alkaline phosphatase in *E. coli*." *J. Mol. Biol.*, **3**, 425. (1–8, 1–9)

Ecker, R. E., and Schaechter, M. (1963), "Bacterial growth under conditions of limited nutrition." *Ann. N.Y. Acad. Sci.*, **102**, 549. (2–3, 3–3, 3–5, 7–1)

von Ehrenstein, G., Weisblum, B., and Benzer, S. (1963), "The function of s-RNA as amino adapter in the synthesis of hemoglobin." *Proc. Natl. Acad. Sci. U.S.*, **49**, 669. (1–4)

Elson, D. (1958), "Latent ribonuclease activity in a ribonucleoprotein." *Biochim. Biophys. Acta*, **27**, 216. (1–3)

Elson, D. (1959a), "Preparation and properties of a ribonucleoprotein isolated from *Escherichia coli.*" *Biochim. Biophys. Acta*, **36**, 362. (1–3)

Elson, D. (1959b), "Latent enzymic activity of a ribonucleoprotein isolated from *Escherichia coli.*" *Biochim. Biophys. Acta*, **36**, 372. (1–3)

Englesberg, E. (1961), "Enzymatic characterization of 17 L-arabinose negative mutants of *E. coli.*" *J. Bacteriol.*, **81**, 996. (1–8)

Epstein, C. J., Goldberger, R. F., and Anfinsen, C. B. (1963), "The genetic control of tertiary protein structure: studies with model systems." *Cold Spring Harbor Symp. Quant. Biol.*, **28**, 439. (1–7)

Falkow, S., Rownd, R., and Baron, L. S. (1962), "Genetic homology between *Escherichia coli* K–12 and *Salmonella.*" *J. Bacteriol.*, **84**, 1303. (2–3)

Fan, D., Higa, A., and Levinthal, C. (1964), "Messenger RNA decay and protection." *J. Mol. Biol.*, **8**, 210. (1–5, 5–4)

Fangman, W. L., and Neidhardt, F. C. (1964a), "Demonstration of an altered aminoacyl ribonucleic acid synthetase in a mutant of *E. coli.*" *J. Biol. Chem.*, **239**, 1839. (5–2)

Fangman, W. L., and Neidhardt, F. C. (1964b), "Protein and ribonucleic acid synthesis in a mutant of *E. coli* with an altered aminoacyl ribonucleic acid synthetase." *J. Biol. Chem.*, **239**, 1844. (5–2)

Feldman, H., and Zachau, H. G. (1964), "Chemical evidence for the 3′-linkage of amino acids to s-RNA." *Biochem. Biophys. Res. Commun.*, **15**, 13. (1–4)

Fessenden, J. M., and Moldave, K. (1961), "Evidence for two protein factors in the transfer of amino acids from soluble-RNA to ribonucleoprotein particles." *Biochem. Biophys. Res. Commun.*, **6**, 232. (1–7)

Flaks, J. G., and Cohen, S. S. (1959), "Virus-induced acquisition of metabolic function. I. Enzymatic formation of 5-hydroxy-methyldeoxycytidylate." *J. Biol. Chem.*, **234**, 1501. (1–2)

Fleissner, E., and Borek, E. (1962), "A new enzyme of RNA synthesis: RNA-methylase." *Proc. Natl. Acad. Sci. U.S.*, **48**, 1199. (1–4)

Forchhammer, J., Kjeldgaard, N. O., and Moldave, K. (1965), "The relative amount and *in vivo* decay of messenger RNA under growth shifts in *E. coli* "TAU-bar'." *FEBS Abstracts*, Vienna, 1965, 288. (3–3, 5–4)

Fraenkel, D. G. (1961), "The control of ribonucleic acid synthesis in *Aerobacter aerogenes.* Ph.D. Thesis, Harvard University, Cambridge, Massachusetts, (3–4)

Fraenkel, D. G., and Neidhardt, F. C. (1961), "Use of chloramphenicol to study control of RNA synthesis in bacteria." *Biochim. Biophys. Acta*, **53**, 96. (4–2, 5–2)

Freese, E. (1959a), "The specific mutagenic effect of base analogues on phage T4." *J. Mol. Biol.*, **1**, 87. (1–2)

Freese, E. (1959b), "The difference between spontaneous and base-analogue induced mutations of phage T4." *Proc. Natl. Acad. Sci. U.S.*, **45**, 622. (1–2)

Freifelder, D. M., and Davison, P. F. (1963), "Physiochemical studies on the reaction between formaldehyde and DNA." *Biophys. J.*, **3**, 49. (6–5)

Freifelder, D., and Maaløe, O. (1964), "Energy requirement for thymineless death in cells of *Escherichia coli.*" *J. Bacteriol.*, **88**, 987. (6–5)

Friesen, J. D. (1965), "Control of bacteriophage RNA synthesis in *Escherichia coli.*" *J. Mol. Biol.*, **13**, 220. (5–2)

Friesen, J. D., and Maaløe, O. (1965), "On the control of deoxyribonucleic acid synthesis by amino acids in *Escherichia coli.*" *Biochim. Biophys. Acta*, **95**, 436. (6–4)

Fuchs, E., Zillig, W., Hofschneider, P. H., and Preuss, A. (1964), "Preparation and properties of RNA-polymerase-particles." *J. Mol. Biol.*, **10**, 546. (1–6, 7–1, 7–2)

Furth, J. J., Hurwitz, J., and Goldman, M. (1961), "The directing role of DNA in RNA synthesis." *Biochem. Biophys. Res. Commun.*, **4**, 362. (1–6)

Garen, A., and Garen, S. (1963), "Genetic evidence on the nature of the repressor for alkaline phosphatase in *E. coli.*" *J. Mol. Biol.*, **6**, 433. (1–9)

Garen, A., and Otsuji, N. (1964), "Isolation of a protein specified by a regulator gene." *J. Mol. Biol.*, **8**, 841. (1–9)

Garen, A., and Siddiqi, O. (1962), "Suppression of mutations in the alkaline phosphatase structural cistron of *E. coli.*" *Proc. Natl. Acad. Sci. U.S.*, **48**, 1121. (1–9, 5–4)

Geiduschek, E. P., Nakamoto, T., and Weiss, S. B. (1961), "The enzymatic synthesis of RNA: complementary interaction with DNA." *Proc. Natl. Acad. Sci. U.S.*, **47**, 1405. (5–1)

Gerhart, J. C., and Pardee, A. B. (1963), "The effect of the feed-back inhibitor, CTP, on subunit interaction in aspartate transcarbamylase." *Cold Spring Harbor Symp. Quant. Biol.*, **28**, 491. (1–8)

Giacomoni, D., and Spiegelman, S. (1962), "Origin and biologic individuality of the genetic dictionary." *Science*, **138**, 1328. (1–6)

Gierer, A. (1963), "Function of aggregated reticulocyte ribosomes in protein synthesis." *J. Mol. Biol.*, **6**, 148. (1–5, 1–7)

Gilbert, W. (1963a), "Polypeptide synthesis in *E. coli*. I. Ribosomes and the active complex." *J. Mol. Biol.*, **6**, 374. (1–7)

Gilbert, W. (1963b), "Polypeptide synthesis in *E. coli*. II. The polypeptide chain and s-RNA." *J. Mol. Biol.*, **6**, 389. (1–5, 1–7)

Gold, M., and Hurwitz, J. (1963). "The enzymatic methylation of the nucleic acids." *Cold Spring Harbor Symp. Quant. Biol.*, **28**, 149. (1–4)

Goldberg, I. H., and Rabinowitz, M. (1962), "Actinomycin D inhibition of deoxyribonucleic acid-dependent synthesis of ribonucleic acid." *Science*, **136**, 315. (1–6)

Goldberg, I. H., Rabinowitz, M., and Reich, E. (1962), "Basis of actinomycin action. I. DNA binding and inhibition of RNA-polymerase synthetic reaction by actinomycin." *Proc. Natl. Acad. Sci. U.S.*, **48**, 2094. (1–6)

Goldberger, R. F., Epstein, C. J., and Anfinsen, C. B. (1963), "Acceleration of a reactivation of reduced bovine pancreatic ribonuclease by a microsomal system from rat liver." *J. Biol. Chem.*, **238**, 628. (1–7)

Goldberger, R. F., Epstein, C. J., and Anfinsen, C. B. (1964), "Purification and properties of a microsomal enzyme system catalyzing the reactivation of reduced ribonuclease." *J. Biol. Chem.*, **239**, 1406. (1–7)

Goldstein, A., and Brown, B. J. (1961), "Addition of amino acid to C-terminal ends of growing protein chains in *Escherichia coli.*" *Biochim. Biophys. Acta*, **53**, 438. (1–5, 1–7)

Goldstein, A., Goldstein, D. B., and Lowney, L. I. (1964), "Protein synthesis at 0° in *E. coli.*" *J. Mol. Biol.*, **9**, 213. (1–7, 3–5)

Goldstein, J., Bennett, T. P., and Craig, C. L. (1964), "Countercurrent distribution studies of *E. coli* B s-RNA." *Proc. Natl. Acad. Sci. U.S.*, **51**, 119. (1–4)

Goodman, H. M., and Rich, A. (1963), "The mechanism of polyribosome action during protein synthesis." *Nature*, **199**, 318. (1–6, 1–7)

Gorini, L., Gundersen, V., and Burger, M. (1961), "Genetics of regulation of enzyme synthesis in the arginine biosynthetic pathway of *Escherichia coli.*" *Cold Spring Harbor Symp. Quant. Biol.*, **26**, 173. (1–8)

Gorini, L., and Kalman, S. M. (1963), "Control by uracil of carbamyl phosphate synthesis in *E. coli.*" *Biochim. Biophys. Acta*, **69**, 355. (1–8)

Gorini, L., and Kataja, E. (1964), "Phenotypic repair by streptomycin of defective genotypes in *E. coli.*" *Proc. Natl. Acad. Sci. U.S.*, **51**, 487. (1–7)

Gorini, L., and Maas, W. K. (1957), "The potential for the formation of a biosynthetic enzyme in *Escherichia coli.*" *Biochim. Biophys. Acta*, **25**, 208. (1–8, 2–2)

Gros, F., and Gros, F. (1958), "Rôle des acides amines dans la synthèse des acides nucléiques chez *E. coli.*" *Exptl. Cell Res.*, **14**, 104. (5–2)

Gros, F., Gilbert, W., Hiatt, H. H., Attardi, G., Spahr, P. F., and Watson, J. D. (1961a), "Molecular and biological characterization of messenger RNA." *Cold Spring Harbor Symp. Quant. Biol.*, **26**, 111. (1–5)

Gros, F., Hiatt, H., Gilbert, W., Kurland, C. G., Risebrough, R. W., and Watson, J. D. (1961b), "Unstable ribonucleic acid revealed by pulse labelling of *Escherichia coli.*" *Nature*, **190**, 581. (1–5)

Gros, F., Dubert, J. M., Tissières, A., Bourgeois, S., Michelson, M., Soffer, R., and Legault, L. (1963a), "Regulation of metabolic breakdown and synthesis of messenger RNA in bacteria." *Cold Spring Harbor Symp. Quant. Biol.*, **28**, 299. (5–4)

Gros, F., Naono, S., Woese, C., Willson, C., and Attardi, G. (1963b), "Studies on the general properties of *E. coli* messenger RNA," in "Informational Macromolecules," eds. Vogel, H. J., Bryson, V., and Lampen, O. J., Academic Press, New York, p. 387. (1–5)

Gros, F., Naono, S., Rouvière, J., Legault, L., and Nierlich, D. (1965), "Control of messenger RNA synthesis at the DNA or ribosomes level." *FEBS Abstracts*, Vienna, 1965, 268. (5–3, 5–4)

Hall, B. D., and Doty, P. (1959), "The preparation and physical chemical properties of ribonucleic acid from microsomal particles." *J. Mol. Biol.*, **1**, 111. (1–3)

Hall, B. D., and Spiegelman, S. (1961), "Sequence complementarity of T2-DNA and T2-specific RNA." *Proc. Natl. Acad. Sci. U.S.*, **47**, 137. (1–5)

Halvorson, H. (1958), "Studies on protein and nucleic acid turnover in growing cultures of yeast." *Biochim. Biophys. Acta*, **27**, 267. (1–7)

Hanawalt, P. C. (1963), "Involvement of synthesis of RNA in thymineless death." *Nature*, **198**, 286. (6–5)

Hanawalt, P. C., Maaløe, O., Cummings, D. J., and Schaechter, M. (1961), "The normal DNA replication cycle. II" *J. Mol. Biol.*, **3**, 156 (reproduced as Appendix IV).

Hardesty, B., Arlinghaus, R., Schaeffer, J., and Schweet, R. (1963), "Hemoglobin and polyphenyl-alanine synthesis with reticulocyte ribosomes." *Cold Spring Harbor Symp. Quant. Biol.*, **28**, 215. (1–7)

Hartman, P. E., Loper, I. C., and Šerman, D. (1960), "Fine structure mapping by complete transduction between histidine-requiring *Salmonella* mutants." *J. Gen. Microbiol.*, **22**, 323. (1–8)

Hartwell, L. H., and Magasanik, B. (1963), "The molecular basis of histidase induction in *Bacillus subtilis*." *J. Mol. Biol.*, **7**, 401. (1–5, 5–4)

Hayashi, M., Hayashi, M. N., and Spiegelman, S. (1963), "Restriction of *in vivo* genetic transcription to one of the complementary strands of DNA." *Proc. Natl. Acad. Sci. U.S.*, **50**, 664. (1–6)

Hayashi, M., Hayashi, M. N., and Spiegelman, S. (1964), "DNA circularity and the mechanism of strand selection in the generation of genetic message." *Proc. Natl. Acad. Sci. U.S.*, **51**, 351. (1–6, 5–1)

Hayashi, M., Spiegelman, S., Franklin, N. C., and Luria, S. E. (1963), "Separation of the RNA-message transcribed in response to a specific inducer." *Proc. Natl. Acad. Sci. U.S.*, **49**, 729. (1–5)

Hecht, L. I., Stephenson, M., and Zamecnik, P. C. (1959), "Binding of amino acids to the end group of a soluble RNA." *Proc. Natl. Acad. Sci. U.S.*, **45**, 505. (1–4)

Helinski, D. R., and Yanofsky, C. (1962), "Correspondence between genetic data and the position of amino acid alterations in a protein." *Proc. Natl. Acad. Sci. U.S.*, **48**, 173. (1–2)

Helling, R. B., and Weinberg, R. (1963), "Complementation studies of arabinose genes in *E. coli*." *Genetics*, **48**, 1397. (1–8)

Helmstetter, C. E., and Cummings, D. J. (1963), "Bacterial synchronization by selection of cells at division." *Proc. Natl. Acad. Sci. U.S.*, **50**, 767. (6–7)

Henning, U., and Yanofsky, C. (1962), "An alteration in the primary structure of a protein predicted on the basis of genetic recombination data." *Proc. Natl. Acad. Sci. U.S.*, **48**, 183. (1–2)

Henrici, A. T. (1928), "Morphologic Variation and the Rate of Growth of Bacteria," Baillière, Tindall & Cox, London. (4–1)

Hershey, A. D. (1953), "Nucleic acid economy in bacteria infected with bacteriophage T2. II. Phage precursor nucleic acid." *J. Gen. Physiol.*, **37**, 1. (1–3, 1–5)

Hershey, A. D., and Bronfenbrenner, J. (1938), "Factors limiting bacterial growth." *J. Gen. Physiol.*, **21**, 721. (2–2)

Hershey, A. D., and Chase, M. (1952), "Independent function of viral protein and nucleic acid in growth of bacteriophage." *J. Gen. Physiol.*, **36**, 39. (1–2)

Hill, C. W., and Echols, H. (1965), "Control of galactose m-RNA level in wild type *E. coli* and in an extreme polar mutant." *Abstr. Biophys. Soc. 9th Ann. Meeting*, San Francisco, 1965, 91. (1–8)

Hirs, C. H. W., Moore, S., and Stein, W. H. (1960), "The sequence of the amino acid in performic acid oxidized ribonuclease." *J. Biol. Chem.*, **235**, 633. (1–7)

Hoagland, M. B., Stephenson, M. L., Scott, J. F., Hecht, L. I., and Zamecnik, P. C. (1958), "A soluble ribonucleic acid intermediate in protein synthesis." *J. Biol. Chem.*, **231**, 241. (1–4)

Hogness, D. S., Cohn, M., and Monod, J. (1955), "Studies on the induced synthesis of β-galactosidase in *Escherichia coli:* the kinetics and mechanism of sulphur incorporation." *Biochim. Biophys. Acta*, **16**, 99. (1–8)

Holley, R. W., Apgar, J., Everett, G. A., Madison, J. T., Marquisee, M., Merrill, S. H., Penwick, J. R., and Zamir, A. (1965), "Structure of a ribonucleic acid." *Science*, **147**, 1462. (1–4)

Horiuchi, T., Tomizawa, J., and Novick, A. (1962), "Isolation and properties of bacteria capable of high rates of β-galactosidase synthesis." *Biochim. Biophys. Acta*, **55**, 152. (1–8)

Hurwitz, J., Evans, A., Babinet, C., and Skalka, A. (1963), "On the copying of DNA in the RNA polymerase reaction." *Cold Spring Harbor Symp. Quant. Biol.*, **28**, 59. (5–1)

Hurwitz, J., Furth, J. J., Anders, M., Ortiz, P. J., and August, J. T. (1961), "The enzymatic incorporation of ribonucleotides into RNA and the role of DNA." *J. Chem. Phys.*, **58**, 934; *Cold Spring Harbor Symp. Quant. Biol.*, **26**, 91. (1–6)

Hurwitz, J., Furth, J. J., Malamy, M., and Alexander, M. (1962), "The role of DNA in RNA synthesis. III. The inhibition of the enzymatic synthesis of RNA and DNA by actinomycin D and proflavin." *Proc. Natl. Acad. Sci. U.S.*, **48**, 1222. (1–6)

Imai, T., Takagi, J., and Isemura, T. (1963), "Recovery of the intact structure of muramidase (lysozyme) after reduction of all disulphide linkages in 8M urea." *J. Biochem. (Tokyo)*, **53**, 1. (1–7)

Ingram, V. M., and Sjöquist, J. A. (1963), "Studies on the structure of purified alanine and valine transfer RNA from yeast." *Cold Spring Harbor Symp. Quant. Biol.*, **28**, 133. (1–4)

Inman, R. B., Schildkraut, C. L., and Kornberg, A. (1965), "Enzymic synthesis of deoxyribonucleic acid. XX. Electron microscopy of products primed by native templates." *J. Mol. Biol.*, **11**, 285. (1–2)

Isemura, T., and Imanishi, A. (1962), "Reversibility of denaturation and molecular stability of *Bacillus subtilis* α-amylase." *J. Biochem. (Tokyo)*, **51**, 172. (1–7)

Jacob, F., and Adelberg, E. A. (1959), "Transfert de caractères génétiques par incorporation au facteur sexuel d'*Escherichia coli*." *Compt. Rend.*, **249**, 189. (1–9)

Jacob, F., and Brenner, S. (1963), "Sur la régulation de la synthèse du DNA chez les bactéries: l'hypothèse du réplicon." *Compt. Rend.*, **256**, 298. (6–1, 6–5)

Jacob, F., and Monod, J. (1961a), "Genetic regulatory mechanisms in the synthesis of proteins." *J. Mol. Biol.*, **3**, 318. (1–1, 1–5, 1–8, 1–9, 5–1)

Jacob, F., and Monod, J. (1961b), "On the regulation of gene activity." *Cold Spring Harbor Symp. Quant. Biol.*, **26**, 193. (1–8, 1–9)

Jacob, F., and Monod, J. (1965), "Genetic mapping of the elements of the lactose region in *Escherichia coli*." *Biochem. Biophys. Res. Commun.* **18**, 693. (1–8)

Jardetsky, O., and Julian, G. R. (1964), "Chloramphenicol inhibition of polyuridylic acid binding to *E. coli* ribosomes." *Nature*, **201**, 397. (1–7)

Josse, J., Kaiser, A. D., and Kornberg, A. (1961), "Enzymatic synthesis of DNA. VIII. Frequencies of nearest neighbor base sequences in DNA." *J. Biol. Chem.*, **236**, 864. (1–2)

Kahan, E., Kahan, F. M., and Hurwitz, J. (1963), "The role of deoxyribonucleic acid in ribonucleic acid synthesis. VI. Specificity of action of actinomycin D." *J. Biol. Chem.*, **238**, 2491. (1–6)

Kalckar, H. M., Kurahashi, K., and Jordan, E. (1959), "Hereditary defects in galactose metabolism in *E. coli*." *Proc. Natl. Acad. Sci. U.S.*, **45**, 1776. (1–8)

Kanazir, D., and Errera, M. (1956), "Alterations of intracellular deoxyribonucleic acid and their biological consequence." *Cold Spring Harbor Symp. Quant. Biol.*, **21**, 19. (6–4)

Karlsson, U., Koorajian, S., Zabin, I., Sjöstrand, F. S., and Miller, A. (1964), "High resolution electron microscopy on highly purified β-galactosidase from *Escherichia coli*." *J. Ultrastruct. Res.*, **10**, 457. (1–8)

Képès, A. (1963), "Kinetics of induced enzyme synthesis. Determination of the mean life of galactosidase-specific messenger-RNA." *Biochim. Biophys. Acta.*, **76**, 293. (1–5, 1–8, 5–4)

Khorana, H. G. (1964), "Chemical synthesis in the study of the nucleic acids." *Sixth Intern. Congr. Biochem., New York, Abstr. 1–S2,* 3. (1–7)

Kihare, H. K., Hu, A. S. L., and Halvorson, H. O. (1961), "The identification of a ribosomal-bound β-glucosidase." *Proc. Natl. Acad. Sci. U.S.,* **47,** 489. (1–3)

Kiho, Y., and Rich, A. (1964), "Induced enzyme formation on bacterial polyribosomes." *Proc. Natl. Acad. Sci. U.S.,* **51,** 111. (1–5)

Kjeldgaard, N. O. (1961), "The kinetics of RNA and protein formation in *Salmonella typhimurium* during the transition between different states of balanced growth." *Biochim. Biophys. Acta,* **49,** 64 (reproduced as Appendix II). (4–1)

Kjeldgaard, N. O. (1963), in "Dynamics of Bacterial Growth," Nyt Nordisk Forlag Arnold Busck, Copenhagen. (3–1, 3–5, 4–5)

Kjeldgaard, N. O., and Kurland, C. G. (1963), "The distribution of soluble and ribosomal RNA as a function of growth rate." *J. Mol. Biol.,* **6,** 341. (3–3)

Kjeldgaard, N. O., Maaløe, O., and Schaechter, M. (1958), "The transition between different physiological states during balanced growth of *Salmonella typhimurium.*" *J. Gen. Microbiol.,* **19,** 607. (4–1)

Kleinschmidt, A. K., Lang, D., Jacherts, D., and Zahn, R. K. (1962), "Darstellung und Längenmessungen des gesamten Deoxyribonucleinsäure-Inhalts von T2 Bakteriophagen." *Biochim. Biophys. Acta,* **61,** 857. (2–3)

Koch, A. L. (1965), "Kinetic evidence for a nucleic acid which regulates RNA biosynthesis." *Nature,* **205,** 800. (4–2)

Koch, A. L., and Levy, H. R. (1955), "Protein turnover in growing cultures of *Escherichia coli.*" *J. Biol. Chem.,* **217,** 947. (1–7)

Kornberg, A., Zimmerman, S. B., Kornberg, S. R., and Josse, J. (1959), "Enzymatic synthesis of deoxyribonucleic acid. VI. Influence of bacteriophage T2 on the synthetic pathway in host cells." *Proc. Natl. Acad. Sci. U.S.,* **45,** 772. (1–2)

Kornberg, H. L. (1963), "Control of biosynthesis from C_2-compounds." *Colloq. Intern. Centre Natl. Rech. Sci. (Paris),* No. 124, 193. (1–9)

Kucan, Ž., and Lipmann, F. (1964), "Differences in chloramphenicol sensitivity of cell-free amino acid polymerization systems." *J. Biol. Chem.,* **239,** 516. (1–7)

Kurland, C. G. (1960), "Molecular characterization of ribonucleic acid from *Escherichia coli* ribosomes. I. Isolation and molecular weight." *J. Mol. Biol.,* **2,** 83. (1–3)

Kurland, C. G., and Maaløe, O. (1962), "Regulation of ribosomal and transfer RNA synthesis." *J. Mol. Biol.,* **4,** 193 (reproduced as Appendix III). (4–2, 5–2)

Kurland, C. G., Nomura, M., and Watson, J. D. (1962), "The physical properties of the chloromycetin particles." *J. Mol. Biol.,* **4,** 388. (1–3)

Langridge, R., Wilson, H. R., Hooper, C. W., Wilkins, M. H. F., and Hamilton, L. D. (1960), "The molecular configuration of deoxyribonucleic acid." *J. Mol. Biol.,* **2,** 19. (1–2)

Lark, C., and Lark, K. G. (1964), "Evidence for two distinct aspects of the mechanism regulating chromosome replication in *Escherichia coli.*" *J. Mol. Biol.,* **10,** 120. (6–4, 6–5, 6–6, 6–7)

Lark, K. G., and Lark, C. (1965), "Regulation of chromosome replication in *Escherichia coli:* Alternate replication of two chromosomes at slow growth rates." *J. Mol. Biol.,* **13,** 105. (6–2, 6–7)

Lark, K. G., and Maaløe, O. (1954), "The induction of cellular and nuclear division in *Salmonella typhimurium* by means of temperature shifts." *Biochim. Biophys. Acta,* **15,** 345. (6–2)

Lark, K. G., Maaløe, O., and Rostock, O. (1955), "Cytological studies of nuclear division in *Salmonella typhimurium.*" *J. Gen. Microbiol.,* **13,** 318. (2–3)

Lark, K. G., Repko, T., and Hoffman, E. J. (1963), "The effect of amino acid deprivation on subsequent deoxyribonucleic acid replication." *Biochim. Biophys. Acta,* **76,** 9. (6–4, 6–6)

Lederberg, E. M. (1960), "Genetic and functional aspects of galactose metabolism in *E. coli* K12." *Symp. Soc. Gen. Microbiol.,* **10,** 115. (1–8)

Lederberg, E. M., Cavalli-Sforza, L., and Lederberg, J. (1964), "Interaction of streptomycin and a suppressor for galactose fermentation in *E. coli* K12." *Proc. Natl. Acad. Sci. U.S.,* **51,** 678. (1–7)

Lee, N., and Englesberg, E. (1962), "Dual effects of structural genes in *E. coli.*" *Proc. Natl. Acad. Sci. U.S.,* **48,** 335. (1–8, 1–9)

Lee, N., and Englesberg, E. (1963), "Coordinate variations in induced synthesis of enzymes associated with mutations in a structural gene." *Proc. Natl. Acad. Sci. U.S.,* **50,** 697. (1–8)

Lehman, I. R. (1959), "Enzymatic synthesis of deoxyribonucleic acid." *Ann. N.Y. Acad. Sci.,* **81,** 745. (1–2)

Lehman, I. R., Bessman, M. J., Simms, E. S., and Kornberg, A. (1958a), "Enzymatic synthesis of deoxyribonucleic acid. I. Preparation of substrates and partial purification of an enzyme from *Escherichia coli.*" *J. Biol. Chem.,* **233,** 163. (1–2)

Lehman, I. R., Zimmerman, S. B., Adler, J., Bessman, M. J., Simms, E. S., and Kornberg, A. (1958b), "Enzymatic synthesis of deoxyribonucleic acid. V. Chemical composition of enzymatically synthesized deoxyribonucleic acid." *Proc. Natl. Acad. Sci. U.S.,* **44,** 1191. (1–2)

Levinthal, C., and Crane, H. R. (1956), "On the unwinding of DNA." *Proc. Natl. Acad. Sci. U.S.,* **42,** 436. (7–1)

Levinthal, C., and Davison, P. F. (1961a), "Degradation of deoxyribonucleic acid under hydrodynamic shearing forces." *J. Mol. Biol.,* **3,** 674. (1–2)

Levinthal, C., and Davison, P. F. (1961b), "Biochemistry of genetic factors." *Ann. Rev. Biochem.,* **30,** 641. (6–1)

Levinthal, C., Keynan, A., and Higa, A. (1962), "Messenger RNA turnover and protein synthesis in *B. subtilis* inhibited by actinomycin D." *Proc. Natl. Acad. Sci. U.S.,* **48,** 1631. (1–5)

Levinthal, C., Signer, E. R., and Fetherolf, K. (1962), "Reactivation and hybridization of reduced alkaline phosphatase." *Proc. Natl. Acad. Sci. U.S* **48,** 1222. (1–7)

Linderstrøm-Lang, K. U. (1950), "Structure and enzymatic break-down of proteins." *Cold Spring Harbor Symp. Quant. Biol.,* **14,** 117. (1–7)

Linderstrøm-Lang, K. U. (1952), "Proteins and Enzymes." Lane Medical Lectures, Stanford University Press, Stanford, **6,** 1. (1–7)

Lipsett, M. N., Heppel, L. A., and Bradley, D. F. (1961), "Complex formation between oligonucleotides and polymers." *J. Biol. Chem.,* **236,** 857. (1–7)

Litman, R. M., and Szybalski, W. (1963), "Enzymatic synthesis of transforming DNA." *Biochem. Biophys. Res. Commun.,* **10,** 473. (1–2)

Loeb, T., and Zinder, N. D. (1961), "A bacteriophage containing RNA." *Proc. Natl. Acad. Sci. U.S.,* **47,** 282. (1–3)

Loftfield, R. B., Hecht, L. I., and Eigner, E. A. (1963), "The measurement of amino acid specificity of transfer RNA." *Biochim. Biophys. Acta,* **72,** 383. (1–4)

Loomis, W. F., Jr., and Magasanik, B. (1964), "The relation of catabolite repression to the induction system for β-galactosidase in *E. coli.*" *J. Mol. Biol.*, **8**, 417. (1–9, 5–1)

Luzzati, V., and Nicolaïeff, A. (1963), "The structure of nucleohistones and nucleoprotamines." *J. Mol. Biol.*, **7**, 142. (7–1)

Maaløe, O. (1961), "The control of normal DNA replication in bacteria." *Cold Spring Harbor Symp. Quant. Biol.*, **26**, 45. (4–4, 6–4)

Maaløe, O. (1962), "Synchronous growth," in "The Bacteria," eds. Gunsalus, I. C., and Stanier, R. Y., Academic Press, New York, Vol. IV., p. 1. (Introduction, 6–7)

Maaløe, O. (1963), "Role of protein synthesis in the DNA replication cycle in bacteria." *J. Cellular Comp. Physiol.*, Suppl. 1, **62**, 31. (6–5)

Maaløe, O., and Hanawalt, P. C. (1961), "Thymine deficiency and the normal DNA replication cycle. I." *J. Mol. Biol.*, **3**, 144. (6–4)

Maaløe, O., and Lark, K. G. (1954), "A study of bacterial populations in which nuclear and cellular divisions are induced by means of temperature shifts." *Proc. Symp. Colston Res. Soc.*, **7**, 159. (2–2)

Maaløe, O., and Rasmussen, K. V. (1963), "On the *in vivo* replication of bacterial DNA." *Colloq. Intern. Centre Natl. Rech. Sci. (Paris)*, No. 124, 165. (6–6)

Maaløe, O., and Richmond, M. H. (1962), "The rate of growth of *Salmonella typhimurium* with proline or glutamate as sole C source." *J. Gen. Microbiol.*, **27**, 269. (4–5)

Maas, W. K. (1961), "Studies on depression of arginine biosynthesis in *Escherichia coli.*" *Cold Spring Harbor Symp. Quant. Biol.*, **26**, 183. (1–8)

Maas, W. K., and Clark, A. J. (1964), "Studies on the mechanism of repression of arginine biosynthesis in *E. coli.* II. Dominance of repressibility in diploids." *J. Mol. Biol.*, **8**, 365. (1–8)

Maas, W. K., Maas, R., Wiame, J. M., and Glansdorff, N. (1964), "Studies on the mechanism of repression of arginine biosynthesis in *E. coli.* I. Dominance of repressibility in zygotes." *J. Mol. Biol.*, **8**, 359. (1–8)

McAuslan, B. R. (1963), "The induction and repression of thymidine kinase in the poxvirus-infected HeLa cell." *Virology*, **21**, 383. (1–9)

McCarthy, B. J. (1962), "The effects of magnesium starvation on the ribosome content of *Escherichia coli.*" *Biochim. Biophys. Acta*, **55**, 880. (4–3)

McQuillen, K., Roberts, R. B., and Britten, R. J. (1959), "Synthesis of nascent protein by ribosomes in *Escherichia coli.*" *Proc. Natl. Acad. Sci. U.S.*, **45**, 1437. (1–3, 3–5)

Magasanik, B. (1963), "The genetic and molecular basis of catabolite repression," in "Informational Macromolecules," eds. Vogel, H. J., Bryson, V., and Lampen, J. O., Academic Press, New York, p. 271. (1–9)

Magasanik, B., Magasanik, A. K., and Neidhardt, F. C. (1959), "Regulation of growth and composition of the bacterial cell." *Ciba Found. Symp. Regulation Cell Metabol.*, 334. (3–4)

Mandelstam, J. (1958), "Turnover of protein in growing and non-growing populations of *Escherichia coli.*" *Biochem. J.*, **69**, 110. (1–7, 3–3, 5–2)

Margolin, P. (1965), "Bipolarity of information transfer from the *Salmonella typhimurium* chromosome." *Science*, **147**, 1456 (7–2)

Marks, P. A., Burka, E., and Schlessinger, D. (1962), "Protein synthesis in erythroid cells. I. Reticulocyte ribosomes active in stimulating amino acid incorporation." *Proc. Natl. Acad. Sci. U.S.*, **48**, 2163. (1–7)

Marmur, J., and Doty, P. (1959), "Heterogeneity in deoxyribonucleic acids.

I. Dependence on composition of the configurational stability of deoxyribonucleic acids." *Nature,* **183,** 1427. (1–2)

Marmur, J., and Doty, P. (1961), "Thermal renaturation of deoxyribonucleic acids." *J. Mol. Biol.,* **3,** 585. (1–2)

Marmur, J., and Greenspan, C. M. (1963), "Transcription *in vivo* of DNA from bacteriophage SP8." *Science,* **142,** 387. (1–6)

Martin, E. M., Yegian, C., and Stent, G. S. (1963a), "Specificity of the amino acid transfer reaction in *E. coli* strains carrying different alleles of the RNA control (RC) gene." *Z. Vererbungslehre,* **94,** 303. (5–2)

Martin, E. M., Yegian, C., and Stent, G. S. (1963b), "The intracellular condition of soluble ribonucleic acid in *E. coli* subjected to amino acid starvation." *Biochem. J.,* **88,** 46. (5–2)

Martin, R. G. (1963), "The one operator-one messenger theory of transcription." *Cold Spring Harbor Symp. Quant. Biol.,* **28,** 357. (1–9)

Mason, D. J., and Powelson, D. M. (1956), "Nuclear division as observed in live bacteria by a new technique." *J. Bacteriol.* **71,** 474. (2–3)

Matthaei, J. H., and Nirenberg, M. W. (1961), "Characteristics and stabilization of DNAase-sensitive protein synthesis in *E. coli* extracts." *Proc. Natl. Acad. Sci. U.S.,* **47,** 1580. (1–5)

Melechen, N. E., and Skaar, P. D. (1962), "The provocation of an early step of induction by thymine deprivation." *Virology,* **16,** 21. (6–5)

Mennigmann, H.-D., and Szybalski, W. (1962), "Molecular mechanism of thymineless death." *Biochem. Biophys. Res. Commun.,* **9,** 398. (6–5)

Merigan, T. C., and Dreyer, W. J. (1963), "Studies on the antigenic combining sites in bacteriophage lysozyme." *Ann. N.Y. Acad. Sci.,* **103,** 765. (1–7)

Meselson, M., and Stahl, F. W. (1958), "The replication of DNA in *Escherichia coli.*" *Proc. Natl. Acad. Sci. U.S.,* **44,** 671. (1–2, 6–1, 6–7)

Midgley, J. E. M. (1962), "The nucleotide base composition of RNA from several bacterial species." *Biochim. Biophys. Acta,* **61,** 513. (1–3, 1–4)

Midgley, J. E. M., and McCarthy, B. (1962), "The synthesis and kinetic behaviour of deoxyribonucleic acid-like ribonucleic acid in bacteria." *Biochim. Biophys. Acta,* **61,** 696. (1–5)

Miura, K.-I. (1962), "The nucleotide composition of ribonucleic acids of soluble and particle fractions in several species of bacteria." *Biochim. Biophys. Acta,* **55,** 62. (1–3, 1–4)

Monod, J. (1942), "Recherches sur la Croissance des Cultures Bactériennes," Hermann & Cie., Paris. (1–9)

Monod, J., Changeux, J. P., and Jacob, F. (1963), "Allosteric proteins and cellular control systems." *J. Mol. Biol.,* **6,** 306. (1–8)

Monod, J., and Cohen-Bazire, G. (1953), "L'effet d'inhibition spécifique dans la biosynthèse de la tryptophanedesmase chez *Aerobacter aerogenes.*" *Compt. Rend.,* **236,** 530. (1–8)

Monod, J., and Cohn, M. (1952), "La biosynthèse induite des enzymes (adaptation enzymatique)." *Advan. Enzymol.,* **13,** 67. (1–8)

Monod, J., Jacob, F., and Gros, F. (1962), "Structural and rate determining factors in the biosynthesis of adaptive enzymes." *Biochem. Soc. Symp. (Cambridge, Engl.),* **21,** 104. (1–8)

Monod, J., Wyman, J., and Changeux, J. D. (1965), "On the nature of allosteric transitions: a plausible model." *J. Mol. Biol.,* **12,** 88. (1–8)

Munch-Petersen, A., and Neuhard, J. (1964), "DeATP metabolism in a thymine-requiring *E. coli* mutant during thymine starvation." *Sixth Intern. Congr. Biochem., New York, Abstr. IX.* S1, 728. (6–5)

Nagata, T. (1963), "The molecular synchrony and sequential replication of DNA in *E. coli.*" *Proc. Natl. Acad. Sci. U.S.*, **49**, 551. (1–2, 7–2)

Nakada, D., Anderson, I. A. C., and Magasanik, B. (1964), "Fate of the ribosomal RNA produced by a "relaxed" mutant of *Escherichia coli.*" *J. Mol. Biol.*, **9**, 472. (1–3)

Nakada, D., and Fan, D. P. (1964), "Protection of β-galactosidase messenger RNA from decay during anaerobiosis in *E. coli.*" *J. Mol. Biol.*, **8**, 223. (1–5)

Nakada, D., and Magasanik, B. (1964), "The roles of inducer and catabolite repressor in the synthesis of β-galactosidase by *Escherichia coli.*" *J. Mol. Biol.*, **8**, 105. (1–5, 5–4)

Nakamoto, T., Conway, T. W., Allende, J. E., Spyrides, G. J., and Lipmann, F. (1963), "Formation of peptide bonds. I. Peptide formation from aminoacyl-s-RNA." *Cold Spring Harbor Symp. Quant. Biol.*, **28**, 227. (1–7)

Nathans, D. (1964), "Puromycin inhibition of protein synthesis: Incorporation of puromycin into peptide chains." *Proc. Natl. Acad. Sci. U.S.*, **51**, 585. (1–7)

Nathans, D., and Lipmann, F. (1961), "Amino acid transfer from amino acyl-ribonucleic acids to protein of ribosomes of *E. coli.*" *Proc. Natl. Acad. Sci. U.S.*, **47**, 497. (1–7)

Nathans, D., Notani, G., Schwartz, J. H., and Zinder, N. D. (1962), "Biosynthesis of the coat protein of coliphage f2 by *E. coli* extracts." *Proc. Natl. Acad. Sci. U.S.*, **48**, 1424. (1–3)

Naughton, M. A., and Dintzis, H. M. (1962), "Sequential biosynthesis of the protein chains of hemoglobin." *Proc. Natl. Acad. Sci. U.S.*, **48**, 1822. (1–7)

Neidhardt, F. C. (1963), "Properties of a bacterial mutant lacking amino acid control of RNA synthesis." *Biochim. Biophys. Acta*, **68**, 365. (5–2)

Neidhardt, F. C., and Eidlic, L. (1963), "Characterization of the RNA formed under conditions of relaxed amino acid control in *E. coli.*" *Biochim. Biophys. Acta*, **68**, 380. (5–3)

Neidhardt, F. C., and Magasanik, B. (1960), "Studies on the role of ribonucleic acid in the growth of bacteria." *Biochim. Biophys. Acta*, **42**, 99. (3–1)

Neu, H. C., and Heppel, L. A. (1964), "The release of ribonuclease into the medium when *Escherichia coli* cells are converted to speroplasts." *J. Biol. Chem.*, **239**, 3893. (1–3)

Neuhard, J., and Munch-Petersen, A. (1965), "Studies on the acid-soluble nucleotide pool in thymine-requiring mutants of *Escherichia coli* during thymine starvation. II. Changes in the amounts of deoxycytidine triphosphate and deoxyadenosine triphosphate in *Escherichia coli 15* $T^-A^-U^-$." *Biochim. Biophys. Acta*, in press. (6–5)

Nirenberg, M. W., and Matthaei, J. H. (1961), "The dependence of cell-free protein synthesis in *E. coli* upon naturally occurring or synthetic polynucleotides." *Proc. Natl. Acad. Sci. U.S.*, **47**, 1588. (1–7)

Nisman, B., and Hirsch, M.-L. (1958), "Etude de l'activation et de l'incorporation des acides aminés par des fractions enzymatiques d'*E. coli.*" *Ann. Inst. Pasteur*, **95**, 615. (5–2)

Noll, H. (1965), "Polysome organization as a control element," in "Developmental and Metabolic Control Mechanisms and Neoplasia." *Symp. Fundamental Cancer Res. 19th Houston, 1965.* (1–7)

Noll, H., Staehlin, T., and Wettstein, F. O. (1963), "Ribosomal aggregates engaged in protein synthesis: Ergosome breakdown and messenger ribonucleic acid transport." *Nature*, **198**, 632. (1–5, 1–7)

Nomura, M., Hall, B. D., and Spiegelman, S. (1960), "Characterization of RNA synthesized in *Escherichia coli* after bacteriophage T2 infection." *J. Mol. Biol.*, **2**, 306. (1–5)

Nomura, M., and Watson, J. D. (1959), "Ribonucleo-protein particles within chloromycetin-inhibited *Escherichia coli.*" *J. Mol. Biol.*, **1**, 204. (1–3)

Novick, A., McCoy, J. M., and Sadler, J. R. (1965, "The non-inducibility of repressor formation." *J. Mol. Biol.*, **12**, 328. (1–9)

Novick, A., and Szilard, L. (1954), "Experiments with the chemostat on the rates of amino acid synthesis in bacteria," in "Dynamics of Growth Processes," ed. Boell, E. J., Princeton University Press, Princeton, p. 21. (1–8)

Novick, A., and Weiner, M. (1957), "Enzyme induction as an all-or-none phenomenon." *Proc. Natl. Acad. Sci. U.S.*, **43**, 553. (1–9)

Ochoa, S., Burma, D. P., Kröger, H., and Weill, J. (1961), "Deoxyribonucleic acid-dependent incorporation of nucleotides from nucleoside triphosphates." *Proc. Natl. Acad. Sci. U.S.*, **47**, 670. (1–6)

Ohtaka, Y., and Uchida, K. (1963). "The chemical structure and stability of yeast ribosomes." *Biochim. Biophys. Acta*, **76**, 94. (1–3)

Oishi, M., Yoshikawa, H., and Sueoka, N. (1964), "Synchronous and dichotomous replications of the *Bacillus subtilis* chromosome during spore germination." *Nature*, **204**, 1069. (6–2)

Okada, T., Yanagisawa, K., and Ryan, F. J. (1960), "Elective production of thymineless mutants." *Nature*, **188**, 340. (6–4)

Okamoto, T., and Takanami, M. (1963), "Interaction of ribosomes and natural polyribonucleotides." *Biochim. Biophys. Acta*, **76**, 266. (1–7)

Ortiz, P. J., August, J. T., Watanabe, M., Kaye, A. M., and Hurwitz, J. (1965), "Ribonucleic acid-dependent ribonucleotide incorporation. II. Inhibition of polyriboadenylate polymerase activity following bacteriophage infection." *J. Biol. Chem.*, **240**, 423. (1–3)

Otaka, E., Osawa, S., and Sibatani, A. (1964), "Stimulation of C^{14}-leucine incorporation into protein *in vitro* by ribosomal RNA of *E. coli.*" *Biochem. Biophys. Res. Commun.*, **15**, 568. (5–4)

Pardee, A. B., Paigen, K., and Prestidge, L. S. (1957), "A study of the ribonucleic acid of normal and chloromycetine inhibited bacteria by zone electrophoresis." *Biochim. Biophys. Acta*, **23**, 162. (1–3)

Pardee, A. B., and Prestidge, L. S. (1956), "The dependence of nucleic acid synthesis on the presence of amino acids in *E. coli.*" *J. Bacteriol.*, **71**, 677. (5–2)

Pardee, A. B., and Prestidge, L. S. (1959), "On the nature of the repressor of β-galactosidase synthesis in *E. coli.*" *Biochim. Biophys. Acta*, **36**, 545. (1–9)

Pardee, A. B., and Prestidge, L. S. (1961), "The initial kinetics of enzyme induction." *Biochim. Biophys. Acta*, **49**, 77. (1–8)

Pauling, L., and Corey, R. B. (1956), "Specific hydrogen-bond formation between pyrimidines and purines in deoxyribonucleic acid." *Arch. Biochem. Biophys.*, **65**, 164. (1–2)

Pauling, L., Corey, R. B., and Branson, H. R. (1951), "The structure of proteins: Two hydrogen-bonded helical configurations of the polypeptide chain." *Proc. Natl. Acad. Sci. U.S.*, **37**, 205. (1–7)

Penman, S., Scherrer, K., Becker, Y., and Darnell, J. E. (1963), "Polyribosomes in normal and poliovirus-infected HeLa cells and their relationship to messenger-RNA." *Proc. Natl. Acad. Sci. U.S.*, **49**, 654. (1–5)

Perrin, D. (1963), "Complementation between products of the β-galactosidase structural gene of *E. coli.*" *Cold Spring Harbor Symp. Quant. Biol.*, **28**, 529. (1–7)

Petermann, M. L., and Hamilton, M. G. (1957), "The purification and properties of cytoplasmic ribonucleoprotein from rat liver." *J. Biol. Chem.* **224,** 725. (1–3)

Pollock, M. R. (1963), "The differential effect of actinomycin D on the biosynthesis of enzymes in *Bacillus subtilis* and *Bacillus cereus.*" *Biochim. Biophys. Acta,* **76,** 80. (1–5)

Preiss, J., Dieckmann, M., and Berg, P. (1961), "The enzymic synthesis of amino acyl derivatives of RNA. IV. The formation of the 3′-hydroxyl terminal trinucleotide sequence of amino acid-acceptor RNA." *J. Biol. Chem.,* **236,** 1748. (1–4)

Pritchard, R. H., and Lark, K. G. (1964), "Induction of replication by thymine starvation at the chromosome origin in *Escherichia coli.*" *J. Mol. Biol.,* **9,** 288. (6–2, 6–6)

Reich, E., Franklin, R. M., Shatkin, A. J., and Tatum, E. L. (1961), "Effect of actinomycin D on cellular nucleic acid synthesis and virus production." *Science,* **134,** 556. (1–6)

Revel, M., and Hiatt, H. H. (1964), "The stability of liver messenger RNA." *Proc. Natl. Acad. Sci. U.S.,* **51,** 810. (1–5)

Rich, A. (1960), "A hybrid helix containing both deoxyribose and ribosepolynucleotides and its relation to the transfer of information between the nucleic acids." *Proc. Natl. Acad. Sci. U.S.,* **46,** 1044. (1–5)

Rich, A., Warner, J. R., and Goodman, H. M. (1963), "The structure and function of polyribosomes." *Cold Spring Harbor Symp. Quant. Biol.,* **28,** 269. (1–7)

Richardson, C. C., Schildkraut, C. L., Aposhian, H. V., Kornberg, A. L., Bodmer, W., and Lederberg, J. (1963), "Studies on the replication of DNA by *E. coli* polymerase," in "Informational Macromolecules," eds. Vogel, H. J., Bryson, V., and Lampen, J. O., Academic Press, New York, p. 13. (1–2)

Richmond, M. H. (1963), "Random replacement of phenylalanine by fluorophenylalanine in alkaline phosphorase formed during biosynthesis by *E. coli.*" *J. Mol. Biol.,* **6,** 284. (1–4)

Rickenberg, H. W., Cohen, G. N., Buttin, G., and Monod, J. (1956), "La galactoside-perméase d'*Escherichia coli.*" *Ann. Inst. Pasteur,* **91,** 829. (1–8)

Risebrough, R. W., Tissières, A., and Watson, J. D. (1962), "Messenger RNA attachment to active ribosomes." *Proc. Natl. Acad. Sci. U.S.,* **48,** 430. (1–5, 1–7)

Roberts, R. B., Abelson, P. H., Cowie, D. B., Bolton, E. T., and Britten, R. J. (1955), "Studies of biosynthesis in *Escherichia coli.*" *Carnegie Inst. Wash. Publ.* No. 607, 28. (3–1)

Rotman, B., and Spiegelman, S. (1954), "On the origin of the carbon in the induced synthesis of β-galactosidase in *Escherichia coli.*" *J. Bacteriol.,* **68,** 419. (1–8)

Ryter, A., and Jacob, F. (1964), "Etude au microscope électronique de la liaison entre noyau et mésosome chez *B. subtilis.*" *Ann. Inst. Pasteur,* **107,** 384. (6–5)

Ryter, A., Kellenberger, E., Birch-Andersen, A., and Maaløe, O. (1958), "Etude au microscope électronique de plasmas contenant de l'acide désoxyribonucleique." *Z. Naturforsch.,* **13,** 597. (3–4)

Sadler, J. R., and Novick, A. (1965), "The properties of repressor and the kinetics of its action." *J. Mol. Biol.,* **12,** 305. (1–9)

Sagik, B. P., Green, M. H., Hayashi, M., and Spiegelman, S. (1962), "Size distribution of 'informational' RNA." *Biophys. J.*, **2**, 409. (1–5)

Sarabhai, A. S., Stretton, A. O. W., Brenner, S., and Bolle, A. (1964), "Colinearity of the gene with the polypeptide chain." *Nature,* **201,** 13. (1–7, 1–9)

Schachman, H. (1963), "Considerations on the tertiary structure of proteins." *Cold Spring Harbor Symp. Quant. Biol.*, **28,** 409. (1–7)

Schaechter, M. (1961), "Patterns of cellular control during unbalanced growth." *Cold Spring Harbor Symp. Quant. Biol.*, **26,** 53. (6–4)

Schaechter, M. (1963), "Bacterial polyribosomes and their participation in protein synthesis *in vivo.*" *J. Mol. Biol.*, **7,** 561. (1–5, 1–7, 3–5)

Schaechter, M., Bentzon, M. W., and Maaløe, O. (1959), "Synthesis of deoxyribonucleic acid during the division cycle of bacteria." *Nature,* **183,** 1207. (6–2)

Schaechter, M., Maaløe, O., and Kjeldgaard, N. O. (1958), "Dependency on medium and temperature of cell size and chemical composition during balanced growth of *Salmonella typhimurium.*" *J. Gen. Microbiol.*, **19,** 592 (reproduced as Appendix I).

Schaechter, M., Williamson, J. P., Hood, J. R., Jr., and Koch, A. L. (1962), "Growth, cell and nuclear divisions in some bacteria." *J. Gen. Microbiol.*, **29,** 421. (6–1, 6–7)

Schildkraut, C. L., Marmur, J., and Doty, P. (1961), "The formation of hybrid DNA molecules and their use in studies of DNA homologies." *J. Mol. Biol.*, **3,** 595. (1–2)

Schildkraut, C. L., Richardson, C. C., and Kornberg, A. (1964), "Enzymatic synthesis of deoxyribonucleic acid. XVII. Some unusual physical properties of the product primed by native DNA templates." *J. Mol. Biol.*, **9,** 24. (6–1)

Schlessinger, D. (1960), "Hypochromicity in ribosomes from *Escherichia coli.*" *J. Mol. Biol.*, **2,** 92. (1–3)

Schlessinger, D. (1963), "Protein synthesis by polyribosomes on protoplast membranes of *B. megaterium.*" *J. Mol. Biol.*, **7,** 569. (1–5, 1–7)

Schwartz, J. H., and Maas, W. K. (1960), "Analysis of the inhibition of growth produced by canavanine in *Escherichia coli.*" *J. Bacteriol.*, **79,** 794. (1–8)

Sekiguchi, M., and Cohen, S. S. (1963), "The selective degradation of phage-induced RNA by polynucleotide phosphorylase." *J. Biol. Chem.*, **238,** 349. (1–3)

Shaeffer, J. R., Arlinghaus, R., and Schweet, R. (1965), "Formation of ribosome-bound intermediates in peptide synthesis." *Abstr. Biophys. Soc. 9th Ann. Meeting,* San Francisco, 1965, 155. (1–7)

Sharon, N., and Lipmann, F. (1957), "Reactivity of analogs with pancreatic tryptophan-activating enzyme." *Arch. Biochem. Biophys.*, **69,** 219. (5–2)

Sicard, N., and Devoret, R. (1962), "Effets de la carence en thymine sur des souches d'*Escherichia coli* lysogènes K 12 T$^-$ et colicinogène 15 T$^-$." *Compt. Rend.*, **255,** 1417. (6–5)

Siminovitch, L., and Graham, A. F. (1956), "The metabolic stability of nucleic acids in *Escherichia coli.*" *Can. J. Microbiol.*, **2,** 585. (1–2, 1–3)

Simon, E. H. (1961), "Transfer of DNA from parent to progeny in a tissue culture line of human carcinoma of the cervix (strain HeLa)." *J. Mol. Biol.*, **3,** 101. (1–2)

Singer, M. F., and Cantoni, G. L. (1960), "Studies on soluble ribonucleic acid of rabbit liver. Terminal groups and nucleotide composition." *Biochim. Biophys. Acta,* **39,** 182. (1–4)

Sinsheimer, R. L. (1959), "A single-stranded deoxyribonucleic acid from bacteriophage φX 174." *J. Mol. Biol.*, **1,** 43. (1–2)

Sinsheimer, R. L. (1961), "The replication of bacteriophage φX 174." *J. Chim. Phys.*, **58**, 986. (1–2)

Sinsheimer, R. L., Starman, B., Nagler, C., and Guthrie, S. (1962), "The process of infection with bacteriophage φX 174. I. Evidence for a 'replicative form.'" *J. Mol. Biol.*, **4**, 142. (1–2)

Smith, E. E. B., Mills, G. T., Bernheimer, H. P., and Austrian, R. (1958), "The presence of an uronic acid epimerase in a strain of pneumococcus type I." *Biochim. Biophys. Acta*, **29**, 640. (1–2)

Smith, R. C., and Maaløe, O. (1964), "Effect of growth rate on the acid-soluble nucleotide composition of *Salmonella typhimurium*." *Biochim. Biophys. Acta*, **86**, 229. (4–2)

Soffer, R. L., and Gros, F. (1964), "Effects of dinitrophenol and proflavine on information transfer mechanisms in *E. coli;* a study *in vivo* and *in vitro*." *Biochim. Biophys. Acta*, **87**, 423. (1–5)

Spahr, P. F. (1962), "Amino acid composition of ribosomes from *Escherichia coli*." *J. Mol. Biol.*, **4**, 395. (1–3)

Spahr, P. F., and Hollingworth, B. R. (1961), "Purification and mechanism of action of ribonuclease from *E. coli* ribosomes." *J. Biol. Chem.*, **236**, 823. (1–3)

Speyer, J. F., Lengyel, P., and Basilio, C. (1962), "Ribosomal localization of streptomycin sensitivity." *Proc. Natl. Acad. Sci. U.S.*, **48**, 684. (1–7)

Spirin, A. S. (1963), "Some problems concerning the macromolecular structure of ribonucleic acids," in "Progress in Nucleic Acid Research," eds. Davidson, J. N., and Cohn, W. E., Academic Press, New York, p. 301. (1–3)

Spitnik-Elson, P. (1962), "The solubilization of ribosomal protein from *E. coli*." *Biochim. Biophys. Acta*, **55**, 741. (1–3)

Spotts, C. R. (1962), "Physiological and biochemical studies on streptomycin dependence in *E. coli*." *J. Gen. Microbiol.*, **28**, 347. (1–7)

Spotts, C. R., and Stanier, R. Y. (1961), "Mechanism of streptomycin action on bacteria: A unitary hypothesis." *Nature*, **192**, 633. (1–7)

Spyrides, G., and Lipmann, F. (1962), "Polypeptide synthesis with sucrose gradient fractions of *E. coli* ribosomes." *Proc. Natl. Acad. Sci. U.S.*, **48**, 1977. (1–7)

Stadtman, E. R., Cohen, G. N., Le Bras, G., and Robichon-Szulmajster, H. (1961), "Selective feedback inhibition and repression of two aspartokinases in the metabolism of *E. coli*." *Cold Spring Harbor Symp. Quant. Biol.*, **26**, 319. (1–8)

Staehlin, T., Brinton, C. C., Wettstein, F. O., and Noll, H. (1963), "Structure and function of *E. coli* ergosomes." *Nature*, **199**, 865. (1–7)

Staehlin, T., Wettstein, F. O., Oura, H., and Noll, H. (1964), "Determination of the coding ratio based on molecular weight of messenger ribonucleic acid associated with ergosomes of different aggregate size." *Nature*, **201**, 264. (1–5)

Steers, E., Craven, G. R., Anfinsen, C. B., and Bethune, J. L. (1965), "Evidence for non-identical chains in the β-galactosidase of *Escherichia coli* K12." *J. Biol. Chem.*, **240**, 2478. (1–8)

Stent, G. S. (1964), "The operon: on its third anniversary. Modulation of transfer RNA species can provide a workable model of an operator-less operon." *Science*, **144**, 816. (5–1, 5–2, 5–4)

Stent, G. S. (1965), "Genetic transcription." Lecture for the Mendel Centennial Symposium, London. *Proc. Royal Soc., London*, in press. (5–3, 5–4, 7–1, 7–2)

Stent, G. S., and Brenner, S. (1961), "A genetic locus for the regulation of ribonucleic acid synthesis." *Proc. Natl. Acad. Sci. U.S.*, **47**, 2005. (5–2)

Stevens, A. (1960), "Incorporation of the adenine ribonucleotide into RNA by cell fraction from *E. coli B*." *Biochem. Biophys. Res. Commun.*, **3**, 92. (1–6)

Strasdine, G. A., Hogg, L. A., and Campbell, J. J. R. (1962), "A ribosomal polynucleotide phosphorylase in *Pseudomona aeruginosa*." *Biochim. Biophys. Acta*, **55**, 231. (1–3)

Sueoka, N. (1960), "Mitotic replication of deoxyribonucleic acid in *Chlamydomonas reinhardi*." *Proc. Natl. Acad. Sci. U.S.*, **46**, 83. (1–2)

Sueoka, N., and Yamane, T. (1962), "Fractionation of amino acyl-acceptor RNA on a methylated albumin column." *Proc. Natl. Acad. Sci. U.S.*, **48**, 1454. (1–4)

Sund, H., and Weber, K. (1963), "Untersuchungen über milchzuckerspaltende Enzyme." *Biochem. Z.*, **337**, 24. (1–8)

Svensson, I., Boman, H. C., Eriksson, K. G., and Kjellin, K. (1963), "Studies on microbial RNA. I. Transfer of methyl groups from methionine to soluble RNA from *E. coli*." *J. Mol. Biol.*, **7**, 254. (1–4)

Swartz, M. N., Trautner, F. A., and Kornberg, A. (1962), "Enzymatic synthesis of DNA. XI. Further studies on nearest neighbour base sequences in DNA." *J. Biol. Chem.*, **237**, 1961. (1–2)

Takai, M., and Kondo, N. (1962), "Studies on the ribosomal ribonucleic acid from *Bacillus cereus*." *Biochim. Biophys. Acta*, **55**, 875. (1–3)

Takanami, M. (1962), "Transfer of amino acids from soluble ribonucleic acid to ribosomes." *Biochim. Biophys. Acta*, **61**, 432. (1–7)

Takanami, M., and Zubay, G. (1964), "An estimate of the size of the ribosomal site for messenger RNA binding." *Proc. Natl. Acad. Sci. U.S.*, **51**, 834. (1–7)

Tal, M., and Elson, D. (1963a), "The location of ribonuclease in *E. coli*." *Biochim. Biophys. Acta*, **76**, 40. (1–3)

Tal, M., and Elson, D. (1963b), "The reversible release of deoxyribonuclease, protein and ribonucleic acid from ribosomes." *Biochim. Biophys. Acta*, **72**, 439. (1–3)

Taylor, A. L., Beckwith, J. R., Pardee, A. B., Austrian, R., and Jacob, F. (1964), "The chromosomal location of the structural gene for orotidylic acid pyrophosphorylase in *E. coli*." *J. Mol. Biol.*, **8**, 771. (1–8)

Thang, M. N., Williams, F. R., and Grunberg-Manago, M. (1963), "Synthèse *in vivo* de la polynucléotide phosphorylase chez *E. coli*. II. Synthèse *de novo* de la polynucléotide phosphorylase en présence de chloramphenicol." *Biochim. Biophys. Acta*, **76**, 572. (5–2, 6–6)

Tissières, A. (1959), "Some properties of soluble ribonucleic acid from *Escherichia coli*." *J. Mol. Biol.*, **1**, 365. (1–4)

Tissières, A., Bourgeois, S., and Gros, F. (1963), "Inhibition of RNA polymerase by RNA," *J. Mol. Biol.*, **7**, 100. (5–3)

Tissières, A., Watson, J. D., Schlessinger, D., and Hollingworth, B. R. (1959), "Ribonucleoprotein particles from *Escherichia coli*." *J. Mol. Biol.*, **1**, 221. (1–3)

Tocchini-Valentini, G. P., Stodolsky, M., Aurisicchio, A., Sarnat, M., Graziosi, F., Weiss, S. B., and Geiduschek, E. P. (1963), "On the asymmetry of RNA synthesis *in vivo*." *Proc. Natl. Acad. Sci. U.S.*, **50**, 935. (1–6)

Tsugita, A., Fraenkel-Conrat, H., Nirenberg, M. W., and Matthaei, J. H. (1962), Demonstration of the messenger role of viral RNA." *Proc. Natl. Acad. Sci. U.S.*, **48**, 846. (1–3)

Umbarger, H. E. (1956), "Evidence for a negative-feedback inhibition in the biosynthesis of isoleucine." *Science*, **123**, 848. (1–8)

Villa-Trevino, S., Farber, E., Staehlin, T., Wettstein, F. O., and Noll, H. (1964), "Breakdown and reassembly of rat liver ergosomes after administration of ethionine or pyromycin." *J. Biol. Chem.*, **239**, 3826. (1–7)

Vogel, H. J. (1961), "Aspects of repression in the regulation of enzyme synthesis: Pathway-wide control and enzyme-specific response." *Cold Spring Harbor Symp. Quant. Biol.*, **26**, 163. (1–8)

Vogel, H. J., Bacon, D. F., and Baich, A. (1963), "Induction of acetylornithine δ-transaminase during pathway-wide repression," in "Informational Macromolecules," eds. Vogel, H. J., Bryson, V., and Lampen, J. O., Academic Press, New York, p. 293. (1–8, 1–9)

Wade, H. E., and Morgan, D. M. (1957), "The nature of the fluctuating ribonucleic acid in *Escherichia coli.*" *Biochem. J.*, **65**, 321. (3–2)

Wade, H. E., and Robinson, H. K. (1963), "Absence of ribonuclease from the ribosomes of *Pseudomonas fluorescens.*" *Nature*, **200**, 661. (1–3)

Waller, J.-P. (1963), "The NH_2-terminal residues of the proteins from cell-free extracts of *E. coli.*" *J. Mol. Biol.*, **7**, 483. (1–2, 1–3)

Waller, J. P., and Harris, J. I. (1961), "Studies on the composition of the protein from *E. coli* ribosomes." *Proc. Natl. Acad. Sci. U.S.*, **47**, 18. (1–3)

Warner, J. R., Knopf, P. M., and Rich, A. (1963), "A multiple ribosomal structure in protein synthesis." *Proc. Natl. Acad. Sci. U.S.*, **49**, 122. (1–5, 1–7)

Warner, J. R., Rich, A., and Hall, C. (1962), "Electron microscope studies of ribosomal clusters synthesizing hemoglobin." *Science*, **138**, 1399. (1–7)

Watson, J. D. (1965), "Molecular Biology of the Gene." W. A. Benjamin, Inc., New York. (Introduction)

Watson, J. D., and Crick, F. H. C. (1953), "The structure of DNA." *Cold Spring Harbor Symp. Quant. Biol.*, **18**, 123. (1–2)

Weisberger, A., Wolfe, S., and Armentrout, S. (1964), "Inhibition of protein synthesis in mammalian cell-free systems by chloramphenicol." *J. Exptl. Med.*, **120**, 161. (1–7)

Weisblum, B., Benzer, S., and Holley, R. W. (1962), "A physical basis for degeneracy in the amino acid code." *Proc. Natl. Acad. Sci. U.S.*, **48**, 1449. (1–4)

Weiss, S. B. (1960), "Enzymatic incorporation of ribonucleoside triphosphates into the interpolynucleotide linkage of RNA." *Proc. Natl. Acad. Sci. U.S.*, **46**, 1020. (1–6)

Weiss, S. B., and Gladstone, L. (1959), "A mammalian system for the incorporation of cytidine-triphosphate into ribonucleic acid." *J. Am. Chem. Soc.*, **81**, 4118. (1–6)

Weiss, S. B., and Nakamoto, F. (1961a), "On the participation of DNA in RNA biosynthesis." *Proc. Natl. Acad. Sci. U.S.*, **47**, 694. (1–6)

Weiss, S. B., and Nakamoto, F. (1961b), "The enzymatic synthesis of RNA: Nearest-neighbor base frequencies." *Proc. Natl. Acad. Sci. U.S.*, **47**, 1400. (1–6)

Weissbach, A., and Korn, D. (1963), "The deoxyribonuclease of *E. coli* K12." *J. Biol. Chem.*, **238**, 3383. (1–3)

Wettstein, F. O., Staehlin, T., and Noll, H. (1963), "Ribosomal aggregate engaged in protein synthesis: Characterization of the ergosomes." *Nature*, **197**, 430. (1–3, 1–5, 1–7, 3–5)

Willson, C., and Gros, F. (1964), "Protein synthesis with an *Escherichia coli* system *in vitro.*" *Biochim. Biophys. Acta*, **80**, 478. (1–5, 5–4)

Willson, C., Perrin, D., Cohn, M., Jacob, F., and Monod, J. (1964), "Non-inducible mutants of the regulator gene in the 'lactose' system of *Escherichia coli.*" *J. Mol. Biol.*, **8**, 582. (1–8, 1–9)

Woese, C., Naono, S., Soffer, R., and Gros, F. (1963), "Studies on the breakdown of messenger RNA." *Biochem. Biophys. Res. Commun.*, **11**, 435. (1–5)

Wood, W. B., and Berg, P. (1962), "The effect of enzymatically synthesized ribonucleic acid on amino acid incorporation by a soluble protein-ribosome system from *Escherichia coli.*" *Proc. Natl. Acad. Sci. U.S.*, **48**, 94. (1–7)

Yankofsky, S. A., and Spiegelman, S. (1962a), "The identification of the ribosomal RNA cistron by sequence complementarity. I. Specificity of complex formation." *Proc. Natl. Acad. Sci. U.S.*, **48**, 1069. (5–1)

Yankofsky, S. A., and Spiegelman, S. (1962b), "The identification of the ribosomal RNA cistron by sequence complementarity. II. Saturation of and competitive interaction at the RNA cistron." *Proc. Natl. Acad. Sci. U.S.*, **48**, 1466. (5–1)

Yankofsky, S. A., and Spiegelman, S. (1963), "Distinct cistrons for the two ribosomal RNA components." *Proc. Natl. Acad. Sci. U.S.*, **49**, 538. (1–6, 3–5, 5–1)

Yanofsky, C. (1963), *Cold Spring Harbor Symp. Quant. Biol.*, **28**, 296. (1–7)

Yanofsky, C., Carlton, B. C., Guest, J. R., Helinski, D. R., and Henning, U. (1964), "On the colinearity of gene structure and protein structure." *Proc. Natl. Acad. Sci. U.S.*, **51**, 266. (1–7)

Yarmolinsky, M. B., and de la Haba, G. L. (1959), "Inhibition by puromycin of amino acid incorporation into protein." *Proc. Natl. Acad. Sci. U.S.*, **45**, 1721. (1–7)

Yarmolinsky, M. B., Jordan, E., and Wiesmayer, H. (1961), "Regulatory mechanisms in the synthesis of enzymes of galactose metabolism." *Cold Spring Harbor Symp. Quant. Biol.*, **26**, 217. (1–8)

Yates, R. A., and Pardee, A. B. (1956), "Control of pyrimidine biosynthesis in *E. coli* by a feedback mechanism." *J. Biol. Chem.*, **221**, 757. (1–8)

Yčas, M., and Vincent, W. S. (1960), "A ribonucleic acid fraction from yeast related in composition to deoxyribonucleic acid." *Proc. Natl. Acad. Sci. U.S.*, **46**, 804. (1–5)

Yoshikawa, H., O'Sullivan, A., and Sueoka, N. (1964), "Sequential replication of the *Bacillus subtilis* chromosome. III. Regulation of initiation." *Proc. Natl. Acad. Sci. U.S.*, **52**, 973. (6–2)

Yoshikawa, H., and Sueoka, N. (1963), "Sequential replication of *Bacillus subtilis* chromosome." *Proc. Natl. Acad. Sci. U.S.*, **49**, 559. (1–2, 6–2)

Zabin, I. (1963a), "Proteins of the lactose system." *Cold Spring Harbor Symp. Quant. Biol.*, **28**, 431. (1–8, 1–9)

Zabin, I. (1963b), "Crystalline thiogalactoside transacetylase." *J. Biol. Chem.*, **238**, 3300. (1–8)

Zabin, I., Képès, A., and Monod, J. (1959), "On enzymic acetylation of isopropyl-β-thiogalactoside and its association with galactoside-permease." *Biochem. Biophys. Res. Commun.*, **1**, 289. (1–8)

Zipser, D. (1963), "Studies on the ribosome-bound β-galactosidase of *E. coli.*" *J. Mol. Biol.*, **7**, 739. (1–3, 1–8)

Zipser, D., and Perrin, D. (1963), "Complementation on ribosomes." *Cold Spring Harbor Symp. Quant. Biol.*, **28**, 583. (1–7)

Zubay, G., and Wilkins, M. H. F. (1960), "X-ray diffraction studies of the structure of ribosomes from *Escherichia coli.*" *J. Mol. Biol.*, **2**, 105. (1–3)

APPENDIXES

From: *J. Gen. Microbiol.* 19, 592–606 (1958)

Reprinted from THE JOURNAL OF GENERAL MICROBIOLOGY
Vol. 19, No. 3, December 1958
 PRINTED IN GREAT BRITAIN

SCHAECHTER, M., MAALØE, O. & KJELDGAARD, N. O. (1958). *J. gen. Microbiol.* 19, 592–606

Dependency on Medium and Temperature of Cell Size and Chemical Composition during Balanced Growth of *Salmonella typhimurium*

BY M. SCHAECHTER*, O. MAALØE AND N. O. KJELDGAARD

State Serum Institute, Copenhagen, Denmark

SUMMARY: Cell mass, the average number of nuclei/cell and the content of RNA and DNA were studied in *Salmonella typhimurium* during balanced (steady state) growth in different media. These quantities could be described as exponential functions of the growth rates afforded by the various media at a given temperature. The size and chemical composition characteristic of a given medium were not influenced by the temperature of cultivation. Thus, under conditions of balanced growth, this organism exists in one of a large number of possible stable physiological states.

The variations in mass/cell are due to changes in the number of nuclei/cell as well as in mass/nucleus. An increase in the number of ribonucleoprotein particles at higher growth rates could, it appears, largely account for the increase in mass/nucleus. Calculations indicate that the rate of protein synthesis per unit RNA is nearly the same at all growth rates.

It is a classic observation that bacterial cells increase in size during the lag which precedes cell division in a newly-inoculated culture, and become smaller again during the period of declining growth (Henrici, 1928). It is also well known that increase in size and enrichment in ribonucleic acid go hand in hand (Malmgren & Hedén, 1947; Morse & Carter, 1949; Wade, 1952; Gale & Folkes, 1953). Previously, interest has been focused mainly on the striking difference between the small, non-dividing cells of an outgrown culture and the larger forms typical of rapid growth. Hence, cells are often described as 'resting' or 'exponentially growing' and these conditions implicitly considered to be alternative physiological states.

We have studied cells of *Salmonella typhimurium* during unrestricted, balanced growth in a variety of media and at different temperatures. The term 'cell' is used throughout this and the following paper to denote either a colony-forming unit or a microscopically visible rod. In both cases the unit may contain more than one nucleus. The terms 'unrestricted and 'balanced' are defined in the discussion. In each case the growth rate, cell size, and the amounts of ribonucleic acid (RNA) and desoxyribonucleic acid (DNA) and the average number of nuclei/cell were determined.

These experiments show that a large number of physiological states exists, each of which is characterized by a particular size and chemical composition of the cells. *At a given temperature*, average mass, RNA, DNA and number of

* Present address: Department of Microbiology, College of Medicine, University of Florida, Gainesville, Florida, U.S.A.

nuclei/cell can be described as exponential functions of the growth rate. *In a given medium*, cell size and composition are almost independent of the growth temperature. The characteristics of the cells would therefore seem to be determined primarily by the pattern of biochemical activities imposed by the medium.

The figures obtained for mass, RNA and DNA/cell permit estimates to be made of the quantities of protein and nucleic acids synthesized/cell/minute in different media at a given temperature. These calculations suggest that, over a wide range of growth rates, the amount of protein synthesized/minute is roughly proportional to the RNA content of the cell; or that, /unit of RNA, the number of protein molecules synthesized/minute is almost independent of the growth rate.

METHODS

Bacteria. The wild-type strain of *Salmonella typhimurium* used in this work was previously employed in this laboratory (Lark & Maaløe, 1954). The tryptophan-requiring mutant *try A*-8 of *S. typhimurium*, kindly supplied by Dr M. Demerec, was used in the continuous-culture experiments.

Culture media. The media employed and the growth rates they supported are listed in Table 1. Amino acids and sugars were added after separate sterilization. All media were adjusted to pH 7·0.

Growth conditions. The organisms were grown in several hundred ml. volumes of medium through which air was constantly bubbled. Balanced growth was maintained by diluting with equal volumes of fresh medium at intervals corresponding to the average generation time. Before sampling, cultures were grown for several hours with frequent checks of the optical density in order to ensure that a constant growth rate had been established. As a rule, the optical density (at 450 mμ, and 1 cm. path) was kept between 0·200 and 0·400. In all media strictly exponential growth is maintained until the optical density reaches 0·800 or more. This optical density corresponds to $1{\cdot}2$–$6{\cdot}2 \times 10^8$ bacteria/ml. and to *c.* 140 μg./ml. bacterial dry weight in the range of culture media employed.

Continuous culture growth. A continuous culture device using an automatic pipetting machine as feeding pump was employed (Formal, Baron & Spilman, 1956). The culture volume of 600 ml. contained in a cylinder 6 cm. in diameter, was aerated through a fritted glass plate. Efficient stirring was produced by the vigorous aeration; thus an added drop of dye solution became uniformly mixed in the culture liquid well within 1 sec. Excess fluid was continuously removed from the surface by suction. The dilution rate D (Monod, 1950) was varied by adjusting both the numbers of strokes delivered by the pipetting machine (10–15/min.) and the volume of medium added/stroke (0·5–1·5 ml.). Mutant *try A*-8 was grown with tryptophan as limiting factor in the casamino-acids medium with 1 μg. tryptophan/ml. Feeding was routinely started just after the culture had exhausted the tryptophan present at the time of inoculation. Sampling for the various analyses was carried out after

Table 1. *Culture media employed*

No.	Medium	Concentration	No. of expt.	Average growth rate in doublings/ hr.
1	Brain + heart infusion	Full strength	1	2·80
2	Nutrient broth	Meat extract + 1 % peptone	3	2·75
3	Yeast extract + glucose	Full strength + 0·2 % glucose	2	2·73
4	Placenta broth	Full strength	1	2·70
5	Nutrient broth	Dil. 1:2 with medium no. 14	3	2·60
6	Nutrient broth	Dil. 1:5 with medium no. 14	9	2·40
7	Casamino acids[(a)]	1·5 % (Difco) + 0·01 % tryptophan in medium no. 14	2	2·00
8	199 Tissue-culture medium	See[(b)]	1	1·88
9	20 amino acids	As in medium No. 8 + salt solution[(c)]	1	1·83
10	Amino acids pool 2[(d)]	As in medium No. 8 + salt solution[(c)]	2	1·46
11	Amino acids pool 3[(e)]	As in medium No. 8 + salt solution[(c)]	2	1·38
12	Amino acids pool 4[(f)]	As in medium No. 8 + salt solution[(c)]	1	1·25
13	Amino acids pool 1[(g)]	As in medium No. 8 + salt solution[(c)]	1	1·22
14	Glucose salt (medium K)	0·2 % + Salt solution[(c)]	9	1·20
15	Succinate salt	0·2 % + Salt solution[(c)]	2	0·94
16	Lactate salt	0·2 % + Salt solution[(c)]	2	0·90
17	Dulcitol salt	0·05 % + Salt solution[(c)]	1	0·83
18	Aspartate salt	0·012 % + Salt solution[(c)]	1	0·83
19	Methionine salt	0·06 % + Salt solution[(c)]	1	0·81
20	Histidine salt	0·04 % + Salt solution[(c)]	1	0·78
21	Threonine salt	0·012 % + Salt solution[(c)]	1	0·63
22	Lysine salt	0·014 % + Salt solution[(c)]	1	0·62

(*a*) This medium, with limiting tryptophan, was employed in the bactostat experiments.

(*b*) Morgan's medium (Salk, Youngner & Ward, 1954) was employed without antibiotics, indicator and solutions H–K, I, J, Q, G and P.

(*c*) Salt solution: $MgSO_4.7H_2O$, 0·1; citric acid, 1·0; $Na_2HPO_4.2H_2O$, 5·0; $Na(NH_4)HPO_4.4H_2O$, 1·74; KCl, 0·74 g./l. Made up as a 50 × concentrate. This solution did not support perceptible growth without the addition of other carbon sources.

(*d*) Threonine, tyrosine, cysteine, histidine, phenylalanine, isoleucine, hydroxyproline and arginine.

(*e*) Phenylalanine, isoleucine, hydroxyproline, arginine, leucine, aspartic acid, glycine and tryptophan.

(*f*) Leucine, aspartic acid, glycine, tryptophan, glutamic acid, alanine, serine and valine.

(*g*) Glutamic acid, alanine, serine, valine, glutamine, lysine, methionine and proline.

not less than 6 hr. of growth. During this period the optical density remained practically constant at about 0·400.

Mass determination. The values of mass/cell are expressed as the optical density at 450 mμ (1 cm. path) given by a suspension containing 10^7 cells/ml. The optical density was found to be proportional to the dry weight, irrespective of the cell size. Optical density 0·100 corresponds to 17–18 μg. dry weight/ml.

Plate counts. Samples of the cultures were diluted in steps representing a total dilution of 2 or 4×10^{-4}. The original sampling was done with a 0·025 or 0·050 ml. constriction pipette and the subsequent steps were carried out with

0·1 ml. serological pipettes. For each value of Fig. 1 plating was done from at least six individual dilutions performed within 10 min. and adjusted to give between 300 and 600 colonies/plate. The viable counts were fitted to the growth curve determined by the optical-density measurements. It was found that the number of viable cells/ml. could be measured with an error of less than 10 %.

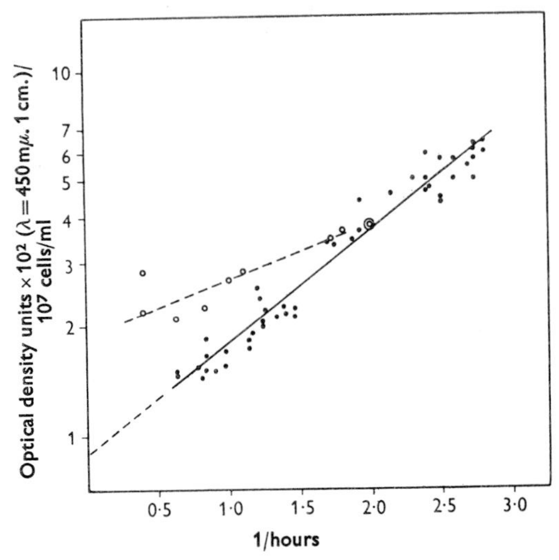

Fig. 1. Dependency of cell mass on growth rate at 37°. From the optical-density (mass) measurements and the viable counts in the different media, values for optical density/10^7 cells/ml. were calculated. The logarithm of these values is plotted against the growth rate expressed as doublings/hr. (●). The stippled line corresponding to the open rings and to the double-ringed point represents results from continuous culture experiments plotted against the dilution rate (○).

Chemical analysis. For nucleic-acid determinations, 40 ml. samples were frozen quickly in a solid CO_2 + ethanol bath. They were thawed and centrifuged in a cooled Servall angle centrifuge at 12,000 rev./min. for 20 min., the sediments were resuspended in 2·5 ml. of cold saline and 0·1 ml. of 70 % perchloric acid was added to 2 ml. of this suspension. The material was heated to 70° for 30 min., centrifuged and the supernate collected for colorimetric sugar tests. Deoxyribose was determined by the procedure of Burton (1956) on 1·0 ml. of the acid extract. Ribose determinations following the method of Kerr & Seraidarian (1945) were performed on 0·1 ml. of the extract. All spectrophotometry was done with a Zeiss Model PMQ II spectrophotometer employing 1 cm. cuvettes. Most of the values presented in Figs. 2 and 3 are averages of four independent determinations.

Nuclear staining. Fixation with OsO_4 and staining with thionine were carried out according to Lark, Maaløe & Rostock (1955), except that acid hydrolysis was extended to 6 min. This procedure is not primarily intended to preserve fine structural detail but, in the organism used, it reveals the same

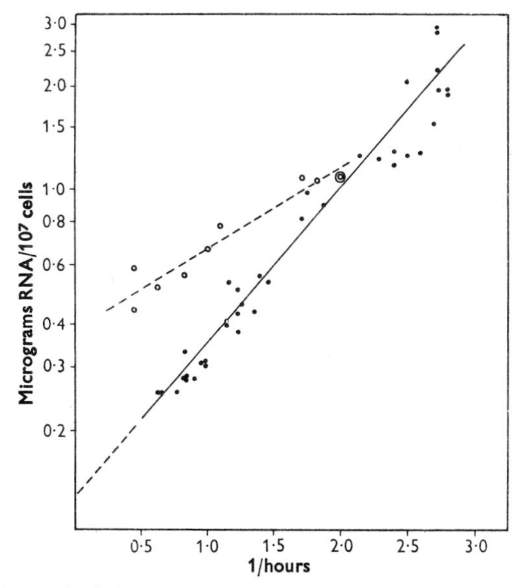

Fig. 2. Dependency of cellular ribonucleic acid on growth rate at 37°. The RNA content of the cultures was calculated from the ribose determinations. (μg. RNA = μg ribose × 4·91). The logarithm of the RNA values (micrograms)/10^7 viable cells is plotted against the growth rate (●). The stippled line corresponding to the open rings and to the double-ringed point represents results from continuous culture experiments, plotted against the dilution rate (○).

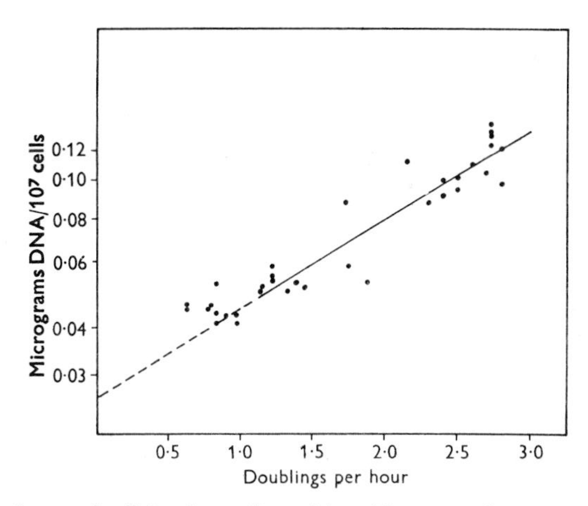

Fig. 3. Dependency of cellular deoxyribonucleic acid on growth rate at 37°. The DNA content of the cultures was calculated from the deoxyribose determinations (μg. DNA = μg. deoxyribose × 2·44). The logarithm of the DNA values μg./10^7 viable cells is plotted against the growth rate.

number of individual staining bodies in each cell as that obtained by other methods. For reasons of ease of observation the stained preparations were examined under phase contrast microscope (Zeiss). Between 300 and 400 cells per sample were scored as one-, two-, or four-nucleated taking into consideration, when possible, that some of the rods consisted of sister cells in different degrees of separation. A subjective criterion had to be employed in order to score a cell containing two adjacent bodies as one- or two-nucleated. However, repeated counts of the same preparation after an interval of months, or duplicate counts by different observers, always gave results compatible with the sampling error.

RESULTS

Balanced growth was maintained at 37° in the different media listed above (Table 1) and samples analysed for mass (optical density) RNA, DNA, viable counts and number of nuclei/cell. The results are presented in Figs. 1–3 in which logarithms of mass, RNA and DNA per viable cell are plotted against

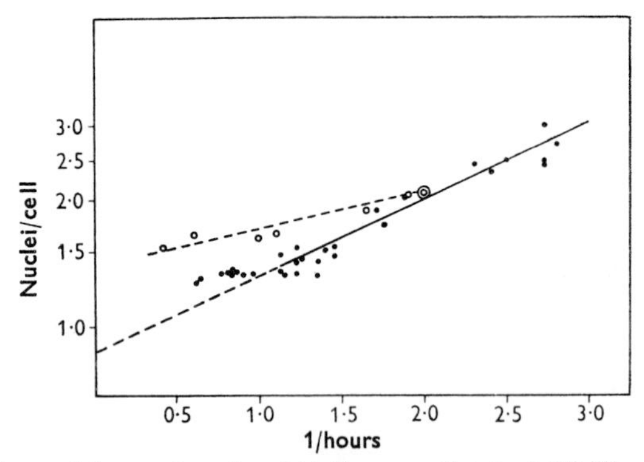

Fig. 4. Dependency of the number of nuclei/cell on growth rate at 37°. The average number of nuclei/cell was calculated from direct counts on stained preparations. The logarithm of the values is plotted against the corresponding growth rate (●). The stippled line corresponding to the open rings and the double-ringed point represents results from continuous culture experiments, plotted against the dilution rate (○).

the growth rate. Figure 4 represents a similar plot for nuclei/cell. Regression analysis showed that the straight lines drawn in Figs. 1–4 adequately represent the observed values. The individual determinations deviate only slightly more from the lines than is to be expected when the combined errors of the chemical analysis and the viable counts are taken into account. For ease of comparison, the increments on the logarithmic scale are the same in all figures.

In Fig. 1, the unbroken line fitted to the solid points shows that cell mass just about doubles/unit increase in doublings/hr. The extrapolation to zero growth rate suggests that the minimal bacterial size would be about half that of a cell growing in glucose-salt medium. This minimal size was actually attained under conditions of nitrogen starvation (see following paper).

Dr K. F. A. Ross kindly carried out measurements on the thickness of formalin-fixed organisms by interference microscopy using a modification of the technique he developed in 1955 (Ross, 1957). He obtained the following figures for the average of ten determinations per sample: $1{\cdot}43\mu$ for a culture growing in medium no. 2 at 2·73 doublings/hr. (d/hr.); $1{\cdot}22\mu$ for 1·85 d/hr. (medium no. 7); $0{\cdot}93\mu$ for 1·00 d/hr. (medium no. 14) and $0{\cdot}87\mu$ for 0·61 d/hr. (medium no. 22). The cell volumes obtained from these figures and from estimates of cell lengths were found to be proportional to the cell mass, as estimated from optical density measurements.

Figs. 2 and 3 show that, per unit increase in doublings/hr., the amount of RNA/cell increases by $\times 2{\cdot}85$ that of DNA/cell by $\times 1{\cdot}73$. The corresponding factor for the average number of nuclei/cell, derived from Fig. 4, is $\times 1{\cdot}55$. At 37°, the four parameters examined may thus be described as exponential functions of the growth rate and can be arranged as follows, with regard to the slopes of the semilogarithmic plots: RNA > mass > DNA ⩾ nuclei/cell.

It is to be understood that all 'per cell values' are based, either on viable counts, or, in the case of nuclei, on cytological observations. Simultaneous haemocytometer and colony counts repeatedly showed that, under conditions of balanced growth, viable and total counts did not differ significantly. Counting unstained cells in the phase contrast microscope showed that, in all media, approximately 75 % of the units appeared to be true single cells, the remaining 25 % were 'doublets' representing incompletely separated sister cells. In Figs. 1–3, an approximate correction for doublets can be made by multiplying the ordinate values by 0·8.

The figures for nuclei /cell (Fig. 4) are based on direct counts of stained preparations. It was not always possible after staining to distinguish between single elements and doublets, particularly when the cells are small. Thus, at the lowest growth rates (smallest cells) uninucleated sister cells which remained attached to one another were probably often scored as binucleates. When the number of nuclei/cell is close to unity a bias of this kind may increase the observed value significantly over the true one. This might be the reason why, in Fig. 4, the experimental points deviate from the straight line at low rates, and it may also explain that the values for DNA/nucleus, which at higher growth rates are found to vary in a random manner around the mean value, decrease slightly, but significantly, in this region.

A number of experiments were carried out with cultures grown at lower temperatures. In Table 2 results obtained at 37° and at 25° with five different media are compared. In all cases, the growth rate at 25° was about half that at 37°; nevertheless, mass, RNA, DNA and number of nuclei/cell remained nearly constant for a given medium. In broth or in the amino-acid medium the figures for nuclei/cell are somewhat higher at 37° than at 25°, but the experiments at 25° are few and the observed difference is probably not significant. Moreover, extensive chemical and cytological studies previously carried out with the same organism showed that, in broth, identical values for DNA and for nuclei/cell are obtained at 25° and at 37° (Lark & Maaløe, 1956; Lark, Maaløe & Rostock, 1955).

In fact, our data suggest that more extensive analyses of 25° cultures would permit graphs to be constructed which would be identical with those of Figs. 1–4 if the growth rate values on the abscissa were reduced to half. Thus, within the temperature range studied, *the size and chemical composition of the cells are related to the growth rate only in so far as it depends on the medium.*

Table 2. *The effect of temperature on cell size and composition*

Medium	No. of expts.	Growth temp. (° C.)	Doublings/ hr.	Optical density* mass	RNA*	DNA*	Nuclei/ cell
No. 6 (broth)	2	25	1·06	5·80	1·64	0·130	2·85
	4	37	2·40	5·00	1·44	0·095	2·50
No. 9 (amino acids)	1	25	0·88	3·66	0·92	0·085	2·05
	2	37	1·83	3·76	0·97	0·056	1·74
No. 14 (glucose)	3	25	0·65	2·32	0·56	0·065	1·46
	5	37	1·20	1·92	0·44	0·048	1·88
No. 15 (succinate)	2	25	0·48	1·47	0·39	0·038	1·31
	2	37	0·93	1·60	0·39	0·042	1·33
No. 16 (lactate)	2	25	0·50	1·50	0·39	0·038	1·30
	2	37	0·90	1·61	0·39	0·039	1·35

* The units for mass, RNA and DNA per cell are the same as in Figs. 1–3, respectively.

The results of the analysis of mass, RNA and nuclei/cell from the continuous culture experiments are presented as open circles in Figs. 1, 2 and 4. The logarithms of cell contents are plotted against the dilution rate D expressed in doublings of culture volume/hr. Monod (1950) and Novick & Szilard (1950) have shown that, in the ideal continuous culture system, D is related to the growth rate μ (in doublings/hr.) by the equation $\mu = D/\ln 2$. As will be seen, this situation was not obtained throughout our experiments. In Figs. 1, 2, and 4 the points marked with a double ring correspond to the maximum rate ($\mu = 2{\cdot}0$) attainable during unrestricted growth of strain *tryA*-8 in the Casamino acid medium with excess tryptophan. Thus, for values of D higher than 1·38, corresponding to $\mu = 2{\cdot}0$, the theoretical growth rate calculated from the above formula exceeds the maximum values for unrestricted growth. D values as high as 1·77, corresponding to a theoretical growth rate of 2·6, have been obtained in our experiments. A similar discrepancy between the calculated and the maximum growth rates was reported by Herbert, Elsworth & Telling (1956) and Powell (1956) who attributed it to imperfect mixing.

It will be seen from Figs. 1, 2 and 4, that the values for mass, RNA and nuclei/cell for organisms grown in continuous culture may also be described as exponential functions of the growth rate. The slopes of the stippled lines drawn in Figs. 1, 2, and 4 are considerably less than those obtained for unrestricted growth, indicating that the lower the dilution rate, the more do the values exceed those from batch cultures. The same trend was observed for DNA, but the data are not included in Fig. 3 because of considerable scatter in the values obtained.

DISCUSSION

Our discussion falls into three parts: (1) An account of the physiological states imposed by the medium under unrestricted and restricted, balanced growth. (2) A representation of related and otherwise relevant data from the literature. (3) An analysis of our findings in terms of the major synthetic activities of the bacterial cell.

(1) In liquid cultures of low bacterial concentration, cells continue to grow for a long time in a virtually unchanging environment. This ideal condition leads to the establishment of a steady state of balanced growth, which can be prolonged at will by appropriate dilutions of the culture. In Campbell's apt formulation (Campbell, 1957), growth is said to be *balanced* over a time interval if, during the interval, every 'extensive' property of the system increases by the same factor. Failure to maintain balanced growth throughout an experiment makes it impossible to relate any measured quantity to the growth rate in a direct way.

When the density of a culture approaches saturation the growth rate gradually decreases and it increases upon subsequent dilution with fresh medium. In either case the changes in rates of cell division and of mass synthesis do not run parallel; as a rule, the rate of cell division remains unchanged for some time after the rate of mass synthesis has been lowered or raised in response to a change in the environment. This general phenomenon, which will be analysed in more detail in the next paper (Kjeldgaard, Maaløe & Schaechter, 1958), accounts for the well-known fact that 'exponentially growing cells' are bigger than 'resting cells'. These common, descriptive terms are sometimes taken to mean that only two physiological cell types exist: a small, resting cell and a larger, exponentially growing cell. This is, however, too simple a picture. Under conditions of *balanced growth*, one of a large number of possible physiological states is established. These states are characterized by the size and chemical composition of the cell; they depend on the culture medium, are not grossly influenced by the temperature of cultivation and can probably be maintained as long as the genetic stability of the culture permits. *At a given temperature*, size and composition are found to depend in a simple manner on the growth rate afforded by the medium. This implies that media which give identical growth rates produce identical physiological states, regardless of the actual constituents of the media. The 'resting state' finds a natural place in this system since, in an outgrown broth culture, the size of the cells is reduced to approximately the value expected for zero growth rate (see Fig. 1).

We have so far considered only batch cultures where all the relevant nutrients are present in excess in the medium. Because the growth rate is limited by the *type* of nutrients and not by their *concentration*, we refer to this situation as 'unrestricted growth'. We assume that the growth rate observed under these conditions is the highest which can be attained with the set of nutrients available to the cell. In a continuous culture device of the type we employed, growth is 'restricted' by the rate at which, say, a required amino acid is added, i.e. by the low extra- and intracellular concentration of that component. Under conditions of unrestricted growth the concentration inside the cell of, say, an amino acid might similarly be thought of as being rate-limiting. This need not be the case, however, since, as discussed later, the growth rate may be controlled at the level of protein synthesis without involving limiting intracellular concentrations of amino acids, etc.

In our continuous culture experiments, new medium was added to the culture in pulses each of which momentarily increased the tryptophan concentration by 1–3 μg/l. According to Novick & Szilard (1950) a constant tryptophan concentration of about 3 μg/l. permits growth of *Escherichia coli*, strain B/1, *t* at maximum rate; but below this concentration the growth rate rapidly decreases. Assuming a similar concentration dependency for strain *tryA*-8 of *Salmonella typhimurium*, every pulse of new medium will create conditions for growth at a relatively high rate for a short period. It is thus possible that, in our system, growth is intermittent, and that under such conditions, the growth rate during the pulse of growth afforded by a pulse of new medium, is not related to the dilution rate D in the simple manner proposed by Monod (1950) and Novick & Szilard (1950). We could therefore assume that the rate of synthesis during each pulse, rather than the overall rate, determines the size and chemical composition of the cell. However, experiments under more nearly ideal conditions of continuous growth are needed before the discrepancy between the results obtained under conditions of restricted and unrestricted growth can be properly analysed.

(2) Attempts to determine concurrently cell mass, nucleic acid content and the number of nuclei as functions of the growth rate have not previously been reported. Several pertinent studies exist in which one or more of these properties were related to the rate of growth. Thus, Wade (1952) obtained results which suggested a linear relation between RNA phosphorus/mg. N and the growth rate of *Escherichia coli*. Our data (Figs. 1, 2) indicate that this relation may actually be exponential; however, over the range studied by Wade and ourselves (0·6–2·8 generations/hr.), the increase in total RNA/unit mass (unlike RNA/cell) is at most twofold, and a clear distinction between linear and exponential functions therefore cannot be made. On the other hand, the overall increase is significantly less in Wade's experiments than in ours (50–60 % and 100 %, respectively). This difference may be due to the use by Wade of very large inocula (initial culture density: $2{\cdot}5 \times 10^8$ to 10^9 organisms/ml.). According to our experience the cells of such a dense culture would not reach, or maintain, the size and RNA concentration characteristic of balanced growth. Wade's careful measurements show that the high growth rate could not always be maintained throughout the experiment; the RNA concentrations, which were related to the *initial* growth rates, may therefore be low compared to the values which would have been obtained had growth been truly balanced.

Caldwell & Hinshelwood (1950) and Caldwell, Mackor & Hinshelwood (1950) determined the RNA concentration (in mg. RNA-phosphorus/mg. N) in different strains of *Aerobacter aerogenes* under various conditions. From the published data it cannot be ascertained whether balanced growth was attained, but their experiments also show that the faster the growth the higher the RNA concentration. In Aerobacter, the observed range of concentration is very high (three- to fourfold) perhaps because the lower growth rates were obtained by adding drugs to the medium or by using selected, slow-growing mutants.

Caldwell & Hinshelwood (1950) also determined the DNA phosphorus in various cultures of *Aerobacter aerogenes*. With increasing values for total nitrogen/cell, a slight, but probably significant rise in DNA/cell was observed. No comparison between these figures and the growth rates can be derived from their data.

Perret (1958), studying *Escherichia coli* strain K12, measured the mean cell length and the number of intracellular structures which appeared as transverse light bands under the phase microscope (probably equivalent to the nuclei described here). He also found that, to the different growth rates obtained in different media and in continuous cultures correspond definite values of cell length and number of 'nuclei'. His figures for nuclei/cell correspond closely to those of Fig. 4.

(3) The existence of a variety of stable physiological states cannot be explained in a simple manner. What follows is an attempt to analyse the significant features of our experimental findings in terms of the major synthetic activities of the cells.

Cytological evidence strongly suggests that the stained bodies referred to as 'nuclei' contain DNA, and we shall assume that most, if not all, the DNA of the cell is located there. A comparison of Figs. 3 and 4 shows that the amount of DNA per stained body is nearly constant, as would be expected if each body represents a nucleus in the physiological and genetic sense. With this in mind it seems opportune to differentiate between variation on the cellular and on the nuclear level. Since at low growth rates the majority of cells are uninucleated it seems natural to consider a single nucleus plus its corresponding cytoplasm, cell wall, etc., as an elementary unit. Multinucleated cells, composed of two or more such units can be thought of as syncytial. We will therefore distinguish between changes in the number of elementary units/cell and in mass/elementary unit. The way in which changes in the number of elementary units/cell come about is treated in the second paper of this series.

The variation in mass per elementary unit will be analysed below in accordance with the following assumptions: (*a*) that a large fraction of the cell's RNA is in the form of ribonucleoprotein particles consisting of about equal parts of RNA and protein and with molecular weight about one million (Schachman, Pardee & Stanier, 1952; Tissières & Watson, 1958); (*b*) that, per nucleus, the cell contains fixed amounts of DNA, cell wall and cell membrane material, varying amounts of free RNA and particles and, finally, a pool of soluble protein and other compounds; and (*c*) that this pool is always made up largely of protein.

The first assumption is supported by data from Wade & Morgan (1957). Comparing resting cells of *Escherichia coli* with cells growing in a complex medium these authors found that the RNA-pentose of particles sedimenting completely in 4 hr. at 100,000 *g* amounted respectively to about 50 and 75 % of the total RNA-pentose. The second assumption is based on estimates of cell diameters and lengths (cf. p. 598) from which it can be estimated that the surface area/nucleus is virtually constant. The actual weight ascribed to cell wall and membrane (see Table 3) is of little importance for our conclusions. The third assumption seems more gratuitous; however, the greater part of the protein of the cell must be in the pool, and since this never exceeds about 60 % of the cell weight (Table 3, column 7) it is fair to assume that the bulk of the pool is protein (free enzymes).

Table 3. *Relative rates of protein synthesis*

1	2	3	4	5	6	7	8	9
							Pool + particle protein synthesized/min.*	
Doublings/ hr.	Dry weight/ cell*	Nuclei/ cell	Dry weight/ nucleus*	RNA/ nucleus*	Particles/ nucleus†	Pool material/ nucleus*‡	Per nucleus	Per particle ($\times 10^4$)
0·6	240	1·25§	192	19	11,300	100	1·1	0·98
		1·10	218	22	13,300	120	1·3	1·0
1·2	360	1·45	250	31	22,400	135	3·1	1·4
2·4	840	2·40	350	65	54,000	176	8·8	1·6
2·8	1090	2·90	376	84	81,000	160	10·6	1·3

* All weights in g. $\times 10^{15}$.

† Calculated on the assumption that, from top to bottom, 50, 60, 70 and 80 % of the RNA is in particles o molecular weight one million, and composed of equal parts of protein and RNA.

‡ Per nucleus, the cell is assumed to consist of: 65×10^{-15} g. of wall, membrane and nuclear material, i.e about one-third by weight of the smallest cell type; (*b*) particles and free RNA; and (*c*) a pool mainly containin soluble protein.

§ Two values given: above, the one directly observed; below, that obtained by extrapolating the linear par of the curve of Fig. 4 (see p. 597).

Table 3 shows representative figures for mass, average number of nuclei/ cell and mass and RNA/nucleus, taken from Figs. 1, 2, and 4 (columns 2, 3, 4, 5). The right-hand side of the Table contains calculations based on these values and on the assumptions listed above. The number of particles and the pool size per nucleus are presented in columns 6 and 7. The relatively small changes in pool size show that variation in *mass/nucleus is due mainly to variation in number of particles/nucleus.*

In Table 3, column 8 presents maximum values for the synthesis of protein/ nucleus/min. (assuming the pool to be all protein and adding to that the particle protein). It is apparent that the *rate* of protein synthesis is directly proportional to the *amount* of RNA, or the number of particles, and that both increase in rough proportion to the growth rate. Small variations in the soluble protein fraction of the pool or in the particle fraction of RNA do not seriously affect these trends. The rate of protein synthesis/unit RNA, or per particle, thus is nearly independent of the growth rate (column 9). This conclusion is of considerable interest because recent biochemical evidence indicates that these particles, which are analogous to the 'microsomal particles' of animal cells, are directly concerned with protein synthesis (see, for example, review by Crick, 1958).

The constancy of the rate of protein synthesis/particle is most readily interpreted on the simple assumption that all particles participate equally in protein synthesis. This may, however, not be the case. By studying externally induced synthesis of β-galactosidase, it has been possible to show that the enzyme-forming system remains intact during growth in the absence of an inducer (Monod, Pappenheimer & Cohen-Bazire, 1952). If we tentatively identify the system producing β-galactosidase with one class of particles, we have a case where particles which continue to be reproduced remain virtually inactive unless an inducer is present. Addition to a culture of, say, an amino acid may cause repression of enzymes concerned with the synthesis of the added compound (see, for example, Vogel, 1957), and it is sometimes taken for granted that the process of repression also involves a reduction of the size of the enzyme-forming systems. If this is not true, as suggested by the results of Monod *et al.* (1952), cells growing in a complex medium would contain a certain fraction of inactive particles (corresponding to the repressed enzymes), whereas cells grown in minimal medium would contain predominantly active ones (little or no repression).

Without knowing what fraction of the particles is actively synthesizing, the true rate of protein synthesis/particle cannot be estimated. Despite this uncertainty it is clear that, unless a majority of the particles are rendered inactive during growth in complex media, the rate of protein synthesis per particle increases much less than does the growth rate.

It is attractive to imagine that the system responsible for a particularly complex process like protein synthesis perhaps functions with nearly the same efficiency under very different growth conditions (with the reservation, of course, that certain enzyme-forming systems may have *their* function specifically repressed). Addition to a culture growing in minimal medium of compounds like amino acids, purines or pyrimidines increases the growth rate presumably by relieving the cells of the necessity for synthesizing the added compounds. If one assumes that the economy of cell growth is actually based on maintaining a high efficiency of protein synthesis it is evident that an increase in growth rate is possible only if the protein synthesizing system of the individual cell is expanded; i.e. if the number of particles/nucleus is increased. For this to happen, the addition of, say, amino acids to the medium must cause a definite increase in the rate of RNA synthesis which, in turn, brings about the observed, *but smaller* increase in growth rate.

In the next paper we shall see that, in agreement with this hypothesis, the initial effect of adding amino acids or broth to a minimal medium culture is to stimulate RNA synthesis preferentially.

We wish hereby to acknowledge the expert technical assistance of Mr O. Rostock. One of the authors (M.S.) was aided by a post-doctoral fellowship grant from the American Cancer Society and one (N.O.K.) by grants from the Danish National Science Foundation and the Lilly Research Foundation.

REFERENCES

Burton, K. (1956). A study of the conditions and mechanism of the diphenylamine reaction for the colorimetric estimation of deoxyribonucleic acid. *Biochem. J.* **62**, 315.

Caldwell, P. C. & Hinshelwood, C. (1950). The nucleic acid content of *Bact. lactis aerogenes*. *J. chem. Soc.* 1415.

Caldwell, P. C., Mackor, E. L. & Hinshelwood, C. (1950). The ribonucleic acid content and cell growth of *Bact. lactis aerogenes*. *J. chem. Soc.* 3151.

Campbell, A. (1957). Synchronization of cell division. *Bact. Rev.* **21**, 263.

Crick, F. H. C. (1958). On protein synthesis. *Symp. Soc. expl. Biol. N.Y.* (in the Press).

Formal, S. B., Baron, L. S. & Spilman, W. (1956). The virulence and immunogenicity of *Salmonella typhosa* grown in continuous culture. *J. Bact.* **72**, 168.

Gale, E. F. & Folkes, J. P. (1953). The assimilation of amino-acids by bacteria. 14. Nucleic acid and protein synthesis in *Staphylococcus aureus*. *Biochem. J.* **53**, 483.

Henrici, A. T. (1928). Morphologic variation and the rate of growth of bacteria. *Microbiology Monographs*. London: Baillière, Tindall and Cox.

Herbert, D., Elsworth, R. & Telling, R. C. (1956). The continuous culture of bacteria: a theoretical and experimental study. *J. gen. Microbiol.* **14**, 601.

Kerr, S. E. & Seraidarian, K. (1945). The separation of purine nucleosides from free purines and the determination of the purines and ribose in these fractions. *J. biol. Chem.* **159**, 211.

Kjeldgaard, N. O., Maaløe, O. Schaechter, M. (1958). The transition between different physiological states during balanced growth of *Salmonella typhimurium*. *J. gen. Microbiol.* **19**, 607.

Lark, K. G. & Maaløe, O. (1954). The induction of cellular and nuclear division in *Salmonella typhimurium* by means of temperature shifts. *Biochim. biophys. Acta*, **15**, 345.

Lark, K. G. & Maaløe, O. (1956). Nucleic acid synthesis and the division cycle of *Salmonella typhimurium*. *Biochim. biophys. Acta*, **21**, 448.

Lark, K. G., Maaløe, O. & Rostock, O. (1955). Cytological studies of nuclear division in *Salmonella typhimurium*. *J. gen. Microbiol.* **13**, 318.

Malmgren, B. & Hedén, C. (1947). Studies of the nucleotide metabolism of bacteria. III. The nucleotide metabolism of Gram negative bacteria. *Acta path. microbiol, scand.* **24**, 448.

Monod, J. (1950). La technique de culture continue, théorie et applications. *Ann. Inst. Pasteur*, **79**, 390.

Monod, J., Pappenheimer, A. M. & Cohen-Bazire, G. (1952). La cinétique de la biosynthèse de la β-galactosidase chez *E. coli* considérée comme fonction de la croissance. *Biochim. biophys. Acta*, **9**, 648.

Morse, M. L. & Carter, C. E. (1949). The synthesis of nucleic acids in cultures of *Escherichia coli* strains B and B/r. *J. Bact.* **58**, 317.

Novick, A. & Szilard, L. (1950). Experiments with the chemostat on spontaneous mutations of bacteria. *Proc. nat. Acad. Sci.* **36**, 708.

Perret, C. J. (1958). The effect of growth-rate on the anatomy of *Escherichia coli*. *J. gen. Microbiol.* **18**, vii.

Powell, E. O. (1956). Growth rate and generation time of bacteria, with special reference to continuous culture. *J. gen. Microbiol.* **15**, 492.

Ross, K. F. A. (1957). The size of living bacteria. *Quart. J. micr. Sci.* **98**, 435.

Salk, J. E., Youngner, J. S. & Ward, E. N. (1954). Use of color change of phenol red as the indicator in titrating poliomyelitis virus or its antibody in a tissue-culture system. *Amer. J. Hyg.* **50**, 214.

Schachman, H. K., Pardee, A. B. & Stanier, R. Y. (1952). Studies on the macromolecular organization of microbial cells. *Arch. Biochem. Biophys.* **38**, 245.

TISSIÈRES, A. & WATSON, J. D. (1958). Ribonucleoprotein particles from *Escherichia coli*. *Nature, Lond.* **182**, 778.

VOGEL, H. J. (1957). Repression and induction as control mechanisms of enzyme biogenesis: the 'adaptive' formation of acetylornithase. In *Chemical Basis of Heredity*, p. 276. Baltimore: The Johns Hopkins Press.

WADE, H. E. (1952). Variation in the phosphorus content of *Escherichia coli* during cultivation. *J. gen. Microbiol.* **7**, 24.

WADE, H. E. & MORGAN, D. M. (1957). The nature of the fluctuating ribonucleic acid in *Escherichia coli*. *Biochem. J.* **65**, 321.

(*Received* 19 *June* 1958)

From: *Biochim. Biophys. Acta* 49, 64–76 (1961)

THE KINETICS OF RIBONUCLEIC ACID- AND PROTEIN FORMATION IN *SALMONELLA TYPHIMURIUM* DURING THE TRANSITION BETWEEN DIFFERENT STATES OF BALANCED GROWTH

NIELS OLE KJELDGAARD

University Institute of Microbiology, Copenhagen (Denmark)

(Received October 17th, 1960)

SUMMARY

1. During an experiment, in which bacteria are transferred from a glucose–ammonia–salts medium into broth at 37° (shift up) the rate of ribonucleic acid synthesis in *Salmonella typhimurium* is greatly increased for the first 30 min. After this period the rate settles at the value characteristic of the broth medium.

2. It is suggested that the diphasic shape of the curve for ribonucleic acid formation is due chiefly to an accelerated synthesis of ribosomal particles.

3. Under steady state conditions of growth a constant relationship is observed between the cell content of ribosomes and the rate of protein synthesis.

4. In a "shift up" experiment, the rate of protein synthesis is initially low, but reaches the rate characteristic of the broth medium about 20 min after the change in growth medium.

5. The data for protein synthesis agree well with the suggested course of ribosome formation and the proportionality constant between ribosome content and rate of protein synthesis observed under steady state conditions.

INTRODUCTION

Bacteria will usually respond to an alteration of the culture medium by changing the growth rate as well as the size and the chemical composition of the cells. At a given temperature a simple exponential relationship exists between the growth rate, the cell size and the cellular content of RNA and DNA[1]. The faster the bacteria grow, the bigger the cells and the higher the content of RNA and DNA, with RNA showing the greater response to the changes in growth rate.

Most of the RNA is present in the cells in the form of ribosomal particles consisting of about 63 % RNA and 37 % protein, and with a molecular weight of a few million[2]. Recent work[3–4] has suggested an important role for these particles in protein formation, presumably as the sites of synthesis. In accordance with this view and on basis of the findings mentioned above, it can be calculated for bacteria that the rate of protein synthesis per unit ribosomal RNA is virtually constant irrespective of the growth rate[1]. This observation suggests that the rate of bacterial growth is in fact limited by the number of ribosomal particles present in the cells[1–5].

Abbreviations: RNA, ribonucleic acid; DNA, deoxyribonucleic acid; Tris, tris(hydroxymethyl)aminomethane; TCA, trichloroacetic acid.

When bacteria growing under conditions of balanced growth in one medium are transferred to another medium which will support a higher growth rate, the following orderly sequence of changes in the rate of synthesis of the cell components is observed[6].

The synthesis of RNA is the first process to respond to the change in environment immediately increasing to the rate characteristic of the new medium. At 37° this change is followed after a few minutes by a similar increase in the rate of synthesis of total cell mass and after 20 and 65 min respectively by changes in the rates of DNA formation and of cell division[6].

It seemed, therefore, that the period following a change in growth medium would be suitable for studying the relation between RNA and protein synthesis. A more detailed study than could be made with conventional chemical methods[6] was undertaken using incorporation of [^{32}P] orthophosphate and [^{14}C]uracil as an index of RNA formation and the uptake of [^{14}C]amino acids as indicators of protein synthesis.

MATERIALS AND METHODS

Bacteria

The wild type strain of *Salmonella typhimurium*, employed in previous studies[1,6], was used throughout the experiments.

Culture media

Low-phosphate Tris minimal medium: Tris 12.0 g; conc. HCl, 6.9 ml; NH_4Cl, 2.0 g; KCl, 2.0 g; $MgCl_2 \cdot 6H_2O$, 0.5 g; $Na_2HPO_4 \cdot 2H_2O$, 50 mg; Na_2SO_4, 20 mg; all dissolved in water and diluted to 1 l.

The pH of the medium is 7.5 and with glucose (0.2 %) as energy source it supports a growth rate of 1.20 doublings/h.

Dilution medium

$MgSO_4 \cdot 7H_2O$, 5.0 g; conc. HCl, 40 ml; $Na_2HPO_4 \cdot 2H_2O$, 250 g; $NaNH_4HPO_4 \cdot 4H_2O$, 87 g; KCl, 37 g, dissolved in about 700 ml of water and diluted to 1 l. When 3 ml of this concentrated solution is diluted into 100 ml of water a medium with the same osmotic strength as the "Tris" medium is obtained.

Low phosphate broth medium

To remove most of the inorganic phosphate from the broth medium, a solution of 2 g of meat extract (Lab-Lemco, Oxo Ltd., London, England) and 2 g of peptone (Orthana Ltd., Copenhagen, Denmark) in 100 ml of water was passed through a 25-ml column of the anion exchanger Amberlite IRA 400 in the OH-form.

The strongly alkaline effluent is neutralized and diluted with an equal volume of Tris medium. Supplemented with 0.2 % glucose this medium supports a growth rate of 2.5 doublings/h.

Tris broth medium

Meat extract (10 g/l) and peptone (10 g/l) dissolved in Tris minimal medium. Supplemented with glucose (0.2 %) the medium supports a growth rate of 2.5 doublings/h.

Preutilized broth medium

Although uracil is taken up from the medium by *Salmonella typhimurium*, preliminary experiments showed that broth contains materials interfering with the utilization of uracil. To remove this material which is preferentially utilized, *Salmonella typhimurium* was grown in the Tris broth medium to an absorbancy of 0.5. The culture was then filtered through a membrane-filter to remove the bacteria and the filtrate sterilized by autoclaving. For the [^{14}C]uracil incorporation experiments, the preutilized medium was supplemented with 5 μg/ml of non radioactive uracil and 0.2 % glucose. The medium supports a growth rate of 2.4 doublings/h.

Chemicals

Carrier free [^{32}P]phosphate as well as ^{14}C labeled DL-[3-^{14}C]tryptophan (17 μC/mg), L-[2-im-^{14}C]histidine (39 μC/mg), generally labeled L-phenylalanine (62 μC/mg), L-arginine (34 μC/mg), and glycine (25 μC/mg) and [2-^{14}C]uracil (91 μC/mg) were obtained from The Radiochemical Centre, Amersham, England. Some of the [^{32}P]-phosphate samples contained particulate ^{32}P containing material, which was held back on the membrane-filters, thus badly interfering with the measurements of the ^{32}P incorporated in the bacteria. The particulate material was completely removed by 30-min hydrolysis in 1 *N* HCl.

Growth conditions

The cultures were grown in 200-ml volumes at 37° and aerated by bubbling with moist air at a rate of 1.5 l/min. A state of balanced growth was reached and maintained by allowing the cells to grow exponentially for several hours keeping the absorbancy below 0.4–0.5, if necessary by repeated dilutions. In the shift experiments, cultures growing in minimal medium at an absorbancy of about 0.200 (in some experiments about 0.400) were diluted into an equal volume of broth at 37° supplemented with the radioactive tracer. Radioactive phosphate was usually added to the broth medium at about 4.0 μC/ml, and [^{14}C]uracil at a concentration of 0.4 μg/ml. The [^{14}C]amino acids were added to the broth cultures at a concentration of 20 μg/ml. The radioactive cultures, usually about 20 ml in volume, were aerated by bubbling with moist air and the absorbancy was as usual kept below 0.4–0.5.

Absorbancies were measured in a Zeiss PMQ II spectrophotometer at 450 mμ with a 1-cm lightpath. An absorbancy of 0.100 corresponds to a bacterial dry weight of 17–18 μg/ml.

Analytical techniques

[^{32}P]phosphate and [^{14}C]uracil experiments: The uptake of the radioactive tracers in the bacteria was followed by sampling the culture at interval after the addition of the tracer and diluting 0.5 ml volumes into (a) 4.5 ml of dilution medium at 37° and (b) 4.5 ml of icecold 5 % TCA. The samples in the first group were immediately after dilution filtered through a 27 mm diameter membrane-filter (Membranfilter-Gesellschaft, Sartorius-Werke A.G., Germany, filtergroup 1, porediameters about 400 mμ), using a technique similar to that described by ROBERTS *et al.*[7]. The filters were carefully washed and glued directly on to 30 mm diameter aluminium planchets for activity counts. The TCA samples were usually kept overnight at 0°, control experiments having shown that the cold acid insoluble fractions remained stable under these conditions for about 24 h (Table I). The samples were filtered, washed and mounted as above.

Whereas the incorporated radioactivity from [^{14}C]uracil is only found in the

TABLE I

STABILITY OF THE COLD ACID INSOLUBLE FRACTION IN *Salmonella typhimurium*

Salmonella typhimurium was grown in broth medium with addition of glucose and $^{32}PO_4^{\equiv}$. After a ten fold increase in cell mass, the culture was filtered on a membrane filter and washed free of radioactivity. The bacteria were rinsed off the filter and resuspended in cold Tris–succinic acid Mg buffer. Samples were diluted with equal volumes of icecold 10% TCA, and incubated at 0 for the indicated periods of time. After centrifugation the supernatants were tested for ^{32}P activity. Another sample of the resuspended bacteria was heated in boiling water for 15 min, centrifuged and the ^{32}P activity in the supernatant measured.

	^{32}P *activities*
Resuspended culture	100%
Cold TCA soluble material	
30 min	10.2%
60 min	9.8%
90 min	10.6%
2 h	10.4%
24 h	11.9%
Supernatant after boiling	98%

cold acid soluble and the hot acid soluble fractions (Table II) in the form of derivatives of uracil and cytosine (the results for *E. coli*[7] were verified for *S. typhimurium*), the ^{32}P will be found distributed over a variety of compounds.

Since elaborate fractionation procedures are almost prohibitive to detailed kinetic studies, the validity of accepting the incorporation of $^{32}PO_4^{\equiv}$ into the cold TCA insoluble fraction as indicator of nucleic acid synthesis was tested in the following experiment. Bacteria were grown for several generations in minimal medium and broth respectively in the presence of the radioactive tracer. After harvesting on membrane-filters the bacteria were washed with dilution medium of the same osmotic strength as the growth medium to avoid losses of pool materials due to osmotic shock[8]. The labeled bacteria were subsequently fractionated according to the procedure of ROBERTS *et al.*[7]. Phosphate determinations were performed on dried bacteria after sulfuric acid digestion by a conventional molybdate method. The results of the measurements are given in Table II.

It will be seen that the phosphorus content of the cells grown in broth medium is increased about 20%, when compared to cells grown in minimal medium. This

TABLE II

FRACTIONATION OF [^{14}C]URACIL AND $^{32}PO_4^{\equiv}$ LABELED CELLS OF *Salmonella typhimurium*

Cultures of *Salmonella typhimurium* were grown in the appropriate medium supplemented with either [^{14}C]uracil or $^{32}PO_4^{\equiv}$. After several generations of growth the culture was harvested, washed and fractionated with (a) icecold 5% TCA (b) 75% ethanol at 50° followed by ether–75% ethanol (1:1) at 50° and (c) 5% TCA at 70°. The total content of phosphorus was measured on dried cell preparations to be 25 µg/mg for cells grown in minimal medium and 31 µg/mg for broth grown cells.

Fraction	*Per cent of incorporated [^{14}C]uracil*	*Per cent of incorporated ^{32}P*		*µg P/mg dry wt. Calculated values*	
	Broth medium	*Minimal medium*	*Broth medium*	*Minimal medium*	*Broth medium*
Cold TCA soluble	7.8	17.0	12.9	4.3	4.2
Ethanol–ether soluble	0.5	13.7	6.0	3.4	1.9
Hot TCA soluble	90	64.2	77.0	16.0	24.6
Residual	2.1	2.1	3.7	1.2	1.2

increase is solely accounted for by an increase in the hot TCA soluble material, and as there is a simultaneous drop in the amount of alcohol–ether soluble phosphorus, the ^{32}P of the hot acid soluble fraction in broth cultures amounts to 89 % of the ^{32}P of the cold acid insoluble fraction, compared to 77 % in minimal medium cultures. To a close approximation, the cold acid insoluble fraction of cells grown in broth medium can therefore be taken as a measure of the nucleic acid, whereas a more detailed fractionation has to be employed in the case of cells grown in minimal medium.

[^{14}*C*]*amino acid experiments*: In these experiments 1-ml samples were taken at intervals after addition of the tracer, diluted into 9 ml of boiling Tris broth and heated at 100° for 10 min[10]. The amino acid pool as well as most of the phosphate containing compounds (Table I) were liberated from the cells by this treatment. The samples were then filtered, washed and mounted for radioactivity determinations.

Radioactivity measurements: The ^{32}P and some of the ^{14}C samples were assayed for activity by a Geiger-Müller end window counter (Frieseke and Hoepner, Erlangen-Bruck, Germany) while other ^{14}C samples were assayed for radioactivity in a methane flow counter.

RESULTS

Incorporation of [^{32}P]orthophosphate

The kinetics of the uptake of radioactive phosphate by *Salmonella typhimurium* cultures grown in broth is shown in Fig. 1. Here, as well as in most of the other figures, the uptake of radioactive material is plotted against the increment in mass expressed as per cent of original cell mass.

The upper curve shows the values for total ^{32}P incorporation and the lower curve the amount of radioactivity which at any moment is present in cold acid insoluble form. The total uptake settles immediately at the definitive rate while the cold acid insoluble fraction shows a period of increasing rate until equilibrium is reached after an increase in cell mass of about 15 %. This indicates that immediate equilibrium is established between the free phosphate pool within the cell and the external phosphate in the growth medium, and that the incorporation into cold acid insoluble form is delayed because the newly formed radioactive material mixes with the preexisting non-radioactive pool.

For a shift experiment where a culture grown in minimal medium is mixed with an equal volume of broth containing [^{32}P]phosphate, the kinetics of incorporation are illustrated in Fig. 2. The curve for total uptake as well as that for acid insoluble material are clearly diphasic, starting at a high rate which, after a mass increment of about 125 % (corresponding to about 30 min of growth) diminishes and settles at the rate characteristic of ^{32}P uptake during balanced growth in broth.

The ^{32}P of the cold acid insoluble fraction is, as pointed out above, largely accounted for by the ^{32}P incorporated into nucleic acids. To confirm that the diphasic shape of the curves on Fig. 2 is indeed due to changes in rate of nucleic acid synthesis, extraction with 70 % ethanol was performed on the cold acid insoluble samples as described by HANAWALT[9]. This extraction removes most of the lipid bound ^{32}P and leaves the nucleic acid and the very small fraction of protein bound ^{32}P. The lower curve on Fig. 2 shows that the ^{32}P values after ethanol treatment still maintain the diphasic shape.

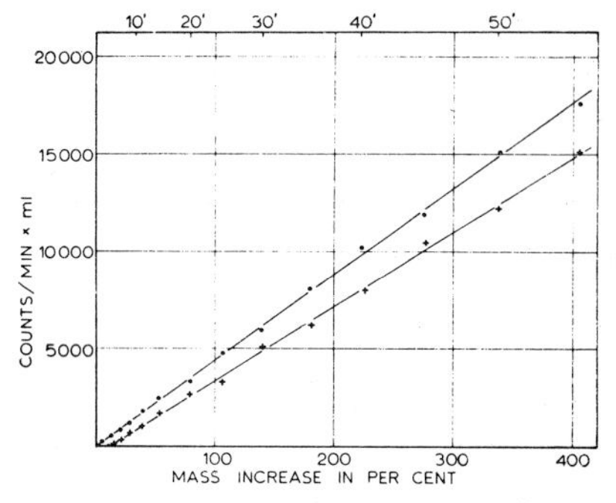

Fig. 1. Kinetics of incorporation of [^{32}P]orthophosphate in *Salmonella typhimurium* during growth in broth medium. Values for total ^{32}P uptake, ●, and uptake into cold TCA insoluble form, +, are plotted against percentage increments in bacterial cell mass. The corresponding time scale is shown at the top of the figure.

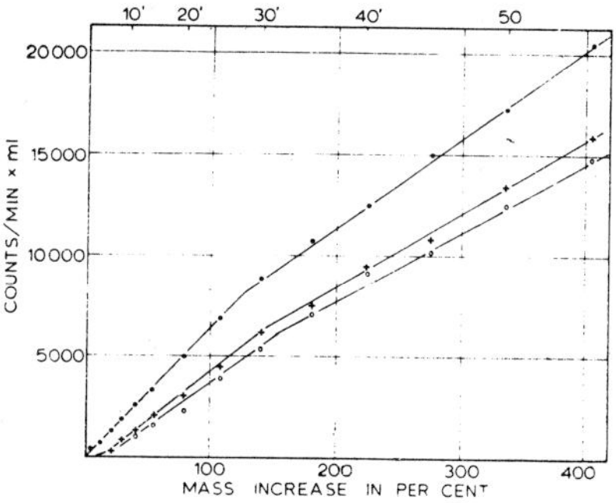

Fig. 2. Kinetics of incorporation of [^{32}P]orthophosphate during a shift up from glucose salts medium to broth. Values for total ^{32}P uptake, ●, uptake in the cold acid insoluble fractions, +, and values after ethanol extraction of the latter fraction, ○, are plotted against increments in mass.

Experiments with [^{14}C]uracil as indicator of nucleic acid synthesis confirmed the diphasic course of incorporation (Fig. 3).

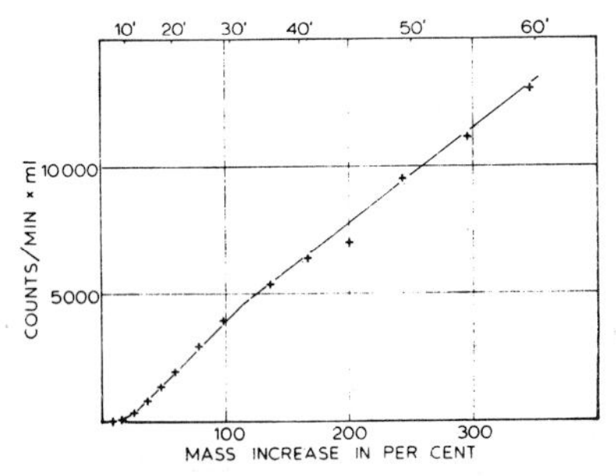

Fig. 3. Kinetics of incorporation of [^{14}C]uracil into the cold acid insoluble fraction during a shift up from minimal medium to broth.

Incorporation of [^{14}C]amino acids

The incorporation of tryptophan, arginine, histidine, phenylalanine and glycine into proteins was followed after transfer of a culture grown in minimal medium to broth. In the minimal medium the cells were grown in the presence of the appropriate amino acid at a concentration of 5 μg/ml in order to avoid influence of possible permease formation and to inhibit or repress the enzyme systems responsible for the formation of the amino acid in question[11–13]. In the glycine experiments, adenine was also added at a concentration of 25 μg/ml to block the incorporation of glycine into adenine and guanine[7].

The kinetics of the incorporation of [^{14}C]amino acids into protein after a shift to broth medium are shown in Fig. 4. Tryptophan, arginine, histidine and phenylalanine which seem to be directly incorporated into proteins[7] show the same general trend. The incorporation curves start at a low rate which, after an increase in mass of about

75 % changes to the faster rate characteristic of the new medium. In the case of glycine (Fig. 5), however, only a very short lag-period, if any, is observed, and the rate of radioactivity uptake settles almost immediately at the definitive value.

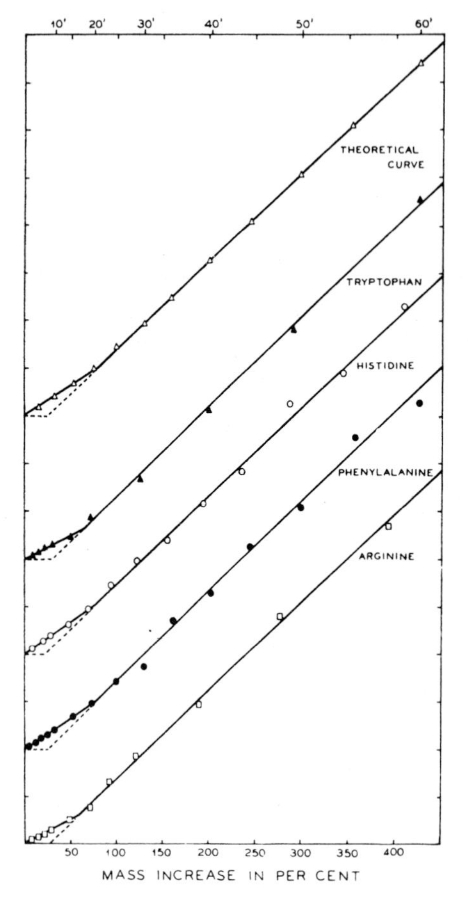

Fig. 4. Incorporation of [^{14}C]amino acids in *Salmonella typhimurium* during a shift up from glucose salts medium into broth. The curves represent the incorporation into stable forms, not removable from the cells by boiling. The uppermost curve shows the theoretical curve for protein formation, calculated as described in the text. All values are plotted in arbitrary units against increments in bacterial cell mass. The corresponding time scale is shown on top of the figure.

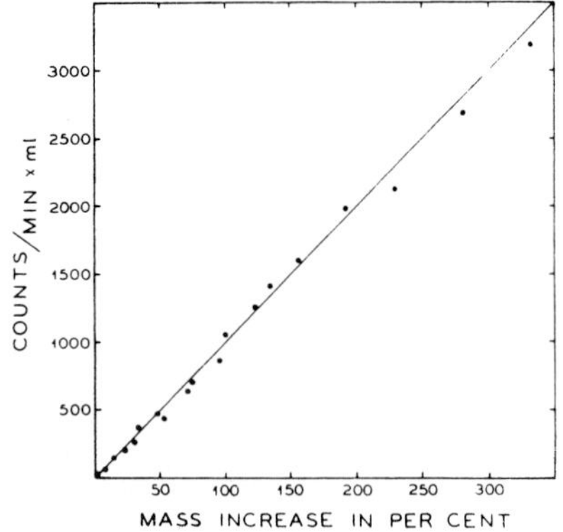

Fig. 5. Incorporation of [^{14}C]glycine during a shift from glucose salts medium into broth. The values for radioactivity uptake into stable forms, not removable by boiling, are plotted against increase in bacterial cell mass.

ANALYSIS OF RESULTS

It is an old observation that bacterial cells vary in size and chemical composition when observed at different stages during the transition from the resting state to the state of exponential growth[14,15]. Such variations could also be detected in cultures of *Salmonella typhimurium* growing under conditions of balanced growth in media supporting different growth rates[1]. It was found that the variations in cell size and cell content of RNA and DNA were exponential functions of the growth rate[1]. Similar results were obtained with *Aerobacter aerogenes* by NEIDHARDT AND MAGASANIK[5].

The cellular composition of *S. typhimurium* at three different growth rates is shown in Fig. 6. The total height of the columns represent the average dry weight of the cells and the subdivisions show its partition among the different cell constituents. The values for dry weight, RNA and DNA are based on previous findings[1], the values for protein content are based on relative measurements on dried cells using the method of LOWRY *et al.*[16]; the absolute protein content of minimal medium cells was calculated assuming the overall amino acid composition of *S. typhimurium* to be the same as that given for *E. coli* by ROBERTS *et al.*[7].

To measure the ribosomal RNA content (Table III), bacteria which had been grown for several generations in the appropriate ^{32}P containing medium were re-suspended in a Tris–succinic acid buffer pH 7.6 with 0.005 *M* Mg^{++} (see ref. 17), disrupted by ultrasonic vibrations in a MSE-Mullard disintegrator and centrifuged for 10 min at 10,000 × *g* to remove cell debris followed by 90 min centrifugation of the supernatant at 40,000 rev./min in a Spinco Model L ultracentrifuge (86-143,000 × *g*). The amount of ^{32}P present in the pellet was taken as a measure of ribosomal ^{32}P. The values of Table III are in fair agreement with the values obtained by WADE AND MORGAN[18].

TABLE III

INCORPORATION OF $^{32}PO_4^{\equiv}$ IN SOLUBLE AND PARTICULATE FRACTIONS OF *Salmonella typhimurium*

Cells grown for several generations in the appropriate medium containing [^{32}P]orthophosphate were harvested and washed and suspended in Tris–succinic acid–Mg buffer. The cells were disrupted by ultrasonic vibrations for 5 min in a MSE-Mullard disintegrator at 20 kc/sec and centrifuged for 10 min at 10,000 × *g* to sediment debris and surviving bacteria. The supernatant was further spun for 90 min at 40,000 rev./min in a Spinco Model L centrifuge (87,000–143,000 × *g*) to sediment the ribosomal particles. The ^{32}P activities in the supernatant and the pellet were determined. The results are here shown related to the activity in the supernatant from the centrifugation at 10,000 × *g*.

	^{32}P *activities*	
	Broth grown cells	*Minimal medium grown cells*
Disrupted cell suspension	110	105
Supernatant 10,000 × *g*	100	100
Supernatant 100,000 × *g*	20	36
Ribosomal pellet	78	63

The cross hatched areas in Fig. 6 represent materials not accounted for above *i.e.* cell wall materials, lipids, carbohydrates.

It will be seen that the ribosomal RNA shows a very pronounced variation with the growth rate. Since the importance of the ribosomal particles in protein synthesis by now seems to be well established[3,4] the amount of ribosomal RNA may be related to the rate of protein synthesis. As previously shown, the ratio between the two values is approximately constant and independent of the growth rate[1]. More rigorously this ratio can be derived from the observed values for protein and ribosome contents at the growth rates 1.2 and 2.4 doublings/h (Fig. 6): during balanced growth the ribosomal RNA (R) of a culture increases according to the equation $R_t = R_0 e^{\alpha t}$ where α equals $\log_e 2$ (0.69) divided by the generation time; assuming the rate of protein synthesis to be proportional to R_t we obtain $dP_t/dt = kR_t = kR_0 e^{\alpha t}$. By integration, the equation for protein formation becomes $P_t = kR_0 e^{\alpha t}/\alpha + c$ (1) where $k = \frac{P_t - P_0}{R_t - R_0} \times \alpha$. Using the values for P and R for the generation times 50 and 25 min we find $k = 0.11$ min^{-1} in both cases. This again means that the quantity of protein synthesized per minute at 37° amounts to 11 % by weight of the ribosomal RNA of the cell. It therefore seems justifiable to maintain that the *rate* of protein synthesis is proportional to the *amount* of ribosomal RNA in the cells.

When a bacterial culture growing under conditions of balanced growth in a glucose salts medium is diluted into an equal volume of broth medium (shift up), cells with a low ribosomal content are suddenly given the external conditions which permit a higher growth rate. In a previous article[6] it was shown that a shift up is followed immediately by an increase in the rate of RNA-formation and shortly thereafter by an increase in the rate of total mass synthesis; the rate of DNA synthesis and of cell division maintain the low pre-shift values for about 20 and 65 min respectively.

The cells thus undergo a gradual change and eventually attain the composition characteristic of cells growing in broth. How these changes come about can be illustrated by the growth curves for the individual cell components (Fig. 7). Such growth curves can be constructed using the data from the histogram (Fig. 6) and the curve for mass synthesis after a shift up from minimal medium to broth.

For simplicity we will consider an imaginary shift up involving only 10^9 cells

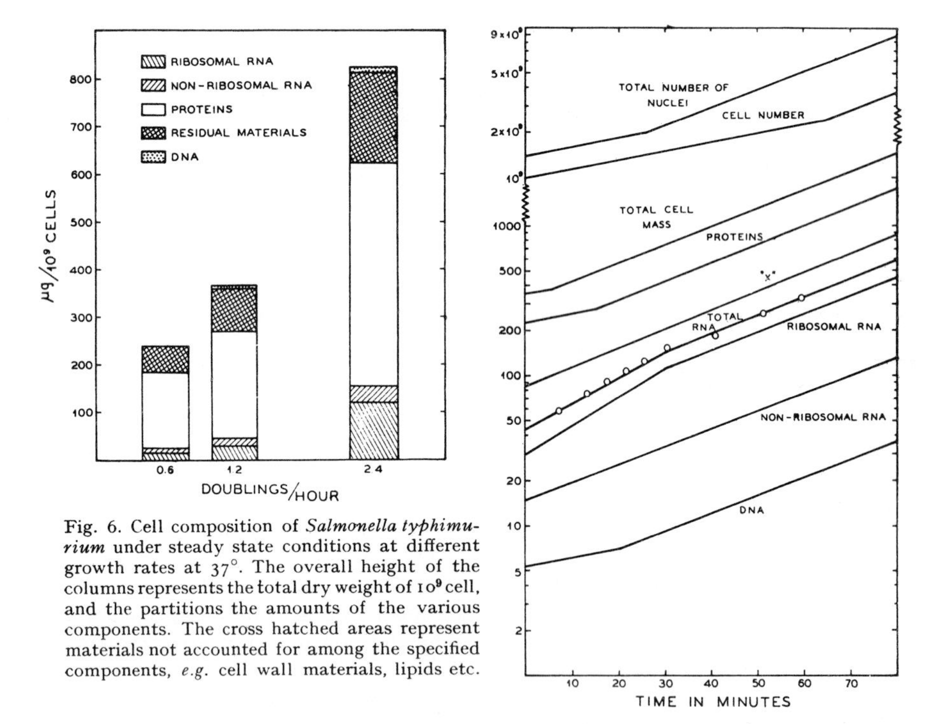

Fig. 6. Cell composition of *Salmonella typhimurium* under steady state conditions at different growth rates at 37°. The overall height of the columns represents the total dry weight of 10^9 cell, and the partitions the amounts of the various components. The cross hatched areas represent materials not accounted for among the specified components, *e.g.* cell wall materials, lipids etc.

Fig. 7. "Growth"-curves for the individual cell constituents following the transfer of 10^9 cells grown in glucose salts medium to broth at 37°. The two top curves show the increase with time of the number of cells and nuclei; the remainder give the increase of the various cell constituents. In all cases the logarithm to the number or the amount in microgram respectively is plotted against time.

which have been grown in minimal medium. After the shift to broth the dry weight of these cells increases exponentially with a doubling time of 25 min, except for a lag period of a few minutes (Fig. 7). The original 340 μg of bacterial dry weight will give rise to 3,000 μg dry weight after a growth period in broth of 80 min. Simultaneously the partition of the dry weight between the various cell components changes to that of broth grown cells. It is known from previous experiments[6] that this change in composition is completed after about 65 min growth in the new medium.

To obtain growth curves for the individual cell components, the amounts of protein, total RNA, ribosomal RNA etc. at time 0 and at 80 min respectively, were plotted at the left and right side of Fig. 7. Curves corresponding to a doubling time of 25 min were then drawn through each point on the right. As will be seen, the curves for non-ribosomal RNA and for "residual material" (x) extrapolate back to the corresponding points on the left side, indicating that these components begin being synthesized at the "broth rate" immediately after the shift. As regards DNA it was previously observed that the low pre-shift rate of synthesis is maintained for about 20 min after a shift up[6]; Fig. 7 shows that a growth curve composed of two segments —a 20 min period at the pre-shift generation time of 50 min plus a 60-min period at the broth rate of synthesis—is adequate to account for the change from the DNA-value at time zero to that found at 80 min. A very similar diphasic curve may be used to describe protein synthesis; this curve will be discussed in detail below.

Finally, to account for the increase in total RNA, and in ribosomal RNA, a period of synthesis at a rate exceeding that characteristic of broth must be introduced. From the experiments illustrated in Figs. 2 and 3 we know that a change to a lower rate occurs about 30 min after the shift up. The curves for total RNA and ribosomal RNA of Fig. 7 are based on this observation, and show an initial high rate of RNA synthesis, corresponding to a doubling time of 16 min, followed at 30 min by a decrease to the definitive broth rate of synthesis.

To justify the use of the observed change in rate of RNA synthesis at 30 min in the construction of the RNA "growth curve" of Fig. 7, the ^{32}P activities presented in Fig. 2 were converted into μg of RNA. From the slope of the curve for cold acid insoluble ^{32}P uptake during balanced growth in broth (Fig. 1) and the RNA content of broth cells, we can obtain a relative measure of radioactivity per microgram of RNA at a given specific ^{32}P activity. Since the shift experiments (Fig. 2) are performed in the same medium with the same specific activity, the data from an idealized incorporation curve for cold acid insoluble ^{32}P where the pool effect has been eliminated, can be converted into μg of RNA. These converted values which are plotted in Fig. 7 show good agreement with the theoretical curve, and it may therefore be assumed that, when the rate of RNA synthesis drops at about 30 min after a shift up, the cells have in fact reached the broth composition with respect to RNA content.

In addition to the individual growth curves just described, Fig. 7 shows curves for the increase in number of nuclei and in number of cells per ml. The former differs from the curve for DNA only in that the rate increase occurs about 5 min later; the latter illustrates the previous finding that cell division continues at the low pre-shift rate for about 65 min after a shift up and then changes to the broth rate[6]. To sum up, Fig. 7 shows that about 30 min after a shift up the cell mass has reached the composition characteristic of growth at the broth rate, and for 30–40 min after that time the cells continue to grow in size without changing their composition.

It will be seen from Fig. 7 that the amount of ribosomal RNA per unit mass as well as per cell increases during the first 30 min after a shift up. On the assumption that the rate of protein synthesis is proportional to the ribosomal content, protein formation would be expected to begin at the pre-shift rate, and to keep pace with the rising ribosomal content until the final broth rate of synthesis is reached. The theoretical curve for protein formation can be calculated under this assumption:

From eqn. (1) above, the increase, ΔP, in amount of protein at time t is derived; $\Delta P_t = \frac{kR_0}{\alpha}(e^{\alpha t} - 1)$. The doubling time for ribosomal RNA after a shift up is 16 min during the first 30 min then changing to 25 min (see Fig. 7). The content of ribosomal RNA of 10^9 cells, which is 30 μg at the time of the shift, is calculated to increase to 106 μg after 30 min of growth. From these figures theoretical values for the increase in amount of protein at different times were calculated and plotted against increase in total cell mass. This theoretical curve for protein synthesis which is shown at the top of Fig. 4, closely resembles the amino acid incorporation curves. In all instances the initial rate of incorporation is approximately half the definitive rate.

Control experiments have shown that equilibrium between the labeled medium and the amino acid pool of the cells is established already 1–2 min after addition of the labeled amino acids. A pool effect similar to that observed in the ^{32}P incorporation experiments therefore cannot be responsible for the low initial rate of ^{14}C uptake, and a competitive effect of preferentially utilized materials in the broth as seen in the case of [^{14}C]uracil is not observed. Furthermore the amino acid in question was always added unlabeled to the minimal medium in which the culture grew before it was transferred to the labeled broth medium, to effect inhibition and repression of the enzymes responsible for the synthesis of the amino acid under investigation[11, 13]. It is important in experiments of this type to control repression, since an increase in the degree of repression after the shift might result in a gradual increase in specific activity inside the cells. Such changes might completely obscure the picture of protein synthesis proper.

In the case of [^{14}C]glycine incorporation different results were obtained. As seen in Fig. 5, no lag was observed and the rate of incorporation settled immediately at the definitive value. No obvious reason for the discrepancy between the data of Figs. 4 and 5 can be given.

A relatively high concentration of glycine in the cell wall or in the protein of the ribosomal particles might explain the findings. However, the latter possibility is unlikely, considering that no striking differences in amino acid composition have been observed between total protein[7] and ribosomal protein[19] of *E.coli*.

DISCUSSION

We have observed earlier that the size and the chemical composition, of bacterial cells vary as a result of changing the environment, and that the variations can be expressed in simple terms as exponential functions of the growth rate at a given temperature[1]. Variation in temperature which of course also affects the growth rate, does not change the cell composition in a given medium to any great extent[1]. Therefore, irrespective of temperature, a given medium defines a steady state condition of growth to which correspond a certain average cell size and a certain chemical composition.

When cells, which have attained the characteristic composition and growth rate in a glucose salts medium, are transferred to broth, a stepwise transition takes place, which brings the cells to a new steady state, characterized by the higher growth rate attained in the new medium. The most striking effect of increasing the growth rate is the large increase in the RNA content and in the amount of ribosomal RNA. This increase in total RNA, as measured by the uptake of ^{32}P orthophosphate and [^{14}C]-uracil is achieved by a greatly increased rate of synthesis during the first 30 min after the transfer to the new medium. After this period, the RNA content per unit cell mass will have reached the value corresponding to the new steady state, and the RNA synthesis then settles at the definitive rate.

Since the amount of ribosomal RNA increases similarly from one steady state to the other, it is suggested that both ribosome formation and the synthesis of ribosomal protein are accelerated during the first 30 min. This suggestion is supported by preliminary ultracentrifugation experiments. In addition NEIDHARDT AND MAGASANIK[5] working with *Aerobacter aerogenes* have found a strongly increased incorporation of [^{14}C]guanine into both soluble and particulate RNA during the first 20 min after shift up and a predominant incorporation of [^{14}C]leucine into particulate proteins.

The ratio between the ribosomal content of the cells in the various steady states and the corresponding rates of protein synthesis is found to be constant and thus independent of the overall growth rate.

By assuming this ratio to remain constant also during the period immediately following a shift from minimal medium to broth, it is possible to calculate the rate of protein synthesis during this transition. From the low value corresponding to the ribosomal content of the slow growing culture, the rate of protein synthesis would be expected to keep up with the rapidly expanding ribosomal system until the final broth rate and the new steady state had been established. The experiments with [^{14}C]amino acids have confirmed these predictions, and thus support the assumption that the constant ratio between ribosomal content and rate of protein synthesis, which is observed under steady state conditions, is valid also under the conditions of imbalance prevailing during the shift up.

Recent observations on mammalian cells and on bacteria[4,20,21] point to the ribosomal particles as the sites of protein synthesis. The constant ratio between the number of ribosomal particles and rate of protein synthesis observed in bacterial cells thus indicate a constant average efficiency of the particles in protein formation.

This constant efficiency is clearly not a reflection of a constant efficiency of production of the various groups of proteins. Induction and repression mechanisms can rapidly start and stop the production of specific proteins, and, as seen in the case of a shift up, the low overall rate of protein synthesis immediately after the medium change coincides with a particularly high rate of formation of ribosomal proteins. In fact, during the first few minutes after the shift the synthesis of ribosomal protein has to account for about 1/3 of the total proteins formed.

No detailed information is yet available concerning the mechanism by which ribosomes function as the specific sites of protein synthesis. RNA templates are generally believed to be responsible for the specificity of the proteins. If the templates are firmly integrated in the structure of the ribosomes, these ribosomes would be subdivided into classes, each functioning in the synthesis of a given protein. On the other hand, the ribosomes may be fairly unspecific sites of synthesis with the actual templates as loosely coupled, shortlived products[22]. It would therefore seem premature to build models relating the average constant efficiency per ribosome in protein formation to the actual function of the individual ribosome or group of ribosomes.

In this connection the problem of "information flow" should be considered. It is commonly assumed that the transfer of information from DNA to RNA-templates is brought about by direct base pairing between the two nucleic acids. During the period of accelerated ribosome formation after a shift up, the overall rate of this copying process would be similarly increased. During the same period DNA synthesis continues at the low pre-shift rate. This dissociation of rates strongly indicates that the rate at which information flows from DNA is independent of the rate of DNA synthesis. The fact that the increase in rate of synthesis of DNA almost coincides with the time at which RNA-synthesis settles at its definitive value may be fortuitous.

ACKNOWLEDGEMENT

The author wishes to express his sincere thanks to Professor OLE MAALØE for help and advice in connection with this work.

REFERENCES

[1] M. SCHAECHTER, O. MAALØE AND N. O. KJELDGAARD, *J. Gen. Microbiol.*, 19 (1958) 592.
[2] A. TISSIERES, J. D. WATSON, D. SCHLESSINGER AND B. R. HOLLINGWORTH, *J. Mol. Biol.*, 1 (1959) 221.
[3] F. H. C. CRICK, *Symposia Soc. Exptl. Biol.*, Cambridge Univ. Press, 1958.
[4] K. MCQUILLEN, R. B. ROBERTS AND R. J. BRITTEN, *Proc. Natl. Acad. Sci. U.S.*, 45 (1959) 1437.
[5] F. C. NEIDHARDT AND B. MAGASANIK, *Biochim. Biophys. Acta*, 42 (1960) 99.
[6] N. O. KJELDGAARD, O. MAALØE AND M. SCHAECHTER, *J. Gen. Microbiol.*, 19 (1958) 607.
[7] R. B. ROBERTS, D. B. COWIE, P. H. ABELSON, E. T. BOLTON AND R. J. BRITTEN, *Studies of Biosynthesis in* Escherichia coli, Carnegie Institution of Washington, Washington D.C. Publication 607, 1957.
[8] R. B. ROBERTS, *Symposium on Molecular Biology*, University of Chicago Press, Chicago, 1959.
[9] P. HANAWALT, *Science*, 130 (1959) 386.
[10] G. N. COHEN AND H. V. RICKENBERG, *Ann. inst. Pasteur*, 91 (1956) 693.
[11] J. MONOD AND G. COHEN-BAZIRE, *Compt. rend.*, 236 (1953) 530.
[12] M. COHN, G. N. COHEN AND J. MONOD, *Compt. rend.*, 236 (1953) 746.
[13] L. GORINI, *Bull. soc. chim. biol.*, 40 (1958) 1939.
[14] A. T. HENRICI, *Morphological Variation and the Rate of Growth of Bacteria*, Baillière, Tindall and Cox, London, 1928.
[15] H. E. WADE, *J. Gen. Microbiol.*, 7 (1952) 24.
[16] O. H. LOWRY, N. J. ROSENBROUGH, A. L. FARR AND R. J. RANDALL, *J. Biol. Chem.*, 193 (1951) 265.
[17] E. T. BOLTON, B. H. HOYER AND D. B. RITTER, in R. B. ROBERTS, *Microsomal Particles and Protein Synthesis*, Pergamon Press, London, 1958.
[18] H. E. WADE AND D. M. MORGAN, *Biochem. J.*, 65 (1957) 321.
[19] P. F. SPAHR, personal communication.
[20] M. RABINOWITZ AND M. E. OLSON, *Exptl. Cell Research*, 10 (1956) 747.
[21] T. PETERS JR., *J. Biol. Chem.*, 229 (1957) 659.
[22] F. JACOB, personal communication.

From: *J. Mol. Biol.* 4, 193–210 (1962)

Regulation of Ribosomal and Transfer RNA Synthesis

C. G. Kurland and O. Maaløe

University Institute of Microbiology, Copenhagen, Denmark

(*Received 27 November 1961*)

Chloramphenicol (CM) initially accelerates the synthesis of transfer as well as ribosomal RNA when cells are growing in minimal medium. This effect is absent in an amino acid medium. High concentrations of CM, which inhibit most protein synthesis, relieve the need for an *external* supply of a required amino acid for RNA synthesis. However, a lag precedes the resumption of RNA synthesis when CM is added to amino-acid-starved cells.

These results suggest that the rate of RNA synthesis is determined by the internal amino acid concentration. This may be accomplished by a repressor mechanism in which the transfer RNA acts as repressor and amino acid adenylate as inducer.

At high CM concentration, the rate of RNA synthesis decreases progressively with time. At intermediate CM concentrations the amount of protein synthesized is paralleled by an *increase* in RNA synthesis, over and above the fixed amount produced at CM concentrations which completely block protein synthesis; i.e. concentrations exceeding 50 μg/ml. In 110 min at 25°C this fixed value amounts to half the normal RNA production. Under these conditions the synthesis of ribosomal RNA decreases steadily whereas transfer RNA is synthesized at a constant rate.

The data suggest that a protein present in log phase cells is necessary for and consumed during the synthesis of ribosomal RNA. This protein is probably the protein component of the CM-particles.

1. Introduction

A given medium will support the growth of bacterial cells at a unique maximum rate. When cell size, gross chemical composition, average number of nuclei per cell, etc., are studied during balanced growth in different media, simple correlations of these extensive properties with the growth rate are observed (Schaechter, Maaløe & Kjeldgaard, 1958; Neidhardt & Magasanik, 1960). In other words, a unique physiological state is established during exponential growth in a given medium.

When cells are shifted from one medium to another, the transition to the new state of growth is characterized by an apparently instantaneous change in the rate of RNA synthesis (Kjeldgaard, Maaløe & Schaechter, 1958; Kjeldgaard, 1961). Thus, if a culture is transferred from a minimal medium containing glucose to one containing the amino acids plus glucose, the rate of RNA synthesis during the first 20 to 30 min after the shift (at 37°C) is greater than the definitive rate characteristic of the amino acid medium. In contrast, the rates of DNA and of protein synthesis increase slowly, and the definitive rates are not reached until about 20 min after the shift (Kjeldgaard, 1961). These facts suggest that, in this situation, the control exerted on the synthesis of RNA does not depend on the amount of DNA or of protein, nor on the rate of synthesis of either.

A similar conclusion may be drawn from the work of Neidhardt & Fraenkel (1961). They observed that when chloramphenicol (CM) was added to cells growing in various minimal media, RNA synthesis was markedly accelerated in spite of the fact that protein synthesis was strongly inhibited. Neidhardt & Fraenkel concluded that the rate of RNA synthesis was not limited by the enzyme content of the cells.

How then does the bacterial cell regulate the rate of RNA synthesis?

A clue to the nature of this regulatory mechanism is provided by the fact that amino acids are required for RNA synthesis. First, it has been shown that bacterial cells which require an amino acid for growth will stop synthesizing RNA when the required amino acid is withdrawn; and, second, it is found that when traces of the required amino acid are added back to the medium in the presence of CM (about 10 μg/ml.), synthesis of RNA is resumed while net protein synthesis remains inhibited by the CM (Gros & Gros, 1956; Pardee & Prestidge, 1956). The authors concluded that amino acids were in some manner "catalytic" to the synthesis of RNA. Extending these studies Aronson & Spiegelman (1958) made the important observation that high concentrations of CM (e.g. 400 μg/ml.) relieve the need for an external supply of the required amino acid for RNA synthesis.

Our experiments suggest that the role of the amino acids in regulating RNA synthesis may be understood by introducing the notion of specific repression. Jacob & Monod (1961) have presented an attractive model according to which the synthesis of a given enzyme, or group of enzymes, can be blocked at the genetic level by specific repressor molecules which in turn can be inactivated by *small* molecules of the proper kind. An important feature of the model is that the function of the repressor molecule calls for two distinct specificities: one for the genetic site with which it must combine to cause repression, and one for the enzyme which inactivates the repressor by coupling it with one of the small inducer molecules if such are present in sufficient concentration. Thus in the case of β-galactosidase, induction of enzyme synthesis should be looked upon as an act of *de*repression effected by lactose or a suitable analogue thereof.

This paper presents data which suggest that the amino acids regulate the synthesis of RNA by playing a role analogous to that played by lactose in regulating the synthesis of β-galactosidase. In our model we tentatively identify the repressor with the transfer RNA and the inducer with the activated amino acids. Thus a molecule of transfer RNA is assumed to be inactivated *as a repressor* when combining with the corresponding amino acid, this process being mediated by the activating enzyme. This is an image of the regulatory role of amino acids which has been developed also by Stent & Brenner (1961) on the basis of their observations on the genetics of the amino acid requirement for RNA synthesis in the 58-161 strain of *E. coli*.

Our data concerning the effects of CM on RNA and protein synthesis in *E. coli* under various physiological conditions are presented below. They include observations which indicate that, in the presence of CM, the synthesis of ribosomal RNA is dependent on a pre-existing protein which is consumed in the process. The synthesis of transfer RNA seems not to be under such a restriction.

2. Materials and Methods

(a) *Materials*

Strain B of *E. coli* was used in all experiments. After treatment with 2-aminopurine, a non-leaky methionine-requiring mutant was isolated by the penicillin selection technique as described by Gorini & Kaufman (1960).

[2-^{14}C]uracil, $^{35}SO_4$ and carrier-free $^{32}PO_4$ were obtained from the Radiochemical Centre, Amersham, England. Before use the $^{32}PO_4$ was hydrolysed for 45 min in concentrated HCl at 90°C. It was then neutralized with ammonia and stored in neutral tris buffer.

The chloramphenicol (CM) was the Parke-Davis product. Stock solutions were stored in the cold and used for at most 10 days. Solutions stored at room temperature take on a yellow color and produce toxic effects in bacterial cells, which are not produced by colorless solutions.

Sodium dodecyl sulfate (SDS) was obtained from L. Light & Co. Ltd., Colnbrook, England. The use of sodium lauryl sulfate was abandoned since it apparently causes degradation of RNA from *E. coli* and *S. typhimurium*.

Two kinds of growth media were used. The first is referred to as minimal medium and contains: 12 g tris, 2 g KCl, 2 g NH_4Cl, 0·5 g $MgCl_2,6H_2O$, 0·178 g $Na_2HPO_4,2H_2O$, 20 mg Na_2SO_4, 6·85 ml. concentrated HCl, 2 g glucose and 20 mg of cytosine and uracil in 1 liter of H_2O. The second medium, the amino acid medium, contains 20 μg/ml. of each of the 20 amino acids added to the minimal medium.

(b) *The measurement of total RNA synthesis*

The effect of CM on the synthesis of total RNA in logarithmically growing cells (optical density (O.D.) about 0·5, at 450 mμ and 1 cm lightpath) was measured by following incorporation of [^{14}C]uracil. Culture volumes of 30 ml. were vigorously aerated in 100-ml. test tubes by bubbling air through a 0·2-ml. pipette; the temperature was maintained at 25$\pm$0·1°C. Samples of 2 ml. each were pipetted into an equal volume of 10% trichloroacetic acid (TCA) at -2°C and held at that temperature. At the end of the experiment the TCA suspensions were passed through membrane filters (CO 5; Membranfiltergesellschaft, Göttingen, Germany), washed with cold 5% TCA and mounted on metal planchettes. The radioactivity was measured in a gas-flow counter (Frieske & Hoepfner); the samples were counted to at least 1000 counts, which in all cases was at least ten times background.

The incorporation of [^{14}C]uracil always took place in the presence of cytosine (20 μg/ml.) to minimize incorporation of [^{14}C]uracil into the DNA which, in cells of this type, constitutes about 10% of the amount of RNA present (Schaechter *et al.*, 1958). The incorporation of [^{14}C]uracil is therefore assumed to be a good measure of the amount of RNA synthesized by the cells in the presence of this label.

Incorporation of [^{14}C]uracil and $^{35}SO_4$ into the TCA precipitable fraction was studied over a wide range of CM concentrations. The technique was as described above except that the incubation volumes were only 10 ml., and that the $^{35}SO_4$ incorporation was measured as hot TCA precipitable material (60 min at 90°C).

(c) *The measurement of $^{32}PO_4$ incorporation into the ribosomal and transfer RNA*

Incorporation of $^{32}PO_4$ was stopped by a twentyfold dilution into a suspension of carrier cells held at -2°C and containing 0·02 M-azide. The cells were harvested in a Servall centrifuge at 10,000 rev/min in the cold, and the pellet resuspended in 1% SDS, 0·005 M EDTA (ethylenediaminetetra-acetate) and frozen. After thawing, the cell material is in the form of a very viscous suspension. This was extracted three times with redistilled phenol and precipitated twice with 67% ethanol plus 0·1 M-acetate pH 4·6 at -2°C for 15 min. It was then incubated with 4 μg/ml. DNase in 0·001 M-Mg^{2+} at room temperature for 15 min. After a final ethanol precipitation the RNA was stored in 0·1 M-acetate at pH 4·6.

The specific activities of the ribosomal and the transfer RNA were measured after centrifugation in a sucrose gradient according to the procedure of McQuillen, Roberts & Britten (1959). A Spinco model L ultracentrifuge and a SW 25 rotor were used. The gradients were centrifuged for 15 hr at 5°C. The distribution of u.v.-absorbing and radioactive TCA precipitable material was analysed as described previously (Gros *et al.*, 1961).

3. Results

(a) *The kinetics of RNA synthesis in the presence of CM*

Strain B of *E. coli* grows with a doubling time of 110 ± 2 min at 25°C in our minimal medium. The incorporation of [^{14}C]uracil into total RNA in cells incubated for one generation with zero, 1, 10 and 100 μg/ml. of CM is shown in Fig. 1. Two distinct effects on RNA synthesis can be demonstrated: first, at all three CM concentrations the *initial* rate of RNA synthesis is 1·5 to 2·0 times greater than that of the control; second, a concentration-dependent deceleration of RNA synthesis is observed at longer times, and at 120 min the incorporation of [^{14}C]uracil amounted to 125, 90 and 65% of that of the control at 1, 10 and 100 μg/ml. of CM, respectively.

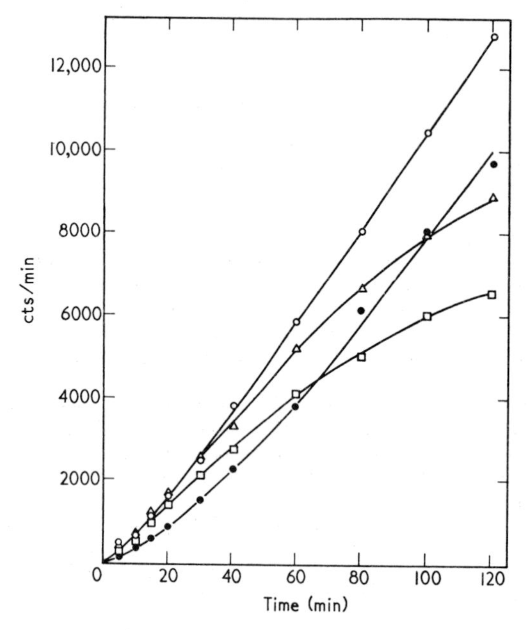

FIG. 1. The incorporation of [^{14}C]uracil into the RNA of cells, grown in minimal medium, during incubation at 25°C with zero (●), 1 (○), 10 (△) and 100 (□) μg/ml. of CM.

The same experiment was performed with cells growing in the amino acid medium with a doubling time of 76 ± 2 min at 25°C. The incorporation of [^{14}C]uracil into cells growing in this medium for 80 min in the presence of zero, 1, 10 and 100 μg/ml. CM is shown in Fig. 2. In contrast to the first experiment very little acceleration of RNA synthesis (5 to 15%) is seen at any concentration of CM. Nevertheless, the concentration-dependent deceleration of RNA synthesis is evident. This is best seen when the incorporation of [^{14}C]uracil in 10 and 100 μg/ml. of CM is compared to that in 1 μg/ml. of CM for both media. Thus, the ratio of [^{14}C]uracil incorporation after 80 min at 10 μg/ml. to that at 1 μg/ml. of CM is 0·82 and 0·70 in minimal medium and in amino acid medium, respectively; the corresponding ratios for 100 μg/ml. and 1 μg/ml. of CM are 0·62 and 0·55.

The marked initial acceleration of RNA synthesis resulting from the addition of CM to cells growing in minimal medium suggests that some control mechanism has been upset by the CM. The facts, (a) that this phenomenon is not dependent on the concentration of CM, and (b) that the acceleration is absent in the amino acid medium, suggest that the initial stimulation is not related to the concentration-dependent deceleration of RNA synthesis occurring at longer times of incubation in both kinds of media.

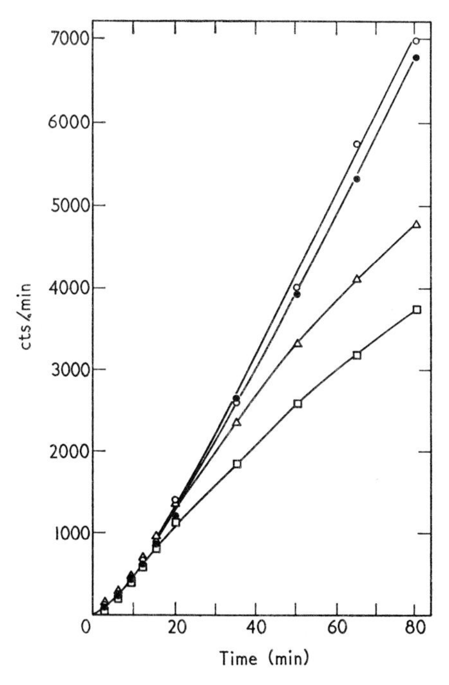

FIG. 2. The incorporation of [^{14}C]uracil into the RNA of cells, grown in amino acid medium, during incubation at 25°C with zero (●), 1 (○), 10 (△) and 100 (□) μg/ml. of CM.

The deceleration of RNA synthesis in the presence of CM might reflect an instability or turnover of RNA (Aronson & Spiegelman, 1958; Neidhardt & Gros, 1957). This possibility was tested as follows. Samples from a minimal medium culture were introduced into four tubes containing sufficient CM to bring the final concentration to 100 μg/ml. [^{14}C]uracil was introduced into these tubes at zero, 30, 60 and 90 min, and in each tube the incorporation of label was followed for 120 min after the addition of [^{14}C]uracil. The results of such an experiment are shown in Fig. 3. Here, continued incorporation for 120 min from time zero gave $9{\cdot}7 \times 10^3$ cts/min, and the sum of the first 30 min of incorporation in each of the staggered samples gave $10{\cdot}7 \times 10^3$ cts/min $[(4{\cdot}5+2{\cdot}5+2{\cdot}2+1{\cdot}5) \times 10^3]$. If the decrease in incorporation at later times of incubation were due entirely to turnover of the RNA in the presence of CM, the sum should have been about 18×10^3 cts/min $(4 \times 4{\cdot}5)$ or about twice the amount of incorporation obtained in 120 min of continuous incorporation starting at time zero. The 10% difference between the figures 9·7 and 10·7 for observed and reconstructed incorporation, respectively, is probably not significant. Therefore, we conclude that little or no turnover of the RNA takes place in the presence of 100 μg/ml. of CM. Furthermore, data to be presented below (see section (d)) indicate that the gradual decrease in the overall rate of RNA synthesis is not due to a general loss of the capacity of the cells to synthesize RNA when incubated with CM.

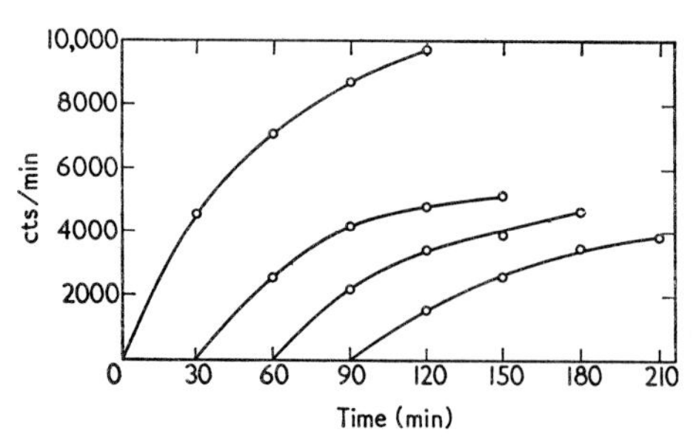

FIG. 3. The incorporation of [^{14}C]uracil into the RNA of cells during incubation in minimal medium containing 100 μg/ml. of CM.

The four curves correspond to samples into which the label was introduced at zero, 30, 60 and 90 min, respectively, after the addition of CM.

(b) *The dose response of RNA and of protein synthesis to CM*

The concentration-dependent effect of CM on RNA synthesis was studied in more detail in experiments of the following type. Samples from a minimal medium culture were pipetted into ten different tubes containing [^{14}C]uracil and concentrations of CM ranging from zero to 1000 μg/ml. The tubes were aerated as usual and the incorporation into TCA precipitable material after 110 min of incubation at 25°C was measured. The results are plotted in Fig. 4, where the amount of RNA synthesis at each CM concentration is expressed as a percentage of the value obtained in the control without CM. The accelerating effect of CM can be seen at low concentrations of CM; however, as the concentration of CM is raised the amount of RNA synthesized decreases. At approximately 50 μg/ml. of CM a constant value of 50 to 60% is reached Thus, in the range from 50 μg/ml. to 1000 μg/ml. of CM, RNA synthesis was uniformly depressed to about half the amount produced by the control cells in the same time.

The effect of different CM concentrations on RNA synthesis has been compared with its effect on overall protein synthesis, which is known to be inhibited by CM (Gale & Folkes, 1953; Wisseman, Smadel, Hahn & Hopps, 1954). The amount of protein synthesized during 110 min of incubation with CM was measured over the same concentration range as above. Hot TCA-precipitable $^{35}SO_4$ incorporation was measured and the data are plotted in Fig. 4. The parallel decrease in RNA and in protein synthesis with increasing CM concentration is quite clear. In particular, the concentration of CM necessary to inhibit 99% of protein synthesis is about the same concentration beyond which RNA synthesis does not further decrease.

The fact that substantial RNA synthesis can proceed at CM concentrations much higher than those at which protein synthesis is no longer observed indicates that RNA synthesis does not require simultaneous synthesis of protein. This fact together with the very definite relationship between the amounts of protein and of RNA synthesized at the lower CM concentrations suggest that protein is consumed during the synthesis of bacterial RNA. A reasonable explanation of these observations would seem to be that, in the act of synthesis, ribosomal RNA combines with ribosomal protein, and that the growing cells contain an excess of this protein. If so, a significant amount of ribosomal RNA could be synthesized in the total absence of protein synthesis, and at CM concentrations which permit protein synthesis at a reduced rate, correspondingly greater amounts of RNA would be synthesized in the 110-min incubation period. This interpretation of the concentration-dependent effect of CM on RNA synthesis is supported by the fact that the synthesis of transfer RNA which is not normally combined with protein is *not* restricted in the same way as the synthesis of ribosomal RNA (see section (d)).

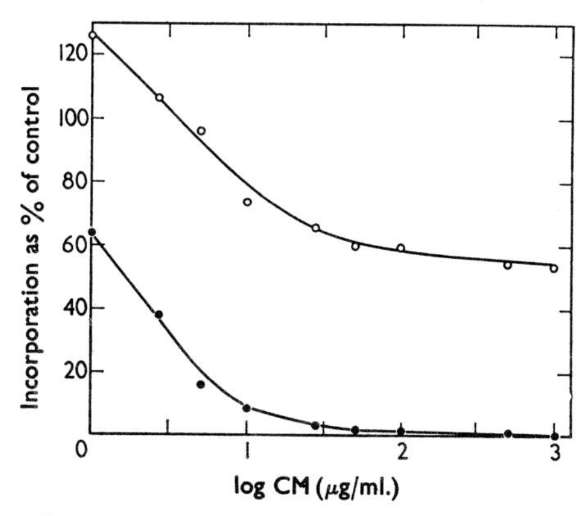

Fig. 4. The incorporation into RNA and protein of [^{14}C]uracil (○) and $^{35}SO_4$ (●), respectively, during incubation in minimal medium containing CM at concentrations ranging from 1 to 1000 μg/ml. The values plotted represent the labeling obtained in 110 min at 25°C *relative* to that of a control sample without CM.

(c) *The effect of CM on the amino acid requirement for RNA synthesis*

According to the data of Lacks & Gros (1959), CM interferes with protein synthesis in bacteria at some point after the addition of the activated amino acid to the transfer RNA. Thus, by blocking protein synthesis CM could have the effect of raising the internal concentration of amino acid in any one of several states, i.e. as free or activated amino acid, or as amino acid-charged RNA. This effect would be more dramatic in cells growing in minimal medium than in cells growing in amino acid medium because the latter already have high internal amino acid concentrations (Britten & McClure, 1961, in the press). The accelerating effect of CM on RNA synthesis in minimal medium and the *absence* of this effect in amino acid medium could therefore result from interfering with a regulatory mechanism which operates through the internal amino acid concentration levels.

The hypothesis that CM causes the accumulation of amino acids in the cell may be tested by studying the effects of CM on the amino acid requirement for RNA synthesis. Mandelstam (1958, 1961) has shown that cells starved for a required amino acid degrade pre-existing protein and from the degradation products resynthesize protein. In *E. coli* this turnover amounts to 4 to 5% of the total cell protein per hour at 35°C. Furthermore, the addition of 20 μg/ml. of CM to amino-acid-starved cells does not affect the degradation process during the first 45 min in spite of the fact that resynthesis of protein is inhibited. Thus, in the presence of CM, an amino acid-starved cell could accumulate an internal pool of amino acids. This prediction was tested by the following experiments.

The methionine-requiring mutant of *E. coli*, strain B, was grown at 25°C to the usual density (O.D. = 0·5). The cells were filtered out of the methionine-containing medium, washed on the filter and resuspended, using minimal medium with no added methionine. The culture was aerated for 20 min at 25°C, during which time the O.D. remained constant, and then distributed into twenty tubes containing [^{14}C]uracil. Ten of these tubes contained methionine (20 μg/ml.) plus concentrations of CM ranging from zero to 1000 μg/ml.; the other ten contained CM but no methionine.

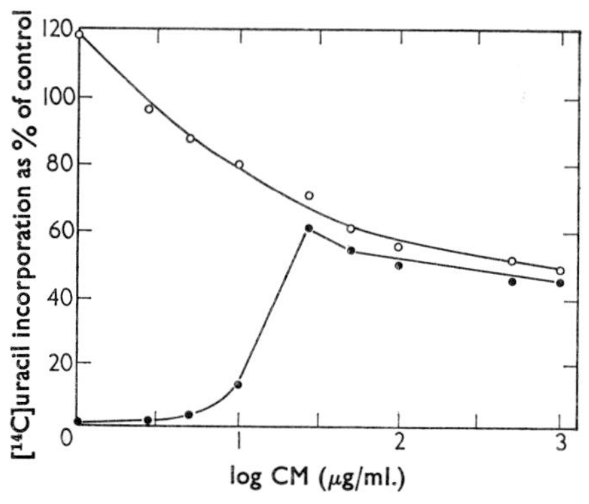

FIG. 5. The incorporation of [^{14}C]uracil into the RNA of methionine-requiring cells which were prestarved of this amino acid and then incubated for 110 min at 25°C at various CM concentrations, in the presence (○) and in the absence (●) of methionine. The labeling is expressed as a percentage of that obtained in a control sample containing methionine but no CM.

The results are presented in Fig. 5 where the incorporation of [^{14}C]uracil is expressed as a percentage of that obtained in the sample containing methionine and no CM. The cells which were incubated in the absence of both CM and methionine incorporated 2·6% as much [^{14}C]uracil as the control sample; this low value undoubtedly represents the amount of uracil incorporated into DNA (Gros & Gros, 1956). The dose response to CM in the presence of methionine is the same as that obtained with the wild-type strain (cf. Fig. 4). In the *absence* of methionine very little RNA is synthesized at low CM concentrations, but in the range from 10 to 25 μg/ml. of CM the amount of RNA synthesis is greatly increased. At higher concentrations of CM, i.e. when protein synthesis is maximally inhibited, *cells incubated with and without methionine synthesize the same amount of RNA*.

If it is true that CM relieves the need for an *external* supply of a required amino acid for RNA synthesis by permitting the accumulation of amino acids in the cells, then a lag would be expected between the time of addition of CM and the onset of RNA synthesis in the absence of methionine. Considering that protein turnover is relatively slow even in the absence of a required amino acid (4 to 5% per hour at 35°C) the expected lag might be long enough to be observed. To test this, cells were starved of methionine as described above and the kinetics of RNA synthesis followed with 100 μg/ml. of CM in the presence as well as in the absence of methionine. As can be seen from Fig. 6, a definite lag of 2 to 3 min in the resumption of RNA synthesis is observed when CM is added to starved cells in the absence of methionine. These results as well as the concentration-dependent release of the amino acid requirement for RNA synthesis (Fig. 5) are consistent with the hypothesis that CM causes the accumulation of amino acids in the cells.

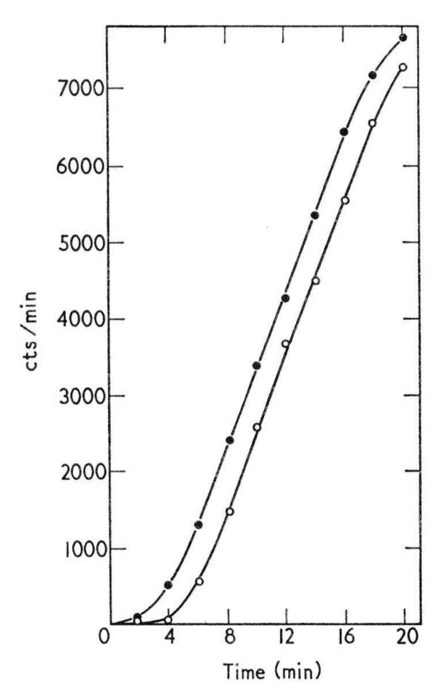

FIG. 6. The kinetics of [^{14}C]uracil incorporation into the RNA of the methionine-requiring strain. The cells were starved of methionine for 20 min and then incubated at 25°C in the presence of 100 μg/ml. of CM, with (●) and without (○) methionine.

It should be stressed that the effects of CM on RNA synthesis in a strain deprived of a required amino acid and the initial acceleration of RNA synthesis observed when CM is added to a minimal medium culture of the wild-type strain are parallel phenomena. In both cases CM can be assumed to increase the intracellular amino acid concentration prior to the onset, or acceleration, of RNA synthesis.

(d) *Ribosomal and transfer RNA synthesis in the presence of CM*

The ribosomal and the transfer RNA together comprise about 98% of the RNA of *E. coli* (Gros *et al.*, 1961, in the press). Since the transfer RNA may constitute as much as one-third of the total RNA (see Fig. 7), the virtual absence of RNA synthesis in cultures without methionine (at zero or at low CM concentrations) means that under these conditions the synthesis of *both* RNA fractions is blocked. It is of obvious interest to know whether the two fractions are affected similarly, (a) during accelerated RNA synthesis, and (b) during the *de*celeration eventually observed at high CM concentrations.

The separate effects of CM on the synthesis of transfer and of ribosomal RNA were examined as follows.

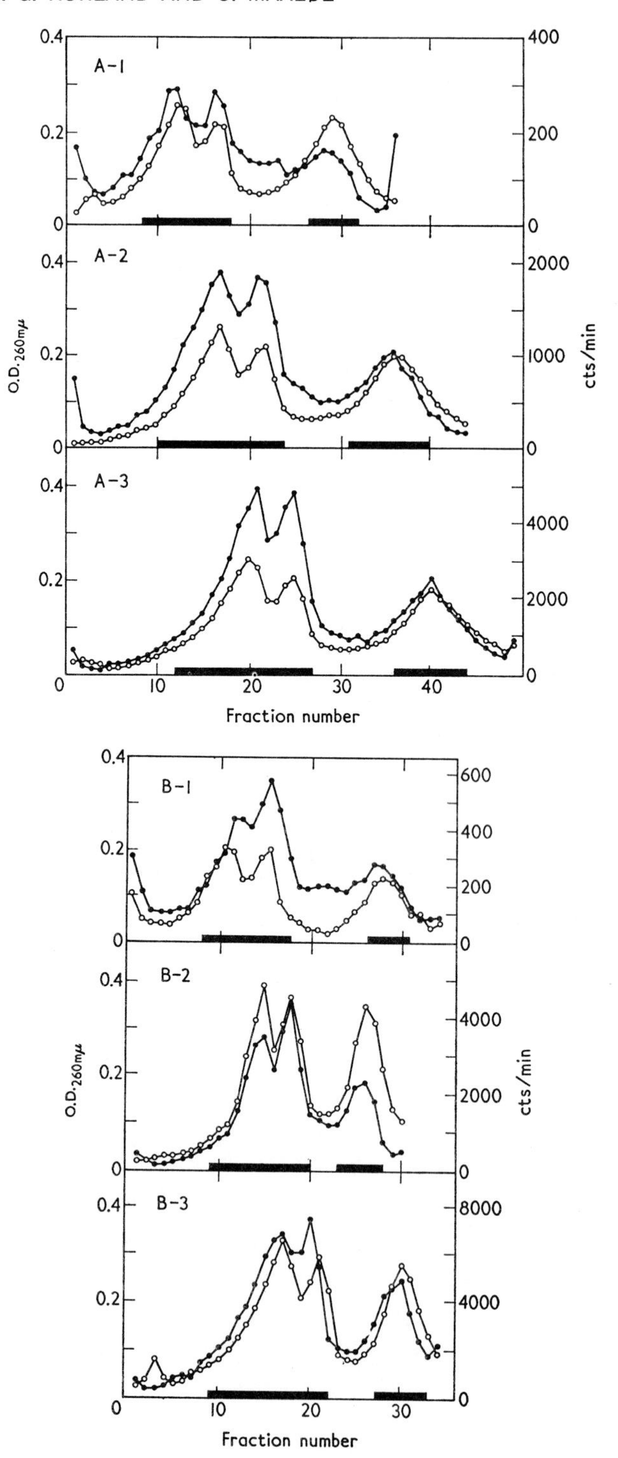

A-1
A-2
A-3
B-1
B-2
B-3
O.D.260mμ
cts/min
Fraction number
0
0.2
0.4
10
20
30
40
200
400
1000
2000
4000
600
8000

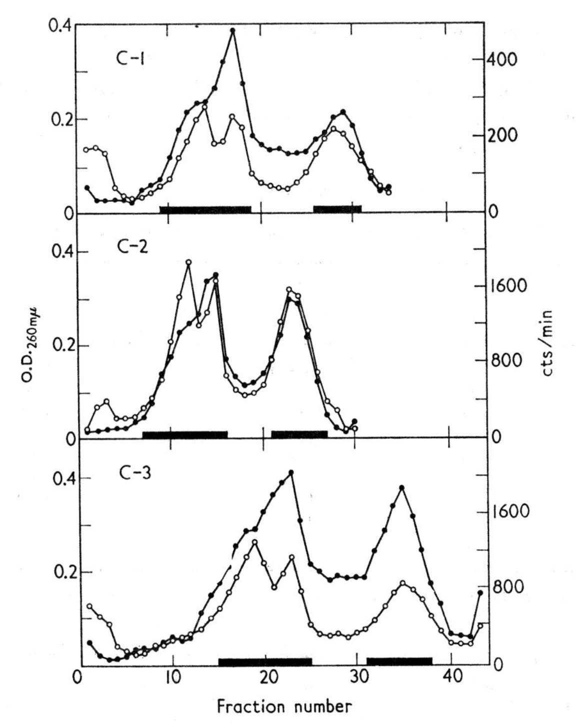

FIG. 7. Zone centrifugation analysis of the distribution of u.v.-absorbing (○) and TCA-precipitable radioactive material (●) in nine samples of phenol-prepared RNA. The cells were labeled with $^{32}PO_4$ in minimal medium containing zero (A), 1 (B) and 100 (C) μg/ml. of CM; at each CM concentration three incubation times were used, *viz.* 20 (1), 60 (2) and 120 (3) min, at 25°C. The specific activities recorded in Table 1 were calculated from the measurements made on the fractions indicated by heavy bars. In each graph, the distribution of u.v.-absorbing material shows the same three peaks representing, from right to left, the 4 s, 16 s and 23 s RNA, respectively. The gradients, of 5 to 20% sucrose, were centrifuged for 15 hr at 5°C and 25,000 rev/min.

RNA was isolated from cells incubated with $^{32}PO_4$ at zero, 1 and 100 μg/ml. of CM. In each case samples were withdrawn after incubation for 20, 60 and 120 min at 25°C All nine samples were mixed with carrier cells (1 : 20) and the RNA was fractionated by zone centrifugation in sucrose gradients. The distributions of u.v.-absorbing and TCA-precipitable radioactive material are shown in Fig. 7; 95% of the u.v.-absorbing material originates from the carrier cells and the radioactivity represents the RNA synthesized during incubation with $^{32}PO_4$.

The specific activities of the RNA fractions were calculated as indicated in Fig. 7. The specific activity of the ribosomal RNA (S_R) is an average of the 16 s and 23 s values (Kurland, 1960) while the transfer RNA specific activity (S_T) is that of the 4 s component (Tissières, 1959). These figures are listed in Table 1 and they have been plotted in two ways: Figs. 8(a), (b) and (c) show the kinetics of labeling of ribosomal and transfer RNA at each of the three CM concentrations to permit comparisons between the two RNA fractions. Figs. 9(a) and (b) show the kinetics of labeling of the individual fractions for comparisons between the three concentrations of CM.

The relatively slow labeling of the transfer RNA as compared to ribosomal RNA (Fig. 8(a)) is noticeable not only at zero but also at 1 μg/ml. of CM. A similar lag is apparent in experiments published by Hayashi & Spiegelman (1961). The nature of this phenomenon is not relevant to the arguments of the present paper; it will be discussed in a later publication.

TABLE 1

The specific activities of transfer and ribosomal RNA

CM (μg/ml.)	Time (min)	S_R (cts/min/O.D.$^{1\,cm}_{260\,m\mu}$ × 10^{-3})	S_T (cts/min/O.D.$^{1\,cm}_{260\,m\mu}$ × 10^{-3})
0	20	0·305	0·175
	60	2·12	1·26
	120	5·43	3·32
1	20	0·660	0·399
	60	2·77	1·70
	120	5·72	4·52
100	20	0·352	0·296
	60	1·16	1·15
	120	1·65	2·10

S_R denotes the specific activity of the ribosomal RNA and S_T that of the transfer RNA.

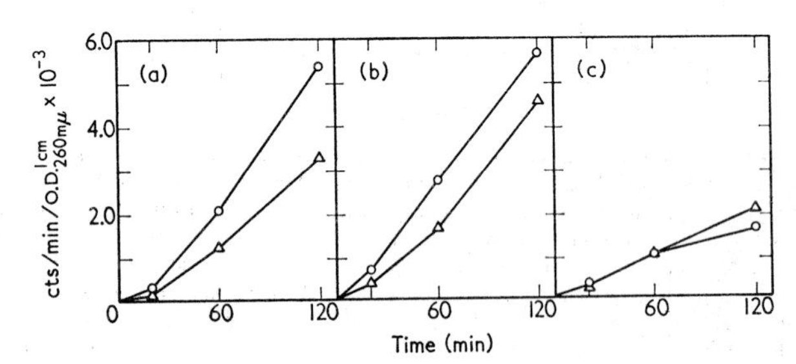

FIG. 8. The kinetics of ribosomal (○) and transfer RNA (△) labeling in the presence of zero (a), 1 (b) and 100 (c) μg/ml. of CM (data from Table 1).

Table 1 and Fig. 9 show that the synthesis of *both* transfer and ribosomal RNA is accelerated by low concentrations of CM. As in the case of uracil incorporation, this effect is most clearly seen at early times of incubation with CM. Thus, after 20 min of incubation at 1 μg/ml. of CM, the specific activities of both fractions are approximately twice as high as in the control samples.

At 100 μg/ml. of CM the relative rates of labeling of the transfer and ribosomal RNA fractions are different: transfer RNA is synthesized at a constant rate, whereas the rate of synthesis of ribosomal RNA decreases gradually during the incubation period. At 120 min the specific activity of the transfer RNA was 1·27 relative to that of the ribosomal RNA, whereas, in the control sample without CM, the final, relative specific activity of the transfer RNA was 0·61. Thus the amount of ribosomal RNA relative to transfer RNA synthesized in 120 min is reduced to about 50% by 100 μg/ml. of CM, i.e. a gradual and selective deceleration of ribosomal RNA synthesis has been demonstrated.

Table 1 shows that, at 60 min, the specific activity of the transfer RNA is approximately the same at zero and at 100 μg/ml. of CM. This means that, at this concentration of CM, the *average* rate of synthesis of the transfer RNA is accelerated relative to the protein content of the cells. Finally, the facts, (a) that the transfer RNA specific activity is greater than that of the ribosomal RNA after 120 min, and (b) that the transfer RNA is synthesized at a constant rate at 100 μg/ml. of CM, show that the gradual deceleration of RNA synthesis is probably not an artifact due to autolysis or a decrease in the general capacity for RNA synthesis.

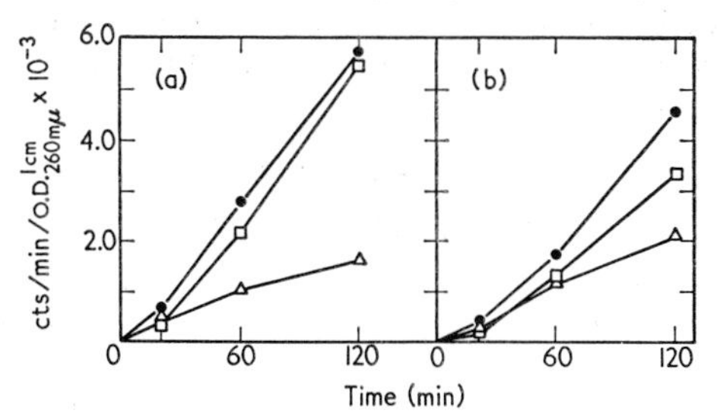

FIG. 9. The kinetics of the labeling of ribosomal (a) and transfer RNA (b) in the presence of zero (□), 1 (●) and 100 (△) μg/ml. of CM (data from Table 1).

At 120 min at 1 μg/ml. of CM the specific activity of the transfer RNA is 36% greater than in the control, whereas that of the ribosomal RNA is only increased by 6%. Thus, even at 1 μg/ml. of CM, where protein synthesis proceeds at two-thirds of the normal rate (see Fig. 4), selective deceleration of ribosomal RNA synthesis can be detected.

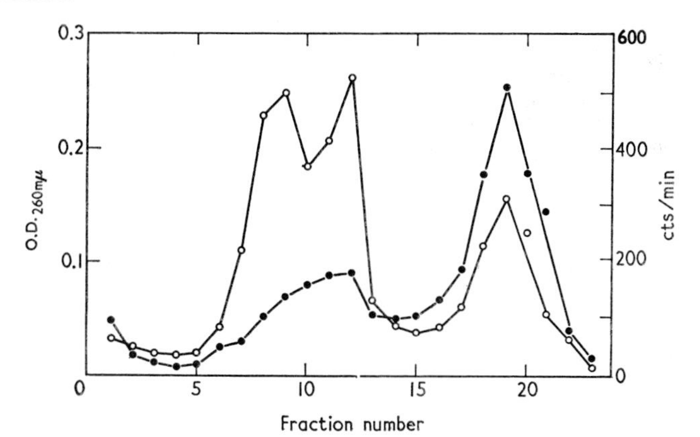

FIG. 10. Zone centrifugation analysis of the distribution of u.v.-absorbing (○) and TCA-precipitable radioactive material (●) in a sample of phenol-prepared RNA. The cells were incubated at 25°C in minimal medium containing 100 μg/ml. of CM. After 120 min, $^{32}PO_4$ was added and labeling continued for 30 min in the presence of the CM.

The preferential synthesis of the transfer RNA in the presence of CM can be clearly demonstrated by another kind of experiment. Cells were incubated with 100 μg/ml. of CM for 120 min; $^{32}PO_4$ was then introduced and labeling continued for 30 min. The distribution of u.v.-absorbing and TCA-precipitable radioactive material obtained by zone centrifugation of this RNA is shown in Fig. 10. The specific activity of the transfer RNA is 4·7 times greater than that of the ribosomal RNA. This should be compared with the RNA labeled for the first 20 min of incubation with 100 μg/ml. of CM. Here, the specific activity of the transfer RNA is 0·84 of that of the ribosomal RNA.

Finally, attention should be drawn to the distribution of label within the ribosomal fraction in the presence of CM. As can be seen from Fig. 7, 16 s ribosomal RNA is synthesized preferentially in the presence of CM. At 100 μg/ml. of CM very little 23 s RNA is synthesized, and even at 1 μg/ml. of CM, where net synthesis of ribosomal RNA is greater than in the control, the bulk of material synthesized is 16 s RNA. The significance of this observation will be considered below.

4. Discussion

(a) *The repressor model*

At CM concentrations which almost completely inhibit protein synthesis, RNA synthesis is independent of an external supply of a required amino acid; at lower concentrations of CM, no RNA is synthesized unless such amino acids are supplied in the medium. These results confirm the seemingly conflicting observations of Aronson & Spiegelman (1958) on the one hand, and of Gros & Gros (1956) and Pardee & Prestidge (1956) on the other. In addition our findings and those of Mandelstam (1958, 1961) suggest that high concentrations of CM relieve the amino acid requirement for RNA synthesis by permitting the accumulation of an internal pool of amino acids derived from the degradation of protein.

An analogous mechanism may explain the accelerating effect on RNA synthesis observed when CM is added to a minimal medium culture. In this situation the internal concentration of amino acids would increase rapidly and considerably when protein synthesis is inhibited by CM. The effect of CM on cells growing in an amino acid medium in which the internal amino acid concentration already is high (Britten & McClure, 1961, in the press) supports this view. In this case, the effect of CM on the internal concentration of amino acids would be expected to be small, and, indeed, RNA synthesis is accelerated very slightly when CM is added to cells growing in an amino acid medium. These considerations lead to the notion that the amino acid requirement for RNA synthesis reflects the operation of a control mechanism through which the *rate* of RNA synthesis is modulated according to the internal concentrations of amino acids.

Amino acids are required for the synthesis of transfer as well as ribosomal RNA. Similarly, the accelerating effect of CM on RNA synthesis in minimal medium affects both fractions. This suggests that the same amino acid mediated control mechanism regulates the rate of synthesis of transfer and of ribosomal RNA.

It has been suggested that RNA synthesis depended on the *simultaneous* synthesis of protein, and that for this reason the amino acids were required (Pardee & Prestidge, 1956). This notion of an obligatory coupling of RNA and protein synthesis must be abandoned since it has been shown that RNA can be produced in the absence of protein synthesis. Aronson & Spiegelman (1958) suggested that a protein might be necessary to stabilize the RNA synthesized in the presence of CM. We find no evidence that RNA synthesized in the absence of protein synthesis is unstable during the first two hours (at 25°C). To avoid confusion, it should be emphasized that this does *not* prove that free ribosomal RNA is stable in the cell; our findings merely suggest that a protein necessary for the synthesis, *or* stabilization, of ribosomal RNA exists in relatively large quantities in the cell, and thus need not be synthesized *after* the addition of CM.

The role played by the amino acids in regulating RNA synthesis may be understood in terms of the repressor model of Jacob & Monod (1961) for the regulation of protein synthesis. The following elements of this model are relevant in our case. (a) A genetically determined molecule, the repressor, blocks the synthesis of a specific macromolecule by inhibiting the activity of the relevant genetic locus. (b) The repressor may be coupled with a specific substrate molecule, the inducer, thereby being inactivated; this is the way in which repression is released. (c) A specific enzyme is required to couple the inducer to the repressor.

To account for our observations we assume that the amino acids, or simple derivatives thereof, act as inducers for RNA synthesis. Since all of the amino acids studied to date seem to be required *inside the cell* (Gros & Gros, 1956; Pardee & Prestidge, 1956), our model would call for either twenty specific repressor molecules or one repressor molecule with specific sites corresponding to each of the twenty amino acids. If the repressors are saturated with amino acids, the rate of RNA synthesis should be maximal. A decrease in *degree* of saturation of the repressors should produce a corresponding decrease in the rate of RNA synthesis. Finally, the absence of RNA synthesis when a required amino acid is withdrawn demands that, if any single class of repressor (or any single site) is completely free of amino acid, ribosomal and transfer RNA synthesis should be completely repressed.

The repressors have not in any case been identified; it is attractive, however, to think that the transfer RNA molecules, already associated with protein synthesis, also act as the repressors of RNA synthesis. If so, the amino acid adenylates could function as the inducers and the activating enzymes (Hoagland, 1955; Hoagland, Keller & Zamecnik, 1956; Berg & Ofengand, 1958) could mediate the coupling of inducer and repressor.

Our model therefore operates with a multiplicity of repressors with a common specific function. A simple way in which this function might be exerted would be through structures common to all classes of repressors. The transfer RNA meets this requirement in the sense that the terminal sequence, cytosine–cytosine–adenosine, occurs in each class. This is the site at which the amino acid is thought to be attached, while the specificity of attachment presumably is determined by nucleotide sequences elsewhere in the molecule (Hecht, Stephenson & Zamecnik, 1959; Berg, Bergmann, Ofengand & Dieckmann, 1961; Preiss, Dieckmann & Berg, 1961). Where then could a segment common to all transfer RNA be imagined to attach to effect repression? First, we have seen that RNA can be synthesized without the simultaneous synthesis of protein; thus RNA synthesis cannot be repressed by blocking the synthesis of a specific protein. Second, no evidence has been produced to indicate that the repressors of RNA synthesis act at a DNA or RNA template determining the nucleotide sequence of the RNA. It is therefore an open question whether the repressors should be thought of as blocking a template, or specifically inhibiting a polymerase necessary to condense the nucleotides into RNA strands.

(b) *The synthesis of the ribosomes*

Most of the RNA synthesized at high concentrations of CM is either transfer RNA or CM-particle RNA (Pardee, Paegin & Prestidge, 1957; Nomura & Watson, 1959).

The CM-particles contain 25% protein, i.e. about half of the protein found in the normal ribosomes (Nomura & Watson, 1959; Tissières, Watson, Schlessinger & Hollingworth, 1959). The RNA of the CM-particle is identical with that of the normal ribosome in base composition (Pardee *et al.*, 1957) and in molecular properties (Kurland, Nomura & Watson, 1962). Indeed, it has been suggested that the CM-particles represent normal precursors to the ribosomes, which accumulate when protein synthesis is inhibited (Nomura & Watson, 1959; Kurland *et al.*, 1962).

The CM-particles are formed under conditions in which protein synthesis cannot be detected, and the protein component of these particles should therefore be derived from protein synthesized before the addition of CM. This deduction was confirmed by isolating CM-particles synthesized at a high CM concentration in the presence of labeled amino acids; the particles contained no label (unpublished results). By transferring ^{32}P-labeled cells to cold medium with a high concentration of CM it has been shown that approximately 25% of the PO_4 in the CM-particle RNA was present in the cell prior to the addition of CM (Nomura & Watson, 1959). Since part of the label found in the CM-particles must come from pool-phosphorus, the value of 25% must be considered an upper limit for the amount of CM-particle RNA derived from pre-existing RNA. Taking this limiting value and assuming that all the label appearing in the CM-particles had originated from ribosomes, the protein of these particles still would account for only half of the protein of the CM-particles. Consequently at least half, and probably more, of the CM-particle protein must have been present in the cell, uncombined with RNA, when CM was added.

In the absence of protein synthesis approximately half the normal amount of RNA is synthesized in 110 min at 25°C. During this period, transfer RNA is synthesized at a constant rate, whereas the rate of synthesis of ribosomal RNA decreases steadily. When the concentration of CM is insufficient to inhibit protein synthesis completely, more RNA is synthesized, and *a greater fraction* of this is ribosomal RNA. Actually, a close correlation was observed between the amount of protein synthesized at low CM concentrations and the *increase* in RNA synthesis over and above the amount produced when protein synthesis is completely inhibited (cf. Fig. 4). This correlation, together with the fact that ribosomal RNA can be made without simultaneous protein synthesis, indicates (a) that in some way protein is necessary for RNA synthesis, and (b) that the protein involved is consumed in the process. This protein must therefore be present in the normal cell in an amount corresponding to the quantity of ribosomal RNA synthesized at high CM concentrations.

The protein required for the synthesis of ribosomal RNA may well be the CM-particle protein itself. We suggest that this protein may contain the polymerizing enzyme, and that, once it is incorporated into a CM-particle, the enzyme activity is masked. The observation that, at high CM concentrations, the rate of synthesis of ribosomal RNA decreases steadily would then imply that, for a given repression level, this rate is determined by the concentration of free CM-particle protein in the cell. In contrast, the rate of synthesis of transfer RNA, which under the same conditions remains constant, would be determined by a different enzyme whose concentration would not change in the presence of CM.

Ribosomal RNA synthesized at a high concentration of CM consists largely of 16 s RNA; at most 10% is in the form of 23 s RNA. It has been shown that purified CM-particles yield 30 to 40% of 23 s RNA (Kurland *et al.*, 1962), some of which may be derived from pre-existing ribosomes. These facts suggest that the 25 s CM-particles, which contain the 23 s RNA, are primarily degradation products of 50 s ribosomes, and that the 18 s CM-particles, which contain the 16 s RNA (Kurland *et al.*, 1961), may be the true precursors of the ribosomes.

The 30 s ribosomes contain 16 s RNA only, whereas 50 s ribosomes contain 23 s as well as 16 s RNA. According to Bolton *et al.* (1959) the 30 s particle is a precursor of the 50 s particle. Therefore, if a 30 s ribosome is a "matured" 18 s CM-particle, no 23 s RNA would be formed until two 30 s particles condense to form a 50 s ribosome (Kurland, 1960). Thus, by preventing the formation of new 30 s ribosomes, CM would also prevent the conversion of newly synthesized 16 s RNA into 23 s RNA.

(c) *The effect of growth medium on RNA synthesis*

Bacteria grow at a unique maximum rate in a given medium. It is known that the chemical composition of cells changes with the composition of the medium. These changes may be looked upon as the visible effects of the interplay of the various regulatory mechanisms operating during growth. It has been pointed out previously (Maaløe, 1960) that an efficient system of controls should lead to a steady state of growth in which no single metabolic step can be said to limit the overall growth rate.

One striking feature of the adjustment of the chemical composition of the cell to the medium is that the rate of protein synthesis per ribosome is virtually constant for media between which the growth rate, at 37°C, varies from 0·6 to 2·8 doublings per hour (Schaechter *et al.*, 1958; Kjeldgaard, 1961). Thus, the faster cells grow the richer they are in RNA. This again means that the cells must possess means of regulating the rate of RNA synthesis *relative* to the overall growth rate. The mechanism for repression of RNA synthesis proposed in this paper may provide this means.

The transition from one state of balanced growth to another is characterized by a sudden change in the rate of RNA synthesis, followed more slowly by corresponding changes in the rates of protein and DNA synthesis. The slow increase in the rate of protein synthesis after a shift to a richer medium is closely correlated with the increase in total RNA per cell (Kjeldgaard, 1961). In other words, to increase the rate of protein synthesis it seems to be necessary to expand the protein-synthesizing system. This again suggests that, *per ribosome*, a fixed maximal rate of protein synthesis is maintained throughout.

The rapid and selective effect on RNA synthesis can be understood on the basis of the repressor model described above: when cells are transferred from a minimal to an amino acid medium, the internal amino acid concentrations may increase significantly in a matter of seconds (Britten & McClure, 1961, in the press); this would lead to a rapid increase in the degree of saturation of the repressors of RNA synthesis with amino acids and a corresponding increase in rate of RNA synthesis.

The lag in the establishment of the definitive rate of protein synthesis may in turn explain the fact that the initial rate of RNA synthesis is *higher* than the definitive rate, when cells are transferred from a minimal to an amino acid medium. According to the repressor model the high initial rate of RNA synthesis reflects peak values for the internal amino acid concentrations produced by placing the cells in the amino acid medium. Later, when the rate of protein synthesis increases, the internal concentrations of amino acids may be assumed to decrease somewhat, resulting in a slight repression of RNA synthesis.

The postulated control of RNA synthesis is formally similar to the repressor mechanisms governing protein synthesis. However, in their relation to growth these processes have, so to say, opposite signs: when the concentration of amino acids is increased, enzyme repression and feed-back inhibition tend to reduce unnecessary synthetic efforts; in contrast, the effect on RNA synthesis is a stimulation resulting in the well-known increase in total RNA per unit cell mass.

The transfer RNA fraction is approximately one-half the size of the ribosomal RNA fraction when cells grow in minimal medium (Fig. 7). It has been our experience that the transfer RNA is approximately one-fourth the ribosomal fraction when cells grow in amino acid medium. The existence of a protein required for ribosomal RNA synthesis could enable the cell to vary the ratio of ribosomal to transfer RNA by varying the rate of synthesis of this protein.

The authors wish to thank Professor C. Levinthal for valuable and stimulating discussions, between planes. Our thanks are also due to Dr. D. Pratt, Mrs. I. W. Kurland and Mr. H. A. Boye for advice and assistance during the course of this investigation. One of us (C. G. K.) was supported by a post-doctoral fellowship (CF-422) from the U.S. Public Health Services.

REFERENCES

Aronson, A. I. & Spiegelman, S. (1958). *Biochim. biophys. Acta*, **29**, 214.
Berg, P., Bergmann, F., Ofengand, E. J. & Dieckmann, M. (1961). *J. Biol. Chem.* **236**, 1726.
Berg, P. & Ofengand, E. J. (1958). *Proc. Nat. Acad. Sci., Wash.* **44**, 78.
Bolton, E. T., Britten, R. J., Cowie, D. B., McCarthy, B. J., McQuillen, K. & Roberts, R. B. (1959). *Yearb. Carnegie Inst.* **58**, 259.
Gale, E. F. & Folkes, J. P. (1953). *Biochem. J.* **53**, 493.
Gorini, L. & Kaufman, H. (1960). *Science*, **131**, 604.
Gros, F. & Gros, F. (1956). *Biochim. biophys. Acta*, **22**, 200.
Gros, F., Hiatt, H., Gilbert, W., Kurland, C. G., Risebrough, R. W. & Watson, J. D. (1961). *Nature*, **190**, 581.
Hayashi, M. & Spiegelman, S. (1961). *Proc. Nat. Acad. Sci., Wash.* **47**, 1564.
Hecht, L. I., Stephenson, M. L. & Zamecnik, P. C. (1959). *Proc. Nat. Acad. Sci., Wash.* **45**, 505.
Hoagland, M. B. (1955). *Biochim. biophys. Acta*, **16**, 288.
Hoagland, M. B., Keller, E. B. & Zamecnik, P. C. (1956). *J. Biol. Chem.* **218**, 345.
Jacob, F. & Monod, J. (1961). *J. Mol. Biol.* **3**, 318.
Kjeldgaard, N. O. (1961). *Biochim. biophys. Acta*, **49**, 64.
Kjeldgaard, N. O., Maaløe, O. & Schaechter, M. (1958). *J. Gen. Microbiol.* **19**, 607.
Kurland, C. G. (1960). *J. Mol. Biol.* **2**, 83.
Kurland, C. G., Nomura, M. & Watson, J. D. (1962). *J. Mol. Biol.* **4**, in the press.
Lacks, S. & Gros, F. (1959). *J. Mol. Biol.* **1**, 301.
Maaløe, O. (1960). *Symp. Soc. Gen. Microbiol.* **X**, 272. Cambridge University Press.
Mandelstam, J. (1958). *Biochem. J.* **69**, 110.
Mandelstam, J. (1961). *Biochem. J.* **79**, 489.
McQuillen, K., Roberts, R. B. & Britten, R. J. (1959). *Proc. Nat. Acad. Sci., Wash.* **45**, 1437.
Neidhardt, F. C. & Fraenkel, D. G. (1961). *Cold Spr. Harb. Symp. Quant. Biol.* **26**, in the press.
Neidhardt, F. C. & Gros, F. (1957). *Biochim. biophys. Acta*, **25**, 513.
Neidhardt, F. C. & Magasanik, B. (1960). *Biochim. biophys. Acta*, **42**, 99.
Nomura, M. & Watson, J. D. (1959). *J. Mol. Biol.* **1**, 204.
Pardee, A. B., Paegin, K. & Prestidge, L. S. (1957). *Biochim. biophys. Acta*, **24**, 215.
Pardee, A. B. & Prestidge, L. S. (1956). *J. Bact.* **71**, 677.
Preiss, J., Dieckmann, M. & Berg, P. (1961). *J. Biol. Chem.* **236**, 1748.
Schaechter, M., Maaløe, O. & Kjeldgaard, N. O. (1958). *J. Gen. Microbiol.* **19**, 592.
Stent, G. S. & Brenner, S. (1961). *Proc. Nat. Acad. Sci., Wash.* In the press.
Tissières, A. (1959). *J. Mol. Biol.* **1**, 365.
Tissières, A., Watson, J. D., Schlessinger, D. & Hollingworth, B. (1959). *J. Mol. Biol.* **1**, 221.
Wisseman, C. L., Smadel, J. E., Hahn, F. E. & Hopps, H. E. (1954). *J. Bact.* **67**, 662.

THE NORMAL DNA REPLICATION CYCLE II

By

Philip C. Hanawalt, Ole Maaløe, Donald J. Cummings
and Moselio Schaechter

The Normal DNA Replication Cycle. II

PHILIP C. HANAWALT,† OLE MAALØE, DONALD J. CUMMINGS‡ AND MOSELIO SCHAECHTER §

University Institute of Microbiology, Copenhagen, Denmark

(*Received 14 October 1960*)

Certain predictions made by the theory developed in our first paper have been examined in autoradiographic experiments. First, individual cells were found to continue DNA synthesis for very different periods after protein and RNA synthesis had been inhibited; this agrees with the assumption that, in the absence of protein and RNA synthesis, DNA replication runs to completion and then stops. Secondly, it was found that if a fraction of the cells of a culture is immune to thymineless death a similar fraction is *un*able to synthesize DNA under conditions of inhibited protein and RNA synthesis; this agrees with our assumption that an immune cell is one that has finished a replication cycle and not yet taken the steps necessary to initiate a new one.

It was further predicted that under certain experimental conditions the cells would go through a complete replication cycle when transferred from a thymine deficient to a thymine containing medium. The actual experiment showed that individual cells in fact produced a quantity of DNA which corresponded to a single replication cycle.

When 5-bromouracil was substituted for thymine it was found that the DNA synthesized in the absence of protein and RNA synthesis was hybrid with respect to bromouracil substitution.

1. Introduction

The theory developed in the preceding paper makes definite predictions concerning DNA synthesis in individual cells. To test these predictions two series of autoradiographic experiments were carried out using tritiated thymidine as a specific label for DNA.||

The first experiment shows how the quantity of DNA synthesized under conditions of inhibited protein and RNA synthesis is distributed in the cell population. As expected, it was found that individual cells contributed very unequally; some would stop synthesizing soon after transfer and contribute little DNA, while other cells continued synthesizing and produced correspondingly more DNA.

The second experiment was designed to analyse the transition from acquired immunity to thymineless death to sensitivity. As shown in the first paper, this transition is paralleled by a slow increase in the rate of DNA synthesis. The present experiment shows that this change in the rate of DNA synthesis is due to a gradual

† Now at the California Institute of Technology, Pasadena, California, U.S.A.

‡ Now at The National Institutes of Health, Bethesda, Maryland, U.S.A.

§ Since September, 1958, at The Department of Microbiology, University of Florida, Gainesville, Florida, U.S.A.

|| The bacterial strains and the abbreviations used to indicate media supplemented in different ways are described on page 147 of the preceding paper.

increase in the *fraction* of cells that actively synthesize DNA; in agreement with our theory, loss of immunity and resumption of DNA synthesis thus seem to go hand in hand. Furthermore, when DNA synthesis is resumed in a (+ T, − AU) medium it can be shown that those cells which participate produce a quantity of DNA corresponding to one complete round of replication and then stop.

In addition to the autoradiographic experiments, preliminary studies of the DNA made in a (+ 5-bromouracil, − AU) medium were made by density gradient centrifugation.

2. Materials and Techniques

The bacterial strains used, the growth media and the bacteriological techniques are described in the preceding paper.

(a) *Autoradiographic procedures*

Tritiated thymidine (360 mc/m-mole) was obtained from the Schwartz Laboratories, Mt. Vernon, N.Y.; in experiments A and B as well as in the control experiment (see p. 158) it was added without carrier to the media to give a final thymidine concentration of 3 μg/ml. The radiochemical purity of this batch of thymidine was not examined at the time it was used, and purification was not attempted. However, the pilot experiment mentioned on page 162 was carried out in Cambridge by Dr. Robert van Tubergen and one of the authors (P.C.H.), and in this experiment a carefully purified thymidine preparation was used. This pilot experiment and our experiment A both showed the *same* large fraction of unlabeled cells. We therefore conclude that the thymidine used in our experiments did not contain radiochemical impurities which under our growth conditions would produce a detectable background of general labeling.

Incorporation of labeled thymidine took place in aerated, 5 ml. cultures. At intervals 0·4 ml. samples were removed and the cells rapidly fixed by squirting the liquid into tubes held at 4°C and containing one drop of 2% formalin.

Standard glass microscope slides (0·8 to 1 mm thick, with one corner filed to designate a "top" side) were soaked for a week in dichromic acid cleaning solution. After thorough rinsing in tap water and then in distilled water the wet slides were dipped in a filtered solution of 0·01% chrome alum + 0·1% gelatin (Knox) at room temperature. The "subbed" slides were allowed to dry in a dust-free room and stored in a dust-free box.

Drops from the formalin-containing tubes were placed on a clean 1% agar surface. After the liquid had been adsorbed by the agar, impression smears were made on "subbed" slides. After drying, the slides were soaked in Carnoy's solution for 20 min at room temperature and then in the following ethanol + distilled water solutions, respectively for 2 min periods: 95% ethanol, 85%, 75%, 50%, 30%, distilled water. The slides were dried overnight at room temperature.

Kodak AR–10 autoradiographic stripping film was placed over the samples by standard procedure in low level lighting from a Wratten 1 safelight (see, e.g. Doniach & Pelc, 1950). Humidity was maintained at 58 to 60% and a 25°C water bath was used for "floating" the emulsion strip. The film was allowed to dry on the slides for three hours in the dark at room temperature in front of a fan. Then the slides were placed in an air- and light-tight box, flushed with dry nitrogen and stored at 4°C.

After an exposure time calculated to give average grain counts of 2 to 4 per labeled cell, the film was developed for 2·5 min at 20°C in Kodak D19b developer and fixed in Kodak non-hardening acid fixer. After rinsing in tap water excess emulsion was carefully trimmed from the edges of the slide and the emulsion allowed to dry. A coverslip was fixed over the emulsion with a drop of 60% glycerol. Cells and grains were easily visible in phase contrast at a magnification × 800. Independent countings of several of the samples by the two authors gave reasonably consistent results.

3. Autoradiographic Experiments

The first series of autoradiograms was prepared by Dr. Schaechter using *E. coli*, strain 15T⁻ taking advantage of the inhibitory effect on protein and RNA synthesis of a transfer from broth to minimal medium (Kjeldgaard, Maaløe & Schaechter, 1958). It is known that mass increase is almost completely blocked for 50 to 60 min after the transfer and that, during this period, DNA increases by about 40%. In experiments with *Salmonella typhimurium* it has further been shown that total RNA drops by 5 to 10% as DNA increases; one may assume that this RNA fraction supplies the cytosine used in DNA synthesis. The experiment of Schaechter consisted in exposing samples of the culture, taken at different times after transfer, to tritiated thymidine for short periods. Autoradiograms were prepared from the samples as described by Schaechter, Bentzon & Maaløe (1959).

These preparations showed that the fraction of cells which incorporated labeled thymidine into trichloroacetic acid (TCA)-insoluble material gradually decreased from 1·0 at time zero to 0·3 to 0·4 at 60 min after transfer. The quantity of thymidine incorporated/min by an actively synthesizing cell decreased only slightly as the fraction of actively synthesizing cells was reduced. From these experiments we conclude that the period during which DNA synthesis continues after transfer varies greatly from cell to cell, that cells that stop synthesizing shortly after transfer contribute little and that cells that continue DNA synthesis for a longer time contribute correspondingly to the overall DNA increase of about 40%. It was not possible from these preparations to obtain reliable measurements for studying the correlation between cell size and the duration of DNA synthesis. Also it should be mentioned that in this experiment total mass increased by about 10% during the first hour after the transfer. Protein and RNA synthesis was thus less efficiently blocked than in previously conducted experiments with *S. typhimurium*. This may account for the fact that even the 60 min sample showed incorporation of thymidine by a considerable fraction of the cells.

The second series of autoradiograms was obtained from rather more complicated experiments: a culture of the triple mutant of *E. coli*, strain 15T⁻A⁻U⁻, growing exponentially in a fully supplemented, (+ T, + AU) medium, was preincubated in (+ T, − AU) medium for 90 min and then transferred to a (− T, + AU) medium. Two portions, A and B, were grown in this medium for 15 and for 45 min respectively before being returned to (+ T, − AU) medium. During the second period in this medium tritiated thymidine (T*) was substituted for thymine, and samples were removed at intervals for autoradiography.

This experiment was designed (1) to test whether the low rate of DNA synthesis observed during the early stages of growth following pre-incubation might be due to participation by a fraction of the cells only; and (2) to determine the quantity of DNA made per cell during the second period in (+ T,* − AU) medium. In order to be able to express this quantity in suitable units of DNA a control experiment was carried out, in which exponentially growing cells were allowed to incorporate tritiated thymidine for various times.

Table 1 presents the data from 6 typical autoradiograms selected from the control series, and from experiments A and B in which the growth periods in (− T, + AU) medium were 15 and 45 min respectively. The most conspicuous feature of these experiments is that in A less than half of the cells took up any radioactive thymidine, whereas in the control culture and in experiment B nearly all the cells did.

Figure 1 shows the complete results from experiments A and B plotted against the time of incubation in medium containing tritiated thymidine. The values on the ordinate express quantities of newly synthesized DNA estimated from the grain counts as explained below (see section in small print). In the case of experiment A correction was made for the fact that only a fraction of the cells took up any label, and all ordinate values thus refer to average quantities of newly made (labeled) DNA *per actively synthesizing cell.* The unit in which these quantities are expressed was derived from the control experiment and corresponds to one complete round of DNA

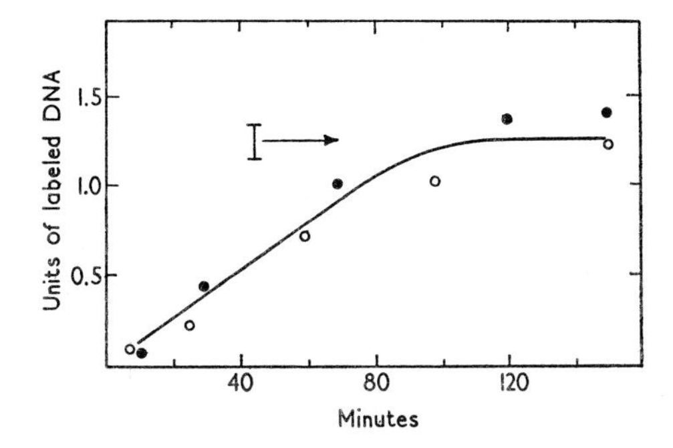

FIG. 1. Experiments A and B are represented by open and filled circles respectively The unit of DNA is defined on page 161. The time axis represents minutes of incorporation in medium containing tritiated thymidine but no A and U. The vertical bar with an arrow shows the interval within which the final yield of labeled DNA is expected to fall (see p. 164).

replication in the presence of the label. As indicated by the curve of Fig. 1, our experiments show that a total of about 1·3 units of DNA was produced per actively synthesizing cell, irrespective of whether all or only a fraction of the cells were engaged in DNA synthesis.

At the end of the 15 and 45 min growth periods in (— T, + AU) medium and after filtration, control samples were incubated for 5 hr in (— T, — AU) medium at 37°C. In experiment A about 70% of the cells and in experiment B 8 to 10% were found to be immune to thymineless death under these conditions (cf. Fig. 5 of our first paper).

Finally, cell division was controlled throughout the experiment by direct colony counts. During the first 90 min in (+ T, — AU) medium the viable cell count increased by about 20%, and during the following 45 min in (— T, + AU) medium a similar small increase was observed; during the second period in (+ T*, — AU) a further increase of about 40% took place. Thus the overall increase was close to one doubling. The significance of these details will be discussed on p. 164.

(a) *Analysis of autoradiograms*

A uniformly labeled population of cells of identical size should produce an autoradiogram in which the number of grains per cell follows a Poisson distribution. In the *control culture* we may assume 100% viability and very nearly the same specific activity of the labeled DNA in all cells. The observed grain distributions were therefore analysed graphically by means of the equation: $\ln(p(x)x!) = x \ln m - m$, in which $p(x)$ is the relative frequency of the class of cells which produced x grains each and m is the mean value of a Poisson distribution. Using the observed frequencies and plotting the left-hand side of the equation ($P(x)$) against x a straight line should obtain if the $p(x)$ values fit a Poisson distribution. The slope and the intercept of this line should yield two estimates of m. These estimates of course should agree with the arithmetic mean of the grain counts. Data from 6 autoradiograms from the control experiments were analysed and found to satisfy these conditions reasonably well, showing that the observed grain distributions approximate to Poisson distributions (two examples are shown in Table 1 and Fig. 2). With reference to experiments A and B below, it should be particularly noted that in all six distributions the $p(o)$ values agreed with the rest of the $p(x)$ values.

TABLE 1

Autoradiographic data

Grains per cell	Control experiment 1	Control experiment 2	Experiment A 1	Experiment A 2	Experiment B 1	Experiment B 2
0	94	34	400	464	60(17)‡	42(12)‡
1	194	80	84	217†	50	32
2	182	88	51	145	80	32
3	144	75	37	75	93	43
4	83	51	27	59	110	51
5	56	31	11	43	98	82
6	20	10	3	20	69	89
7	8	5	1	10	44	38
8		1		5	11	15
9				1	4	6
Cells scored	781	375	613	1039	619	430
m_a	2·27	2·51	0·79	1·38	3·66	4·23
m_e	2·38	2·48	2·14	2·94	3·78	4·37
m_e/t	0·40	0·50	0·71	0·59	0·76	0·63

m_a = arithmetic mean of grain counts.
m_e = graphically estimated mean; t = time in days of exposure of autoradiographic film.
In control experiments 1 and 2 incorporation of label was continued for 50 and 65 min respectively; the corresponding estimates of m_e/t for total labeling were 0·72 and 0·76 (see p. 161).
In experiment A both samples represent incorporation for 150 min.
In experiment B samples 1 and 2 represent incorporation for 120 and 150 min respectively.
† The probable reason for this excessive value is discussed on page 162.
‡ The figures in brackets are corrected $p(o)$ values assuming that 7% of the cells had remained unlabeled (see p. 162); the effect of this correction is illustrated in Fig. 2.

The graphical method used to estimate the mean values (the m_e of Table 1) permits an evaluation of the error of this estimate. In the control experiment as well as in experiments A and B below, the individual estimates of m are believed to be correct within $\pm$ 10%. A more exact calculation of the standard deviations of the estimates of slopes would be difficult since the observed $p(x)$-values carry extremely different weights.

Considering that cells of an exponentially growing culture contain anywhere from 1 to 2 genomes per nucleus, and since some variation in the number of nuclei per cell was noticed, it was at first surprising that the observed grain distributions did not deviate significantly from Poisson distributions. We therefore calculated the distribution to be expected from the simplifying assumption that replication starts at the time of cell division and continues at a constant rate throughout the division cycle. Based on this assumption the cell population can be divided into, e.g. 10 classes with respectively 1·0 to 1·1; 1·1 to 1·2; . . . and 1·9 to 2·0 genomes per nucleus. Here the class with least DNA comprises the newly divided cells and is almost twice as large as the class with most DNA (the cells about to divide). In a culture homogeneously labeled with tritiated thymidine each class should give a grain distribution of the Poisson type with a mean value proportional to the average DNA content per cell of the class. Disregarding variation in the number of nuclei per cell, these mean values should vary twofold. Assigning arbitrary mean values from 2·1 to 3·9 to the 10 classes and summing the individual distributions we obtained an approximation to the theoretical grain distribution for the whole population. Analysed graphically as described above this distribution exhibited a slight upward concavity; however, the deviation from the line representing the Poisson distribution with mean 2·9 was small and would completely escape notice in our experiments in which at most 1,000 cells were scored per autoradiogram.

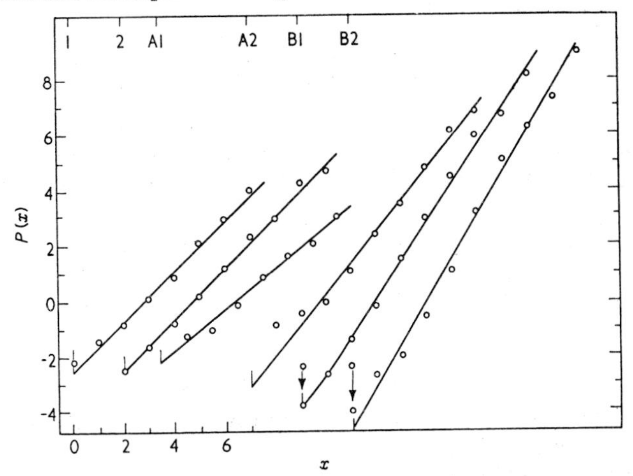

FIG. 2. The six lines represent the grain distributions of Table 1. The x on the abscissa refers to curve No. 1 and indicates the number of grains/cell in the class whose frequency-function, $P(x) = \log_e (p(x)x!)$, figures on the ordinate. The other curves are displaced to the right and on top of the frame the position is indicated of the individual zero-classes. Curves A1 and A2 are based on the assumption that 60% of the cells did not incorporate any label; notice that by this correction fair agreement was obtained between the estimates of ln$m$ from the slope and of m itself from the intercept. On curves B1 and B2 two $P(o)$ values are shown; the upper ones correspond to the observed $p(o)$, the lower ones to the corrected values shown in brackets in Table 1.

In the control experiment the usual generation time of 42 min was observed, and since the definitive rate of incorporation of thymine into DNA is established without a noticeable lag (see p. 149 of this issue), values for grains per day per *totally* labeled cell could be calculated. The figures 0·72 and 0·76 were obtained from experiments 1 and 2 of Table 1 (50 and 65 min incorporation periods respectively). From the total of 6 autoradiograms, representing incorporation times from 30 to 80 min a weighed mean of 0·753 was obtained. In an exponentially growing culture the *average* DNA content per nucleus is taken to be 1·44 times that of a genome (see p. 159 of this issue). The figure 0·753/1·44 = 0·52 is therefore our estimate of the average number of grains that would be produced per day by a cell which was allowed to incorporate tritiated thymidine throughout one round of replication of its DNA. This figure was chosen as unit on the ordinate of Fig. 1.

Experiment A. In this experiment the zero-fraction is obviously much larger than would correspond to a Poisson distribution. We therefore tested the hypothesis that the cell population studied consisted of a large fraction of cells which had not incorporated any thymidine, plus a fraction of labeled cells giving rise to a grain distribution of the

Poisson type. In the above equation ln$m$ depends on the *ratio* between the relative frequencies only; thus, plotting $P(x)$ against x, and disregarding the zero-fraction, a straight line should be obtained even if the sum of cells scored included a large fraction of unlabeled cells. The slope of this line would be an estimate of the mean value of the Poisson distribution of the fraction of *labeled* cells. If the unlabeled fraction is large this estimate of the mean will be strikingly high compared with the arithmetic mean.

Experiment A involved the scoring of 12 different autoradiograms, of which two were from an independent pilot experiment (see p. 157). The graphical analysis of the data led to the conclusion that the cell populations could be adequately described as composed of about 60% of unlabeled cells plus a labeled fraction exhibiting a Poisson distribution of grains. Table 1 and Fig. 2 present the scorings of two autoradiograms of this series. A1 with a high and A2 with a very low zero-fraction. The low zero-fraction correlated with an excessively large number of cells associated with single grains, presumably a result of the high background of grains in that preparation. When about 60% of the cells are unlabeled a high background, by adding a "false grain" to, e.g. 10% of *all* cells, increases the one-fraction out of proportion and at the same time markedly reduces the zero-fraction. In Table 1 the postulated heterogeneity with respect to labeling is indicated by the large discrepancy between the arithmetic and the graphically estimated mean values of experiments A1 and A2.

Experiment B. In this case 9 autoradiograms were scored and the data analysed graphically. The grain distributions all closely resembled Poisson distributions, but, generally, the zero-fractions were slightly too large. This was particularly apparent in cases where the estimated mean values were high as in the distributions B1 and B2 presented in Table 1. The best fits to Poisson distributions were obtained by assuming that 5 to 10% of the cells had remained unlabeled and that the rest of the population was homogeneously labeled (see Fig. 2). This high degree of homogeneity in the population is indicated by the close agreement between the arithmetic and the estimated mean values shown in Table 1.

4. Density Gradient Analysis

In a few experiments 5-bromouracil (Bu) was substituted for thymine in media with and without A and U.

First, growth and viability were studied in a (+ Bu, + AU) medium. Optical density (O.D.) was found to increase exponentially at the normal growth rate for about 100 min; after that time the rate slowly decreased. In contrast, the viable count after a small initial increase dropped exponentially with a half-life of about 20 min. At 140 min when the growth rate, in terms of O.D. increment, had been reduced to half only 10% of the cells survived as colony formers. In these respects the process resembles thymineless death in a (−T, + AU) medium. Second, in a (+ Bu, − AU) medium the usual very slight increase in O.D. was observed and *no* loss of viability occurred over a period of 5 hr.

Bromouracil labeled with ^{14}C in the 2-position (Bu*) was used to follow incorporation into the nucleic acids. In the (+ Bu*, + AU) medium the differential labeling (counts/minute/unit increase in O.D.) remained constant over more than a fourfold increase in O.D. This suggests that at least two rounds of DNA replication took place during which Bu replaced T. Consequently, a large fraction of the newly formed DNA should carry the analogue in both strands. In the (+ Bu*, − AU) medium the label was initially incorporated at a rate comparable to that obtained in (+ Bu*, + AU) medium.† However, after 80 to 90 min incorporation had almost stopped. We con-

† Some of our observations indicate that if the medium contains no U, an appreciable part of the label reaches RNA. This finding was not unexpected since it has previously been shown that *E. coli* may convert Bu to U which then may be incorporated into RNA (Wacher, personal communication).

clude that DNA synthesis probably continued in the (+ Bu, — AU) medium in the same manner and to much the same extent as in the (+ T, — AU) medium.

The Bu-substituted DNA synthesized under these conditions was extracted and its density determined by Dr. Cummings. Extraction and centrifugation in the CsCl gradient were carried out as described by Meselson & Stahl (1958).

In the gradient the DNA extracted from cells incubated in a (+ Bu, — AU) medium was found to separate into two *distinct* and *symmetrical* bands. From the positions of the bands the density of the two fractions was calculated to be 1·75 and 1·70, corresponding to half-substituted and to normal DNA respectively. In four samples, one taken just before Bu was substituted for T, and three taken after 15, 40 and 90 min in the (+ Bu, — AU) medium, the DNA recoveries were in good agreement with the expected increase in total DNA. In the 90 min sample the ratio of heavy to total DNA was approximately 0·6; at earlier times the ratio was correspondingly decreased. This preliminary study included control experiments with DNA extracted after prolonged growth in a (+ Bu, + AU) medium. As mentioned above, Bu* was incorporated to an extent indicating that DNA containing Bu in both strands should have been formed; nevertheless, we failed to extract any material banding in the position corresponding to fully Bu-substituted DNA. We have no explanation to offer for this failure.

5. Discussion

The theory presented in our first paper contains the following postulates: (1) that the division cycle of the bacterial cell consists of two periods, one during which a complete round of DNA replication takes place, and one during which *no* DNA is made; and (2) that inhibition of protein and RNA synthesis does *not* interfere with the replication process itself, but prevents the initiation of a new round of replication. Two predictions made by this theory have been examined, both of which concern DNA synthesis in the individual cells of a culture. It was therefore necessary to use autoradiographic techniques.

The first, and also the simplest case is that of a culture in which protein and RNA synthesis is suddenly inhibited. Clearly, the prediction is that cells that, at the time of inhibition, had almost finished replication should continue DNA synthesis for a short time only, whereas cells that had just begun replication should continue synthesis for a longer time and effectively double their DNA under the condition of inhibited protein and RNA synthesis. The experiment of Schaechter confirms this expectation in a qualitative manner, showing that after inhibition of protein and RNA synthesis a gradually decreasing *fraction* of the cells participate in DNA synthesis. As mentioned on page 158 the method used produces temporary inhibition of protein and RNA synthesis only; it is therefore understandable that DNA synthesis does not come to a complete stop at any time during this experiment.

The second prediction is based on our observations on susceptibility and immunity to thymineless death in a (— T, — AU) medium. First it was shown that complete immunity developed gradually in a culture if DNA synthesis was allowed to proceed in the absence of protein and RNA synthesis, i.e. in a (+ T, — AU) medium. This was interpreted to mean that all cells eventually finished their DNA replication, and that they remained in the non-synthesizing state in which they suffered no damage if T was also removed from the medium (see I, p. 153). In other words, susceptibility to thymineless death was taken to indicate that a cell was actively synthesizing DNA *at the time* when T was removed. Next we observed that the immunity acquired during incubation in (+ T, − AU) medium was lost *gradually* during subsequent growth. If an immune cell is one that has finished a replication cycle and not yet taken the steps necessary to start a new one, *loss* of immunity should indicate that these steps have been taken and that the cell is now able to resume DNA synthesis. Thus, at the time when, e.g. 50% of the cells of a culture have become susceptible the culture should be composed of an equal number of DNA synthesizing and of non-synthesizing cells.

In experiments A and B we observed that about 30% and about 90% of the cells respectively were susceptible to thymineless death at the end of the growth periods in (− T, + AU) medium. These figures then should be compared with the autoradiographic data which showed that about 40% of the cells in experiment A, and 90 to 95% in experiment B actively incorporated tritiated thymidine when transferred to the (+ T*, − AU) medium.

The figures 30 and 40 for the percentages of susceptible and actively synthesizing cells respectively may not be significantly different; nevertheless, it should be pointed out that a likely correction for the effect of cell division reduces the figure 40 considerably. We have seen that about 40% of the cells divided in the (+ T, − AU) medium if the preceding growth period in (− T, + AU) medium was 45 minutes. Presumably, division and resumption of DNA synthesis are correlated events, and we may therefore assume that in experiment A about 40% *of the actively synthesizing cells* divided during the period in which they incorporated the label, and that the rest of the cells did not divide. If this is so, the true percentage of active cells at time zero in experiment A would be 32 and not 40.

The quantity of DNA synthesized during the incorporation of tritiated thymidine may now be compared with that predicted by our theory. The reasoning runs as follows: during the first period in (+ T, − AU) medium replication is thought to run to completion, and each original nucleus should thus be represented by 2 complete genomes (as pointed out on page 153, the few cells that divide during this period probably complete a new round of replication after division). In the second period in the (+ T, − AU) medium a new and complete round of replication is assumed to take place. This should result in the production of 4 half-labeled genomes per original nucleus, and an average of 2 units of DNA per original cell (see p. 159). This figure should be corrected for cell division. Since altogether 60 to 70% of the cells divide during the growth period in (− T, + AU) and the labeling period in (+ T*, − AU) media, the 2 units of DNA per cell reduces to about 1·25. This corrected value agrees reasonably well with the figures 1·2 and 1·4 from experiments A and B respectively (see Fig. 1).

The average curve drawn in Fig. 1 shows that systematically experiment B gave slightly higher values than experiment A. Thus, although the final levels are not significantly different, DNA synthesis probably was somewhat slower in experiment A than in B. This could be due to the average DNA/mass ratio being considerably greater in experiment A than in B; see the schematic diagram (Fig. 6) of the preceding paper.

In general, the results of experiments A and B agree with the predictions of our theory: First, we have shown that if a certain fraction of the cells of a culture is *immune* to thymineless death, a similar fraction is unable to synthesize DNA, and *vice versa*. Second, we find that cells which are believed to begin a new replication cycle when transferred to a (+ T,* − AU) medium produce a quantity of DNA corresponding to one complete cycle and not more.

Finally, we shall discuss the results obtained by density gradient centrifugation. As explained on page 163, Bu can be substituted for T in a (+ T, − AU) medium without apparently changing the course of DNA synthesis. According to our theory total DNA should increase by about 40% in a (+ Bu, − AU) medium, and the new material should consist of fully Bu-substituted strands paired with "old" strands containing T. In the ideal case of instantaneous and complete inhibition of protein and RNA synthesis no material containing Bu in both strands should be formed. If total DNA increases from 1·0 to 1·4 arbitrary units, we would therefore expect to find 0·6 units of normal DNA and 0·8 units of material containing Bu in one strand only. The ratio of hybrid to total DNA predicted by theory is thus 0·57, a value with which the observed ratio of 0·6 agrees almost perfectly.

This excellent fit should be viewed with some reservation, however: as discussed in our first paper (p. 153), it is likely that a small fraction of the cells finish replication soon after transfer to a (+ T, − AU) medium, then divide and go through a complete new round before stopping. If 20% of the cells went through a second cycle total DNA would increase by about 55% and the expected ratio of hybrid to total DNA would be about 0·67 instead of 0·57. Moreover, a few per cent of the newly synthesized DNA would be fully Bu-substituted. Under our experimental conditions these few per cent probably would not have been detected; nevertheless, in this connection it must be remembered that *no* fully substituted DNA was recovered in the control experiment although such material probably was formed. The best argument against significant quantities of fully substituted DNA being produced during incubation in the (+ Bu, − AU) medium is that the increase in total DNA could be accounted for almost completely by the increase in the hybrid DNA recovered from the individual samples.

The fact that a homogeneous fraction of hybrid DNA was formed during incubation in the (+ Bu, − AU) medium is less ambiguous. It shows that the "excess DNA" produced in the absence of protein and RNA synthesis probably is formed through the normal, semi-conservative replication process first demonstrated by Meselson & Stahl (1958).

The authors wish to thank Dr. Robert van Tubergen for his generous help in carrying out the pilot experiment discussed on page 162. One of us (P.C.H.) acknowledges the award of a U.S. Public Health Postdoctoral Fellowship.

REFERENCES

Doniach, I. & Pelc, S. R. (1950). *Brit. J. Radiol.* **23**, 184.
Kjeldgaard, N. O., Maaløe, O. & Schaechter, M. (1958). *J. Gen. Microbiol.* **19**, 607.
Meselson, M. & Stahl, F. W. (1958). *Proc. Nat. Acad. Sci., Wash.* **44**, 671.
Schaechter, M., Bentzon, M. W. & Maaløe, O. (1959). *Nature*, **183**, 1207.

INDEX

"Allosteric" proteins, 41
(*see also* Feed-back inhibition)
Amino acid analogues (*see* RNA synthesis, effect of amino acid analogues)
Amino acid starvation, effect on charging of tRNA, 137–138
effect on RNA synthesis, 128
(*see also* RNA synthesis)
Autoradiography, of free DNA labeled with ^{3}H, 9–10, 154–155, 160–161
of normal cells labeled with ^{3}H, 157–158
of starved cells labeled with ^{3}H, 170–171

Bacterial genome, autoradiographic analysis of, 9–10, 67
number of, per cell, 74
per nucleus, 67
size of, 67–68
Bacterial nucleus, definition of, 64–65
DNA content of, 66–67
number of, per cell, 65
number of genomes per nucleus, 67
packing of DNA in, 189–190
volume of, 189
(*see also* Bacterial genome)
Balanced growth, definition of, 63–64
rate limiting factors in, 123–124
Bromouracil (Bu), as density label in DNA, 178
(*see also* DNA synthesis)
toxic effects of, 180–181

Catabolite repression, 54
in the design of experiments, 54
Cell composition, compared to *in vitro* systems, 86–87
at different growth rates, 75–76
dry weight per unit volume, 87–90
numbers of macromolecules per genome, 90
Cell division, and DNA replication, 116–117
after shift-down, 117–119
after shift-up, 116–117
synchronization of, 2, 157–158
synchronous, 182–186
Cell mass, per genome, 74
at different growth rates, 62–63
measurement of, 61–62
Chloramphenicol (CM), effect on protein synthesis, 39
Codon, 7
Colinearity, 6
Control of macromolecular synthesis, role of feed-back inhibition in, 106–107, 163–164
by frequency of initiation, 162–163

DNA, autoradiography of, 9–10, 154–155, 160–161
 base composition of, 7
 effect of shift-down, 117–119
 effect of shift-up, 115–116
 hydrodynamic shear of, 10
 initiation of replication of, 9
 in vitro replication of, 8–9, 156–157
 in vivo replication of, 154–157
 "melting" of, 8
 quantity per cell, 74
 structure of, 7
DNA-dependent RNA synthesis, enzymology of, 30
DNA/mass ratio, in normal and in starved cells, 168–170, 171–172, 180
DNA synthesis, during amino acid starvation, 164–167
 analysis of, by combined density and tracer labeling, 178–180
 effect of chloramphenicol on, 184–187
 genetic analysis of, 159
 requirement of protein synthesis for initiation of, 167–168
 rate of individual acts of replication, 158–162
 review of, 8–12

Electron microscopy, of fast and slow growing cells, 86
Enzyme induction, arabinose system, 45–46
 β-galactosidase system, 43–44
 galactose system, 44–45
 genetics of β-galactosidase system, 44
Enzyme repression, alkaline phosphatase, 48
 arginine pathway, 47–48
 genetic evidence (*see* individual enzyme systems and Section 1–9)
 histidine pathway, 46–47
 pyrimidine pathway, 47
Ergosomes (*see* Polysomes)

Feed-back inhibition, mechanism of, 41
Fluorouracil (FU), assimilation of, 151
 effect of, on translation (*see* mRNA, effect of fluorouracil)

β-Galactosidase (*see* Enzyme induction, β-galactose system)
Genome (*see* Bacterial genome)
Growing point (g.p.) (*see* Replication)
Growth media, composition of, 83
Growth rates, effect of temperature on, 68
 (*see also* Steady states of growth)

"Measurements," as a particular class of experiment, 2, 160
Messenger RNA (mRNA), breakdown of, 151–152
 characterization of, by radiochemical means, 22–24
 effect of 5-fluorouracil in, 31, 150
 estimation of, by means of fluorouracil, 150–151
  by means of protein synthesis *in vitro*, 24, 143–147
  by radiochemical means, 28–29, 35, 140–141
 half-life of, 26
 homology with DNA, 23–24
 "punctuation marks," 52
 quantities of, 29
  at different growth rates, 147–149
 in relaxed strains, 149–150
 ribosome association, 23
 ribosome attachment, 38
 size of, 52–53
 synthesis during amino acid starvation, 140–142, 147
 synthesis in constitutive strains, 44–45, 108–109
 transcription of one DNA strand only, 31–32
 translation of multicistronic messages, 53–54

Operon, 49
Operator, 49
Operator model, genetic implications of, 49–50

Polynucleotide chains, rate of synthesis of, 106–108, 163, 195
Polypeptide chains, direction of synthesis of, 34
  (*see also* Translation)
 number produced per mRNA, 95–96
 rate of growth of, 162–163, 195

Polypeptides, *in vitro* synthesis of, 36–38
Polysomes, 13
formation of, 36
function of, 35, 36
size of, 25, 35
Protein synthesis, effect on, of amino acid concentration *in vivo*, 113
of antibiotics (*see* individual antibiotics)
of shift-down, 119
of shift-up, 110–113
in vitro, as a tool to estimate mRNA, 145–147
rate of, per ribosome, 90–94, 109–110
per unit rRNA, 81
per unit of total RNA, 76–78, 83–84
review of, 34–38
Proteins (bacterial), composition of, 71–72
contents of, per cell and per genome, 70–71
enzyme balance *in vivo*, 121–123
"naturation" of, 38
stability of *in vivo*, 33
Puromycin, effect on protein synthesis, 39

R- and O-loci (*see* Operator model)
"Relaxed" strains, behavior in shift experiments, 134
control of RNA synthesis in, 135
definition of, 132–133
(*see also* RNA synthesis, in stringent and relaxed strains)
new isolates, 133–134, 136
Replication of DNA, direction of, 195–196
at several growing points, 160, 181
initiation of, at a fixed point, 155–156
as a function of rate of protein synthesis, 176–177
in synchronously dividing cells, 184–186
review of, 8–12, 154–157 (*see also* DNA synthesis)
unwinding of, in synchronously dividing cells, 184–186
Replicon model, 176
Repressor substance, function of, 49
nature of, 50–51
temperature-labile, 51
Ribosomes, "chloramphenicol" particles, 16–17
composition of, 14
distribution of, in cells, 189
enzymes associated with, 15
nonspecificity of, 18
numbers of, at different growth rates, 82–83
stability of, 13
synthesis of, after Mg starvation, 112
after a shift-up, 110
tRNA associated with, 84–86
RNA, extraction and analysis of, 79–81
metabolic stability of, 12
quantity per genome, 74
quantity at different growth rates, 72
rRNA/tRNA ratio, 78–79
RNA synthesis, control of ribosomal RNA (rRNA) synthesis, 152
effect on, of amino acid analogues, 131–132
of amino acid starvation, 128
of amino acids, 130
of chloramphenicol, 128–129, 130–131
of shift-down, 119
of shift-up, 99–102, 116–117
of tRNA *in vitro*, 136–137, 138–139
in vitro, 29–31, 192
latent capacity for, 106
mechanical interaction with DNA template, 192–194
polymerase concentration *in vivo*, 106–108
rate of, in shift experiments, 102–106
regulation of synthesis of individual species, 125–127, 151–152
ribosomal protein and regulation of rRNA synthesis, 152–153
rRNA molecules produced per second, 94
rRNA sites, number of per genome, 94–95
in stringent and relaxed strains, 132–133
substrate concentration *in vivo*, 106–108

RNA synthesis (*cont.*)
topological problems *in vivo*, 190–192, 196
tRNA and its role in control of, 130
unwinding of new molecules from DNA template, 194–195

Shift experiments, combined shift-up and shift-down, 119
definition of, 98
Shift-up and shift-down (*see e.g.* RNA synthesis, effect of shift-up)
Steady states of growth, effect of temperature on, 68
experimental criteria, 59
approach to equilibrium, 58–59
properties of, 56–57
transitions between, 97–98
Streptomycin, effect on protein synthesis, 39–40
effect on translation, 40

Thymine starvation, effect on deoxynucleotide pools, 174–176
Thymineless death (t.l.d.), effect of low thymine concentrations, 173–174
immunity to, 165–167
kinetics of, 173
mechanism of, 172–173
properties of the $15T^-$ strain of *E. coli*, 178
and RNA synthesis, 177–178
Transcription, 5
(*see also* RNA synthesis)
Transfer RNA (tRNA), role in control of RNA synthesis, 139–140
(*see also* RNA synthesis)
specificity of, 19
Translation, 5
(*see also* Protein synthesis and Messenger RNA)